# STUDY GUIDE

## For Chemical Principles, Fourth Edition

***by Dickerson, Gray, Darensbourg, and Darensbourg***

**Patricia L. Samuel**
*Boston University*

**The Benjamin/Cummings Publishing Company, Inc.**
***Menlo Park, California • Reading, Massachusetts***
***London • Amsterdam • Don Mills, Ontario • Sydney***

Production Editor:  Jenny DeGroot
Copy Editor:  Cindy Martin
Proofreader:  Teri Twombly
Typist:  Lynne Alexander



ISBN 0-8053-2424-0

BCDEFGHIJ-AL-8987654

The Benjamin/Cummings Publishing Company, Inc.
2727 Sand Hill Rd.
Menlo Park, California  94025

For

Roger and Emily

# To the Student

This book is designed to help you study efficiently. In each chapter you will find the following elements:

- Chapter Overview and Objectives: The main topics in the chapter are summarized here. The learning objectives are specific skills you should master before leaving the chapter and proceeding to the next one.

- Section Summaries: These summarize the important ideas in each section of the chapter. Worked examples and alternate explanations of concepts are provided as well.

- Terms to Know: Important vocabulary words are listed in alphabetical order near the end of the chapter. In chemistry, as in any of the sciences, language is very powerful, so be sure that you can correctly define the terms in these lists.

- Test Yourself: A selection of problems for you to work closes each chapter. Completely worked out solutions to these are found in the Appendix. Be sure to answer all the self-study questions and problems at the end of each chapter in the text as well.

As you use the Study Guide, you will encounter many diagrams and charts, especially in Chapters 2 through 5. Their purpose is to help you see how to solve a problem before the calculations are given. Flowcharts summarize the thought processes involved in solving problems. The unknown, i.e. the answer you are seeking, is usually found at the top of a flowchart. Once you have identified the unknown, you can work backwards to the information that is given in the problem.

Take advantage of all the resources for learning available to you. These resources include not only the text, this Study Guide, and material in the library, but also your instructor and other students. Studying with another person in the course can be enormously helpful. You will need to set aside some regularly scheduled time for studying. Also, lectures will benefit you most if you have read the material beforehand. Chemistry is an exciting science. Have fun!

# To the Instructor

The intent of this Study Guide is not only to explain and reinforce chemical concepts, but also to teach students problem-solving logic. While some general chemistry students have weak mathematical backgrounds, the majority of those who experience difficulty lack training and experience in applying the mathematics they know to physical situations. Specific skills, such as dimensional analysis and the use of logarithms, are presented in the early chapters. Other helpful notes are included throughout the guide in the examples, which are worked out step by step. In addition, the thought processes used in solving problems are deliberately articulated in the examples. This is most evident in Chapters 2 and 3, where flow diagrams are used, and in Chapters 4 and 5.

Each chapter begins with an overview and list of objectives. Key ideas are summarized, and reinforced with examples. Important terms are collected in a vocabulary list at the end of each chapter. After working the problems in the text, students can test themselves with the questions following each chapter of the Study Guide. Detailed solutions to these questions are provided in the Appendix.

The problem-solving techniques used in this guide have been classroom-tested. Using the Study Guide together with the text allows you to design your course such that weaker students are given the extra support they need, while the attention of the well-prepared ones is maintained.

Special thanks go to colleague Margaret Kastner for reviewing the manuscript and for very helpful discussion. I would also like to acknowledge Valerie Fassbender, who provided most of the solutions to the Test Yourself questions.

P. L. Samuel

# Contents

# 1 Atoms, Molecules, and Ions

## CHAPTER OVERVIEW AND OBJECTIVES

This introductory chapter summarizes much that is known about atoms, ions, and molecules. Later chapters discuss how this information is acquired as well as questions about matter and its behavior which have not yet been answered and are topics of current chemical research.

When you finish this chapter you should be able to:

1. Define the terms printed in boldface type in the text and emphasized here;

2. Tell how many protons, neutrons, and electrons are present in an isotope of an atom or monatomic ion;

3. Understand the chemical counting unit the mole, and use it quantitatively, in combination with molecular weights and formula weights;

4. Briefly describe the attractive forces which exist between atoms, molecules, and ions in compounds and solutions;

5. Write formulas and names for ionic compounds derived from the ions listed in Section 1-6.

## SECTION 1-1: THE STRUCTURE OF ATOMS

The terms that follow are part of the basic vocabulary you need to know when talking about atoms. If any of the definitions are new to you, be sure to take special note.

- atom: an electrically neutral particle of matter consisting of a nucleus and electrons
- nucleus: the portion of an atom containing most of its mass; very dense (mass/volume ratio is large) and positively charged
- electron, $\bar{e}$: small, very light subatomic particle with a charge of -1
- proton, p: subatomic particle with +1 charge found in the nucleus, of mass about 1 amu
- neutron, n: neutral (uncharged) subatomic particle found in the nucleus, with mass of about 1 amu
- atomic mass unit, amu: a unit of mass equal to 1/12 the mass of one atom of carbon-12, which consists of 6p, 6n, and 6$\bar{e}$
- symbol: the letter designation for an element; first letter only capitalized, e.g., Zn, the symbol for the metallic element zinc
- element: matter consisting of atoms all having the same atomic number

- o <u>formula</u>: letter designation for chemical species containing more than one atom, e.g., HF, formula for hydrogen fluoride, which contains one atom of hydrogen and one of fluorine
- o <u>atomic number</u>, $Z$: the number of protons in the nucleus of an atom
- o <u>mass number</u>, $A$: the number of protons and neutrons in the nucleus

Because atoms are electrically neutral, they contain equal numbers of electrons and protons. The number of neutrons in an atom can, and does, vary.

<u>Example 1</u>

How many protons, neutrons, and electrons are there in these atoms?

| | | | |
|---|---|---|---|
| a. | Tc: | $Z = 43$ | $A = 99$ |
| b. | B: | $Z = 5$ | $A = 11$ |
| c. | B: | $Z = 5$ | $A = 8$ |
| d. | Am: | $Z = 95$ | $A = 243$ |

<u>Solution</u>: The names of these atoms are given on the back endpapers of the text. The atomic number, $Z$, is the number of protons and the number of electrons in an atom. The mass number, $A$, is the sum of the protons and neutrons.

| | | | | |
|---|---|---|---|---|
| a. | Tc, technetium: | 43p, | $43\bar{e}$, | 56n |
| b. | B, boron: | 5p, | $5\bar{e}$, | 6n |
| c. | B, boron: | 5p, | $5\bar{e}$, | 3n |
| d. | Am, americium: | 95p, | $95\bar{e}$, | 148n |

Notice that cases b and c are atoms of the same element, boron, because both have the same number of protons.

<u>Example 2</u>

What is the difference between NO and No?

<u>Solution</u>: No is the symbol for the element nobellium, element 102. NO is the formula for the compound nitric oxide, or nitrogen monoxide. You can tell that NO is a formula of a compound and not the symbol for an element, because it contains more than one capital letter. A molecule of nitric oxide contains one atom of nitrogen, N, and one atom of oxygen, O.

## SECTION 1-2: ISOTOPES

<u>Isotopes</u> are atoms of the same element having different numbers of neutrons. In Example 1, two isotopes of the element boron are given, boron-11 and boron-8. Symbols for isotopes follow the form

$$^{A}_{Z}X$$

where subscript $Z$ = atomic number
superscript $A$ = mass number

Symbols for the two isotopes of boron are $^{11}_{5}B$ and $^{8}_{5}B$.

The atomic weight of an isotope is its mass expressed in atomic mass units, amu. The atomic weight is somewhat less than the sum of the masses of the protons, neutrons, and electrons in the atom because some mass is converted to energy to provide the binding energy for the nucleus. The mass that is lost is called the mass excess of the atom.

Example 3

Calculate the mass excess for $^{11}_{5}B$, atomic weight 11.00931.

Solution: The mass excess is the difference between the sum of the masses of the protons, neutrons, and electrons in the atom and the observed atomic weight:

$$\text{mass excess} = (\text{mass p} + \text{mass n} + \text{mass } \bar{e}) - \text{atomic weight}$$

There are 5p, $5\bar{e}$, and 6n in an atom of boron-11.

$$\begin{aligned}\text{mass excess} &= (5p)(1.00728 \text{ amu/p}) + (6n)(1.00867 \text{ amu/n}) + (5\bar{e})(0.00055 \text{ amu}/\bar{e}) - 11.00931 \text{ amu} \\ &= (5.03640 + 6.05202 + 0.00275) \text{ amu} - 11.00931 \text{ amu} \\ &= (11.09117 - 11.00931) \text{ amu} = 0.08186 \text{ amu}\end{aligned}$$

The natural atomic weight of an element is the weighted average of the atomic weights of the isotopes of that element which are found in nature. It is the natural atomic weights that are listed in the table at the end of the text and in the periodic table.

Example 4

Lithium has two naturally occurring isotopes, lithium-6 and lithium-7, atomic weight 7.01600. The natural atomic weight of lithium is 6.941. Naturally occurring lithium is 92.58% of the heavier isotope. Calculate the atomic weight of lithium-6.

Given: natural atomic weight of Li, 6.941 amu
atomic weight $^{7}Li$ = 7.01600
92.58% of naturally occurring Li is $^{7}Li$

Find: atomic weight of $^{6}Li$

Solution: Start with the fact that the natural atomic weight of Li is 6.941 amu and write an equation showing how that is calculated as a weighted average.

$$\text{natural atomic weight} = (\%^{7}\text{Li})(\text{atomic weight } ^{7}\text{Li}) + (\%^{6}\text{Li})(\text{atomic weight } ^{6}\text{Li})$$

Everything in this equation is given in the statement of the problem except the atomic weight of $^{6}Li$ (the unknown) and its percent natural abundance. Because there are only two isotopes, however,

$$\%^{6}\text{Li} + \%^{7}\text{Li} = 100\%$$

$$\%^{6}\text{Li} = 100.00\% - 92.58\% = 7.42\%$$

Now we have one equation and one unknown, and the rest is a matter of arithmetic. Substitute the appropriate numbers into the equation and let $x$ = atomic weight of $^{6}Li$.

$$6.941 \text{ amu} = (92.58\%)(7.01600 \text{ amu}) + (7.42\%)(x)$$

92.58% written as a decimal is 0.9258, 7.42% is 0.0742.

$$6.941 \text{ amu} = (0.9258)(7.01600 \text{ amu}) + 0.0742x$$

$$6.941 \text{ amu} = 6.4954 \text{ amu} + 0.0742x$$

(Carry along an extra significant figure until you reach the final answer.)

$$(6.941 - 6.4954) \text{ amu} = 0.0742x = 0.446 \text{ amu}$$

$$x = 0.446 \text{ amu}/0.0742 = 6.01 \text{ amu}$$

(Notes on significant figures (sig. fig.): Only three sig. fig. are allowed in the answer to 6.941 - 6.4954 because the least number of sig. fig. to the right of the decimal point is three. Only three sig. fig. are allowed in the final answer because the least number of sig. fig. in the quotient 0.446/0.0742 is three.)

## SECTION 1-3: MOLECULES

A molecule is an electrically neutral chemical species composed of two or more atoms held together by covalent bonds. A covalent bond is formed by the sharing of electrons between atoms. Molecules may contain atoms of one element, such as $H_2$, $N_2$, $S_8$, and $P_4$, or more than one element, such as $CO_2$ or HF. Molecules containing atoms of more than one kind of element are compounds. A molecular formula tells how many of each kind of atom there are in a molecule.

Example 5

Perchloric acid molecules contain 1 atom of hydrogen, 1 atom of chlorine and 4 atoms of oxygen. Write the molecular formula.

Solution: We need the symbols of hydrogen, chlorine, and oxygen. They can be found in the table at the back of the text and are H, Cl, and O, respectively. The formula is then

$$HClO_4$$

The subscripts telling the number of each kind of atom are written to the right of the symbol for the element: $N_2$, not $_2N$. For instance, $NO_2$ and $N_2O$ are different compounds. $NO_2$ contains 1 N atom and 2 O atoms, while $N_2O$ is composed of 2 N atoms and only 1 O atom.

Molecular diagrams indicate which atoms are bonded together, but don't show the shape of the molecule. You cannot draw a molecular diagram just by looking at the molecular formula. For $NO_2$, you can write both

| O - N - O | or | N - O - O |
|---|---|---|
| (correct) | | (incorrect) |

Molecular weight is just the sum of the natural atomic weights of the atoms in a molecule. You need to know the molecular formula of a molecule in order to calculate its molecular weight.

Example 6

What is the molecular weight of acetic acid, $CH_3COOH$?

Solution: The formula could also be written $C_2H_3O_2H$ or $C_2H_4O_2$.

$$\text{molecular weight (MW)} = \text{sum of atomic weights (AW)}$$

$$\begin{aligned}\text{MW of acetic acid} = &\ (4\ \text{H atoms})(1.008\ \text{amu/H atom}) \\ &+ (2\ \text{C atoms})(12.011\ \text{amu/C atom}) \\ &+ (2\ \text{O atoms})(15.999\ \text{amu/O atom})\end{aligned}$$

$$\text{MW} = (4.032 + 24.022 + 31.998)\ \text{amu} = 60.052\ \text{amu}$$

## SECTION 1-4: FORCES BETWEEN MOLECULES

Forces between molecules are much, much weaker than the covalent bonds which hold atoms together within molecules. For example, you can spread water out into a thin layer of molecules with your hands, but you can't rip the molecules apart into individual hydrogen and oxygen atoms without applying a large amount of energy. Be sure to learn the terms in the list that follows:

- van der Waals forces: weak attractive forces between molecules which generally increase with increasing molecular weight
- temperature: quantitative measure of heat energy, which is a consequence of molecular motion; heat and temperature are different but are often confused
- solid state: phase of matter having definite shape and volume because molecules are organized into a crystalline lattice
- liquid state: phase of matter having definite volume but variable shape because intermolecular attractions are weaker than those in the solid state
- gaseous state: phase of matter characterized by having neither definite volume nor shape, and by wild, chaotic molecular motion, due to nearly nonexistent intermolecular forces
- melting point, $T_m$: temperature of transition between the solid and liquid phases of a substance
- boiling point, $T_b$: temperature of transition between the liquid and gas phases of a substance
- polar molecule: one in which the electrons in the covalent bonds are not shared equally between the atoms, e.g., HF, $\overset{\delta^+\delta^-}{\text{H–F}}$, CO, $\overset{\delta^+\delta^-}{\text{C–O}}$
- electronegativity: degree of attraction an atom has for the electrons in a covalent bond which it makes with another atom
- hydrogen bond: an especially strong attraction (but not as strong as a covalent bond) between a hydrogen atom in one molecule and a F, O, or N atom in another molecule, or in another section of a large molecule

## SECTION 1-5: MOLECULES AND MOLES

The most important term to understand in this section is the chemical counting unit called the mole. A mole of anything is $6.022 \times 10^{23}$, or Avogadro's number, of that thing. Anything at all can be counted by moles. In concept, a mole is just like other counting units:

| | |
|---|---|
| dozen | 12 things |
| gross | 144 things |
| ream | 500 things, usually sheets of paper |
| decade | 10 things |
| score | 20 things, usually years |
| century | 100 years |

Granted, a mole is a huge number of things, but it has to be, because what is usually counted by moles are atoms and molecules, and these are incredibly small. In order to see and measure a collection of atoms or molecules, we have to count out a tremendous number of them. An entire mole of hydrogen molecules, $H_2$, weighs only 2 grams; that's $6.022 \times 10^{23}$, Avogadro's number, of $H_2$ molecules.

To get a feel for just how huge a number Avogadro's number is, take your pulse, and calculate how many years it would take to count up a mole of heartbeats.

In chemical calculations, the mole unit helps make the transition between counting out individual atoms or molecules and measuring out enough atoms or molecules of a substance to weigh (mass) on a laboratory balance. The mole is the link between the microscopic world of atoms and molecules and the macroscopic world of bulk materials that we deal with every day.

Example 7

A sample of carbon tetrachloride, $CCl_4$, contains 0.250 mol $CCl_4$ molecules.

a. How many molecules does it contain?

Solution: The size of 1 mole of anything is $6.022 \times 10^{23}$. Thus, 0.250 mol of anything contains $(1/4)(6.022 \times 10^{23}) = 1.50 \times 10^{23}$ things. Thus, there are $1.50 \times 10^{23}$ molecules in the sample.

b. How many atoms of C and of Cl does it contain?

Solution: Examine the molecular formula. In one molecule of $CCl_4$, there are 1 C and 4 Cl atoms. The sample contains $1.50 \times 10^{23}$ molecules, so there are an equal number of C atoms, and 4 times as many Cl atoms, or $6.02 \times 10^{23}$ Cl atoms.

c. How much does the sample weigh, in grams?

Solution: The definition of the mole states that exactly 12 g of $^{12}C$ contains Avogadro's number of $^{12}C$ atoms. In practical terms, this means that the atomic weight of an atom, expressed in grams, contains one mole of atoms. Similarly, the molecular weight of a molecule, given in grams, contains one mole of molecules.

In the case given here, there is 0.250 mol of $CCl_4$ molecules. One mole of $CCl_4$ weighs as much as the molecular weight in grams, or $(12.011 + (4 \times 35.453))$ g = 153.823 g. Then 0.250 mol weighs

$$(0.250 \text{ mol})(153.823 \text{ g mol}^{-1}) = 38.456 \text{ g} = 38.5 \text{ g}$$

d. Another sample of $CCl_4$ weighs 10.00 g. How many moles of $CCl_4$ does this sample contain?

Solution: We can immediately say that a 10.00 g sample contains less than one mole, because the molecular weight is 153.823 g/mol. A 10.0 g sample is about 1/15 mole.

$$10.00\ g/(153.823\ g/mol) = 6.501 \times 10^{-2}\ mol$$

## SECTION 1-6: IONS

In contrast to molecular compounds, in which intermolecular forces are fairly weak, salts, or compounds composed of ions, are bound together by strong coulombic attractions. Ions are chemical species that are electrically charged either through loss or gain of electrons. Compounds composed of ions are electrically neutral overall; thus, the total negative charge from the anions must equal the total positive charge on the cations. The strength of the attraction between positive and negative ions is reflected in their extremely high melting and boiling points (relative to those of molecular solids). Both the magnitude of the charges on the ions and their arrangement in the crystal lattice contribute to the attractive forces which bind an ionic crystal together.

Cations are produced from electrically neutral atoms by oxidation, the loss of one or more electrons. When neutral atoms are reduced, or gain electrons, anions result. An oxidation process is always accompanied by a reduction process. Only electrons shift from one atom to another during oxidation-reduction reactions; the number of protons in each atom does not change.

Although ionic compounds melt only at very high temperatures, most readily dissolve in polar liquids such as water, methyl alcohol ($CH_3OH$) and acetonitrile ($CH_3CN$). In solution the ions are solvated by solvent molecules, a process which stabilizes an ion by dispersing its charge over many atoms. Figure 1-6 illustrates this process for an aqueous solution of a salt.

### Example 8

Calcium phosphate is a major constituent of bones and teeth. It is a salt composed of $Ca^{2+}$ and $PO_4^{3-}$ ions.

a. Write the formula for calcium phosphate.

Solution: Compounds are always neutral, so there must be equal numbers of positive and negative charges represented in the formula of a salt. Thus

$$-(\text{number of } Ca^{2+} \text{ ions})(+2 \text{ charge}) = (\text{number of } PO_4^{3-} \text{ ions})(-3 \text{ charge})$$

By inspection we can write $Ca_3(PO_4)_2$ as the formula of calcium phosphate. The symbol $Ca^{2+}$ stands for a cation resulting from the loss of two electrons by Ca. The formula $PO_4^{3-}$ tells us that one phosphorus and four oxygen atoms are covalently bonded together as a unit, and that three extra electrons have been added to this group. (Note: when no charge is written to the upper right of a chemical symbol or formula, the material symbolized has no charge.)

b. Calculate the formula weight of $Ca_3PO_4$.

Solution: Formula weights (F.W.) are calculated in exactly the same way as molecular weights. The mass of one mole of a salt in grams is equal to its formula weight expressed in grams. In a formula unit of $Ca_3(PO_4)_2$ there are 3 Ca atoms, 2 P atoms, and 8 O atoms, or 2 $PO_4^{3-}$ ions and 3 $Ca^{2+}$ ions.

$$\begin{aligned}\text{F.W. } [Ca_3(PO_4)_2] &= (3 \text{ mol Ca/mol } Ca_3(PO_4)_2)(40.08 \text{ g/mol Ca}) \\ &\quad + (2 \text{ mol P/mol } Ca_3(PO_4)_2)(30.97 \text{ g/mol P}) \\ &\quad + (8 \text{ mol O/mol } Ca_3(PO_4)_2)(16.00 \text{ g/mol O}) \\ &= 310.18 \text{ g/mol } Ca_3(PO_4)_2\end{aligned}$$

The rules for naming ions and ionic compounds are given in the text. Your instructor will tell you how much of this chemical nomenclature you are expected to know. Much of this material must be learned by memorizing it, so use whatever memory aids work best for you.

## DIMENSIONAL ANALYSIS

The Systeme Internationale (SI) of units is explained in Appendix 1 of the text. The authors assume that you will be able to use these units when solving problems, and also that you will be able to convert between SI and other units, such as English ones, as necessary.

Dimensional analysis is a powerful problem-solving tool which uses units as a guide for setting up problems, and also as a check on the reasonableness of answers. When solving problems in science, units should always be written out explicitly in every step. They are, after all, part of the quantities used in scientific calculations, and are just as important as the numbers. The examples which follow illustrate some ways in which dimensional analysis can be helpful.

### Example 9

You are going to build a doghouse, using 2 inch × 4 inch lumber (two-by-fours) for the frame. Preservative-treated yellow pine 2 × 4's are priced at 30¢ per linear foot. What will 90 linear feet of this lumber cost?

Solution: The units of the desired unknown are money, expressed in cents or dollars. The units of price are money divided by length. The word per means "divided by." To have money units in the answer while length cancels out, multiply price by length:

$$\text{total cost} = \left(\frac{30¢}{\cancel{ft}}\right)(90\ \cancel{ft})$$

$$\text{total cost} = 2700¢ = \$27.00$$

If we had divided price by length,

$$\frac{30¢/\text{ft}}{90\ \text{ft}} = 0.3\bar{3}¢/\text{ft}^2$$

the answer would come out in units of money per unit area, which is not what we are looking for, and would not make sense in this situation.

### Example 10

The density of mercury is 13.6 g/cm$^3$. It is sold commercially by the "flask" (a flask weighs 76 pounds). What is the volume of one flask of mercury, expressed in liters and as pints?

Given: density of mercury (Hg), 13.6 g/cm$^3$
1 flask = 76 lb

Find: volume of 1 flask in liters and pints

<u>Solution</u>: This problem involves not only calculating the unknown volume from mass and density, but also converting from one set of units to another. Any conversion factor is really a ratio whose value is one. Conversion factors do not change the value of quantities, they merely allow these quantities to be expressed differently. In Example 9, for instance, the total cost of lumber was expressed two ways, 2700¢ and $27.00. The amount of money is not changed by using units of cents instead of dollars. The conversion factor is

1 dollar = 100 cents or

100 cents/dollar = 1

In this example, the unknown volume is to be expressed in two units, L and pt, neither of which is directly used in the given information. Moreover, two different mass units, g and lb, are given. Thus, the factors we will need are those which convert

g to lb

$cm^3$ to L to pt

These factors are

1 lb = 454 g or 454 g/lb = 1

1 L = 1000 $cm^3$ or 1000 $cm^3$/L = 1

1 L = 1.06 qt or 1.06 qt/L = 1

1 qt = 2 pt or 2 pt/qt = 1

The 1's in the factors are exact numbers. These exact numbers can have as many significant figures as needed.

Armed with this information, we can use dimensional analysis to guide us in setting up the problem. The answer must have units of volume. It is to be obtained by combining density, in dimensions of mass per unit volume, with mass. Mass divided by density gives units

$$\frac{\text{mass}}{\text{mass/volume}} = \frac{\cancel{\text{mass}} \times \text{volume}}{\cancel{\text{mass}}} = \text{volume}$$

which is what we are looking for. As a check, try multiplying instead:

$$(\text{mass})(\text{mass/volume}) = \frac{\text{mass}^2}{\text{volume}}$$

Units of $\text{mass}^2$/volume are clearly ridiculous, and thus point out that multiplication is the wrong arithmetical operation for this problem. To obtain volume in liters, then,

$$V(L) = \frac{(76\ \text{lb})(454\ \text{g/lb})(1\ \text{L}/10^3\ \text{cm}^3)}{13.6\ \text{g/cm}^3}$$

$$V(L) = \frac{(76 \not{lb})(454 \not{g})(\not{cm^3})(1\ L)}{(13.6 \not{g})(\not{lb})(10^3 \not{cm^3})}$$

V(L) = 2.537 L = 2.5 L, to the correct number of significant figures

(Note: Be sure to study Appendix 3, Significant Figures and Exponential (Scientific) Notation, thoroughly.) Now convert volume from L to pt.

$$V(pt) = (2.537 \not{L})(1.06\ \not{qt}/\not{L})(2\ pt/\not{qt})$$

Retain extra significant figures in intermediate steps for accuracy. You should do this calculation using 2.5 L and compare your answer with the one given.

V(pt) = 5.38 pt = 5.4 pt

Example 11

What is the area in square meters of a triangle of height 3.0 ft and base 2.0 ft?

Given: △, h = 3.0 ft, b = 2.0 ft

Find: area in $m^2$

Solution: As in the previous example, we must calculate an unknown quantity as well as convert between units. In this case, the unknown will have units of area, or length squared, while the knowns have units of length. You must be particularly careful when working problems like this to use units throughout the process and to remember that arithmetical operations, such as squaring, are performed on entire quantities, numbers and units, not just on one or the other.

Recall that the area of a triangle is

area = ½ × base × height

$A = \frac{1}{2}bh$

The desired dimensions are to be expressed in $m^2$, while $b$ and $h$ are given in ft. Two approaches can be used:

- convert $b$ and $h$ from ft to m, then find $A$
- find $A$ in $ft^2$, then convert to $m^2$

The second method will be used here. You should check it by using the first one.

$$A = \tfrac{1}{2}(3.0\ ft)(2.0\ ft) = \tfrac{1}{2}(6.0\ ft^2) = 3.0\ ft^2$$

A conversion factor from ft to m is not given, but the conversion from cm to in. is given. Thus,

2.54 cm = 1 in

12 in = 1 ft

$100 \text{ cm} = 1 \text{ m}$, or $1 \text{ cm} = 10^{-2} \text{ m}$

Convert ft to m, then square to get the conversion from $ft^2$ to $m^2$.

$$(1 \cancel{ft})\left(\frac{12 \cancel{in}}{\cancel{ft}}\right)\left(\frac{2.54 \cancel{cm}}{\cancel{in}}\right)\left(\frac{10^{-2} \text{ m}}{\cancel{cm}}\right) = 0.305 \text{ m, or } 1 \text{ ft} = 0.305 \text{ m}$$

$$(1 \text{ ft})^2 = (0.305 \text{ m})^2$$

Don't forget to square both number and unit!

$$1 \text{ ft}^2 = 0.0929 \text{ m}^2, \text{ or } 0.0929 \text{ m}^2/\text{ft}^2 = 1$$

$A = (3.0 \cancel{ft^2})(0.0929 \text{ m}^2/\cancel{ft^2}) = 0.2787 \text{ m}^2 = 0.28 \text{ m}^2$, to the correct number of significant figures.

Check this work by using the other conversion method, i.e., changing ft to m, then calculating $A$.

## Terms to Know

atom
anion
atomic mass unit
atomic number
atomic weight
Avogadro's number
binding energy
boiling point
cation
covalent bond
electron
electronegativity
element
formula
gaseous state
hydrogen bond
isotope
liquid state
mass excess
mass number
melting point
mole
molecular weight
molecule
natural atomic weight
neutron
nucleus
oxidation
polar molecule
proton
reduction
solid state
symbol
temperature
van der Waals forces

Test Yourself

1. How many protons, neutrons, and electrons are there in one a) $^{58}Co^{2+}$ ion, b) $^{79}Se^{2-}$ ion?

2. Calculate the mass excess for $^{15}_{7}N$, atomic weight 15.00011.

3. Naturally occurring argon is composed of three isotopes, argon-36, argon-38, and argon-40. The percent abundances of these are 0.337%, 0.063%, and 99.60%, respectively. Calculate the natural atomic weight of argon. The atomic weights of the isotopes are 35.96755, 37.96272, and 39.948, respectively.

4. The natural atomic weight of the metal vanadium is 50.942. It is composed of two isotopes, vanadium-50, atomic weight 49.9472, and vanadium-51, atomic weight 50.9440. Calculate the percent abundances of these isotopes.

5. Write the formula and calculate the formula weight for the following: a) silver dichromate, b) nickel (II) phosphate, c) calcium chlorite, d) aluminum thiosulfate.

6. How many years are required to count up a mole of heartbeats, using a pulse rate of 72/min?

7. What is the mass of 0.125 mole of silver dichromate?

8. How many chromium atoms are present in the sample in question 7?

9. How many moles of calcium chlorite are contained in 25.00 g of it?

# 2 Conservation of Mass and Energy

CHAPTER OVERVIEW AND OBJECTIVES

Three principles of conservation undergird this chapter:

- o matter is conserved in ordinary chemical reactions
- o net charge is conserved
- o energy is conserved

These principles may seem rather obvious, but their implications can be subtle. Applications of these conservation principles will arise over and over throughout your study of chemistry, so it is very important that you acquire a thorough understanding of them now.

You will notice that diagrams and flow charts are often used as aids to problem solving. They can be quite helpful when analyzing a problem and charting a path, or paths, to a solution. Problem solving is also made easier by first deducing how to solve the problem, and after that, performing the required calculations. The final step should always be checking the answer: Is it a reasonable one or not? Depend to some extent on your common sense, and not exclusively on your calculator!

When you finish this chapter you should be able to

1. Account for amounts of matter measured as mass, moles, or individual molecules, atoms or ions.

2. Apply the principle of conservation of matter to ordinary chemical processes:

   - o write and balance the chemical equations starting from word descriptions of the reactions;
   - o use balanced chemical equations to predict amounts of products generated, or reactants required;
   - o use the objective above in conjunction with the concept of percent yield;
   - o understand and apply the solution unit of molarity and use the normality unit with solutions of acids and bases;
   - o understand and apply the concept of acid-base neutralization.

3. Apply the principle of conservation of energy to chemical processes:

   - o understand the following concepts: potential and kinetic energy, work, heat, and mechanical force;
   - o apply the principle of energy conservation to chemical processes and phase changes using Hess' law.

## SECTION 2-1: ATOMIC WEIGHTS, MOLECULAR WEIGHTS, AND MOLES

Review the calculation of molecular weights for compounds of known molecular formula in Chapter 1. Also review the discussion of the mole. Keep in mind that the mole is simply a huge counting unit, analogous to units such as a gross or a ream. The reason that Avogadro's number is such a large number of particles is that things usually measured by the mole--atoms, molecules, and electrons--are so very small. In order to accurately weigh out such small, light particles, a huge number of them must be weighed together.

The mole is crucial to chemical calculations because it relates individual atoms and molecules to measurable quantities of them. It is the link between the microscopic world on the atomic level and our macroscopic one, in which we deal not with single atoms or molecules, but with tremendously large groups of atoms and molecules.

The following example summarizes the relationships between the mass and the number of moles, molecules, and atoms in a sample of material.

### Example 1

Trichloroethylene, $C_2HCl_3$, is commonly used as a dry-cleaning fluid, because it dissolves most fats and oils. For a 15.00-g sample of trichloroethylene, calculate the following:

a. number of moles of $C_2HCl_3$

b. number of moles of chlorine atoms

c. number of $C_2HCl_3$ molecules

d. number of carbon atoms

e. mass percent of Cl in $C_2HCl_3$

f. mass of Cl in this sample

The relationships among quantities a.-f. are diagrammed as shown:

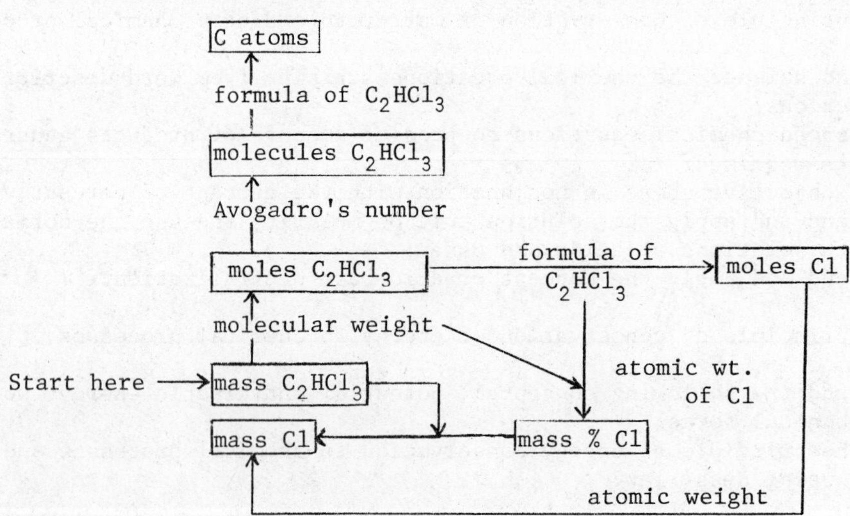


a. molecular weight $C_2HCl_3$ = 2(12.011 g/mol) + 1.0079 g/mol + 3(35.453 g/mol) = 131.29 g/mol

moles $C_2HCl_3$ = 15.00 g/(131.39 g/mol) = 0.1142 mol

b. moles Cl = $(3Cl/C_2HCl_3) \times 0.1142$ mol = 0.3426 mol

c. molecules $C_2HCl_3 = 6.022 \times 10^{23}$ molecules/mole × 0.1142 mol
$= 6.877 \times 10^{22}$ molecules

d. C atoms = 2 C atoms/$C_2HCl_3$ molecule × $6.877 \times 10^{22}$ molecules
$= 1.375 \times 10^{23}$ atoms

e. $$\% \text{ Cl} = \frac{3\text{Cl}/\text{C}_2\text{HCl}_3 \times 35.453 \text{ g/mol Cl}}{131.39 \text{ g/mol}} = 80.949\%$$

f. mass Cl (two methods)

method 1: 80.949% Cl × 15.00 g $C_2HCl_3$ = 12.14 g Cl

method 2: 0.3426 mol Cl × 35.453 g/mol = 12.15 g Cl

## SECTION 2-2: CHEMICAL ANALYSES

One of the tools chemists use for identifying compounds is elemental analysis. It is routinely employed in laboratories where synthesis of new compounds is being attempted. From the elemental analysis, that is, the mass percentages of various elements in the compound, the empirical formula can be determined. The empirical formula expresses the relative numbers of atoms of each element in a compound as their simplest whole-number ratios. The molecular formula may or may not correspond to the empirical formula, but is some whole-number multiple of it. To determine the molecular formula of a compound, the molecular weight must be measured in a separate experiment.

### Example 2

Ethyl vanillate, a by-product of paper manufacturing, is an inexpensive substitute for vanillin, which is extracted from vanilla beans.

a. Find the empirical formula of ethyl vanillate, which contains only C, H, and O and is 61.22% C and 6.16% H.

Given: compound containing C, H, and O
% C and % H by mass

Find: empirical formula

Solution: The empirical formula is an expression of the relative numbers of atoms of each element in a compound. Thus relative masses of atoms, expressed as mass percentage, must be converted to relative numbers of atoms or moles of atoms.

The flowchart shown illustrates the process for finding an empirical formula from an elemental analysis. To use the diagram, begin at the bottom and read up.

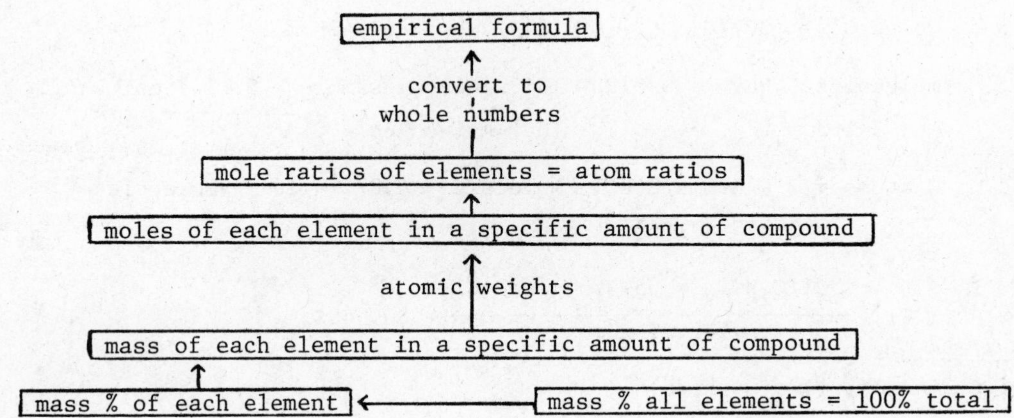


$$\% \text{ O} = 100\% - (\% \text{ C} + \% \text{ H})$$

(Oxygen analyses are rarely performed because they are not very accurate.)

$$\% \text{ O} = 100\% - (61.22 + 6.16)\% = 32.62\%$$

Choose any mass of compound you wish. This mass is completely arbitrary; 100.00 g will be used in this calculation.

$$\text{mass O} = (32.62\%)(100.00 \text{ g}) = 32.62 \text{ g}$$

$$\text{mass C} = (61.22\%)(100.00 \text{ g}) = 61.22 \text{ g}$$

$$\text{mass H} = (6.16\%)(100.00 \text{ g}) = 6.16 \text{ g}$$

$$\text{moles O} = \frac{32.62 \text{ g}}{15.9994 \text{ g/mol}} = 2.039 \text{ mol}$$

$$\text{moles C} = \frac{61.22 \text{ g}}{12.011 \text{ g/mol}} = 5.097 \text{ mol}$$

$$\text{moles H} = \frac{6.16 \text{ g}}{1.0079 \text{ g/mol}} = 6.11 \text{ mol}$$

$$\text{moles C/moles O} = 5.097/2.039 = 2.4998 = 5/2$$

$$\text{moles H/moles C} = 6.11/5.097 = 1.199 = 6/5$$

These are identical to the atom ratios, related by Avogadro's number. Therefore, the empirical formula is $C_5H_6O_2$.

Additional experimental evidence is necessary to determine the molecular formula.

b. In a separate experiment, the molecular weight of ethyl vanillate is found to be 196. What is its molecular formula?

Given: empirical formula, $C_5H_6O_2$
molecular weight, 196

Find: molecular formula

Solution: The molecular weight is related to the formula weight of the empirical formula by the same factor that relates the empirical and molecular formulas. Thus,

$$\text{formula weight of } C_5H_6O_2 = 5(12.011) + 6(1.008) + 2(15.999) = 98.101$$

$$\text{molecular wt/formula wt} = 196/98.101 \simeq 2$$

Therefore, the molecular formula is $(C_5H_6O_2)_2$ or $C_{10}H_{12}O_4$.

Example 3

Sometimes the data from an elemental analysis are not presented as mass percentages of each element, but as masses of products formed from the combustion of a known mass of the compound being analyzed. In these combustion reactions carbon is converted to $CO_2$, hydrogen to $H_2O$, nitrogen to $NO_2$, and sulfur to $SO_2$. The moles of these combustion products can then be related to the moles of each atom present in the original sample of compound. For the elements C, N, and S, one mole of product is formed for each mole of C, N, or S atoms present originally. Only ½ mole $H_2O$/mole H atoms is produced because there are two H atoms per $H_2O$ molecule.

A compound containing only C, H, and O is burned in excess oxygen, yielding 1.47 g $CO_2$ and 0.361 g $H_2O$. The original sample weighed 655 mg. What is the empirical formula of this compound?

Given: 655 mg of compound containing only C, H, and O
1.47 g $CO_2$ produced from combustion
0.361 g $H_2O$ produced from combustion

Find: empirical formula

Solution: As with all empirical formula problems, it is necessary to find out the moles or atoms of each element in a specified quantity of compound. This can be done once the molar relationships between C and H atoms in the compound and $CO_2$ and $H_2O$ molecules are established. Oxygen will be calculated by difference. The equation for combustion is

$$C_xH_yO_z + \text{excess } O_2 \longrightarrow xCO_2 + (y/2)H_2O$$

Read the flowchart shown from the bottom up.

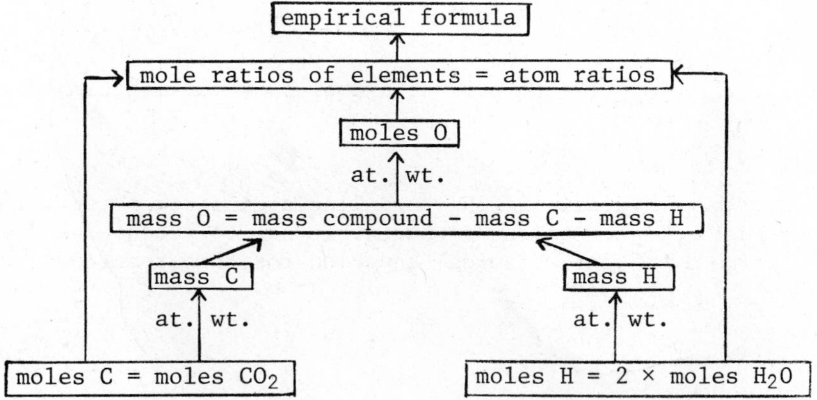

$$\text{moles } CO_2 = \text{moles C} = \frac{1.47\text{ g}}{44.01\text{ g/mol}} = 3.338 \times 10^{-2}\text{ mol}$$

$$\text{moles } H_2O = (\tfrac{1}{2}) \times \text{moles H} = \frac{0.361\text{ g}}{18.015\text{ g/mol}} = 2.003 \times 10^{-2}\text{ mol}$$

$$\text{moles H} = 2(2.003 \times 10^{-2})\text{ mol} = 4.006 \times 10^{-2}\text{ mol}$$

$$\begin{aligned}\text{mass O} &= 0.655\text{ g} - \text{mass C} - \text{mass H} \\ &= 0.655\text{ g} - (3.338 \times 10^{-2}\text{ mol})(12.011\text{ g/mol}) \\ &\quad - (4.006 \times 10^{-2}\text{ mol})(1.008\text{ g/mol}) \\ &= 0.655\text{ g} - 0.4009\text{ g} - 0.0404\text{ g}\end{aligned}$$

$$\text{mass O} = 0.214\text{ g}$$

$$\text{moles O} = \frac{0.214\text{ g}}{15.999\text{ g/mol}} = 1.338 \times 10^{-2}\text{ mol}$$

$$\frac{\text{moles C}}{\text{moles O}} = \frac{3.338 \times 10^{-2}}{1.338 \times 10^{-2}} = 2.495 = 2.5 = 5/2$$

$$\frac{\text{moles H}}{\text{moles C}} = \frac{4.006 \times 10^{-2}}{3.338 \times 10^{-2}} = 1.200 = 12/10 = 6/5$$

Therefore, the empirical formula = $C_5H_6O_2$.

One compound having this empirical formula is ethyl vanillate. (See Example 2.)

## SECTION 2-3: CHEMICAL EQUATIONS

Here is a method for writing and balancing equations which you may find helpful.

1. If the equation is stated in words, decide what the reactants and products are.

2. Write a skeleton equation with reactants to the left and products to the right of the arrow connecting them. Include physical states when known.

3. Use the principle of conservation of mass to balance the equation. Begin with atoms that appear in only one reactant and one product. Charges must also balance.

4. Check your work.

These rules will be applied to several examples of varying complexity.

### Example 4

A mixture of liquid hydrazine, $N_2H_4$, and liquid dinitrogen tetroxide can be used as a rocket fuel. These compounds react together to produce gaseous water and nitrogen. Write a balanced chemical equation for this reaction.

Solution: step 1: reactants are $N_2H_4(l)$ and $N_2O_4(l)$
products are $N_2(g)$ and $H_2O(g)$

step 2: $N_2H_4(l) + N_2O_4(l) \longrightarrow N_2(g) + H_2O(g)$

step 3: H and O appear only once on each side of the equation, so these are balanced first. Balancing O requires that there be 8 H atoms, since there are 4 $H_2O$ molecules.

$$2N_2H_4(l) + N_2O_4(l) \longrightarrow N_2(g) + 4H_2O(g)$$

Next, balance N. There are 6 N atoms on the left, which require 3 $N_2$ molecules on the right.

$$2N_2H_4(l) + N_2O_4(l) \longrightarrow 3N_2(g) + 4H_2O(g)$$

step 4:

| left side | | right side |
|---|---|---|
| 4 | O | 4 |
| 8 | H | 8 |
| 6 | N | 6 |

The equation is balanced.

Example 5

The first step in the manufacture of potassium permanganate is oxidation of solid manganese(IV) oxide with oxygen in potassium hydroxide solution. The products are aqueous potassium manganate, $K_2MnO_4$, and water. Write a balanced equation describing this process.

Solution: step 1: reactants: $MnO_2(s)$, $O_2(g)$, $KOH(aq)$
products: $K_2MnO_4(aq)$, $H_2O(l)$

step 2: $MnO_2(s) + O_2(g) + KOH(aq) \longrightarrow K_2MnO_4(aq) + H_2O(l)$

step 3: Mn, K, and H appear only once on each side of the equation and can be balanced first.

$$MnO_2(s) + O_2(g) + 2KOH(aq) \longrightarrow K_2MnO_4(aq) + H_2O(l)$$

Mn, K, and H are balanced; O is not. There are six O atoms on the left and five on the right. Adding either more $K_2MnO_4$ or $H_2O$ will require rebalancing K, Mn, and H. Adding more $H_2O$ requires more KOH.

$$MnO_2(s) + O_2(g) + 4KOH(aq) \longrightarrow K_2MnO_4(aq) + 2H_2O(l)$$

step 4:

| left side | | right side |
|---|---|---|
| 2 | Mn | 2 |
| 4 | H | 4 |
| 4 | K | 4 |
| 10 | O | 10 |

The equation is balanced.

Example 6

When silver is oxidized by nitric acid, nitric oxide is produced, rather than hydrogen. Balance the equation for this reaction. The other products are silver(I) and water.

steps 1 and 2:

$$Ag(s) + NO_3^-(aq) + H^+(aq) \longrightarrow Ag^+(aq) + NO(g) + H_2O(l)$$

Solution: Since nitric acid is ionized in aqueous solution, it is written in ionic form. (Notice that the counter-ion for $Ag^+$ has been omitted since it is a spectator ion, i.e., it does not participate in the reaction.)

step 3: Ag and N seem to be balanced. More O atoms are needed on the right.

$$Ag(s) + NO_3^-(aq) + H^+(aq) \longrightarrow Ag^+(aq) + NO(g) + 2H_2O(l)$$

More H atoms are needed on the left.

$$Ag(s) + NO_3^-(aq) + 4H^+(aq) \longrightarrow Ag^+(aq) + NO(g) + 2H_2O(l)$$

step 4:

| left side | | right side |
|---|---|---|
| 1 | Ag | 1 |
| 1 | N | 1 |
| 3 | O | 3 |
| 4 | H | 4 |
| +3 | charge | +1 |

Although mass is balanced, charge is not; more positive ions are needed on the right.

$$3Ag(s) + NO_3^-(aq) + 4H^+(aq) \longrightarrow 3Ag^+(aq) + NO(g) + 2H_2O(l)$$

check:

| left side | | right side |
|---|---|---|
| 3 | Ag | 3 |
| 1 | N | 1 |
| 3 | O | 3 |
| 4 | H | 4 |
| +3 | charge | +3 |

Now the equation is balanced.

What kind of information can be obtained from a balanced equation? Let's use the equation just balanced as an illustration.

$$3Ag(s) + NO_3^-(aq) + 4H^+(aq) \longrightarrow 3Ag^+(aq) + NO(g) + 2H_2O(l)$$

1. The minimum numbers of atoms, ions, or molecules of each starting material that are necessary for reaction, as well as the maximum numbers of product molecules that can result

2. The relative numbers of atoms, ions, or molecules of reactants and products

3. The relative numbers of moles of reactants and products

4. The relative masses of reactants, obtained indirectly through the use of atomic and formula weights

In the equation above, there must be at least three silver atoms, one nitrate ion, and four hydrogen ions present for reaction to occur. This mixture is capable of producing three silver ions, one nitric oxide molecule, and two molecules of water. There must be silver atoms, nitrate ions, and hydrogen ions in the proportions 3:1:4 for complete reaction. Silver ions, nitric oxide molecules, and water molecules will be produced in proportions 3:1:2.

Scaling the reaction up to observable quantities, the number of moles of starting materials that will react are in proportions of $Ag:NO_3^-:H^+$ equal to 3:1:4. This does not mean that three moles of silver, for instance, must be present, only that the relative molar amounts of reactants be in the proportions given by the stoichiometric coefficients in the balanced equation. For example, the number of moles of hydrogen ion that will react with a given number of moles of silver ion is in the proportion of 4 to 3, or 1 1/3 to 1.

Since the masses of starting materials and products are related to their molar amounts through their formula weights, a balanced chemical equation tells, indirectly, the relative masses of reactants and products. The ratios of masses of the materials involved in chemical transformations was what was measured by early chemists. Careful quantitative measurements of reaction yields led to such things as the scale of atomic weights, the discovery of certain elements and compounds, and the elucidation of some molecular formulas. The chart shown summarizes the molar and mass information available from the equation in question.

$$3Ag + NO_3^- + 4H^+ \longrightarrow 3Ag^+ + NO + 2H_2O$$

| | Ag | $NO_3^-$ | $H^+$ | $Ag^+$ | NO | $H_2O$ |
|---|---|---|---|---|---|---|
| at. or molec. wt. | 107.89 | 62.00 | 1.008 | 107.89 | 30.01 | 18.015 |
| molar proportions | 3 | 1 | 4 | 3 | 1 | 2 |
| mass proportions | 323.67<br>80.28 | 62.00<br>15.38 | 4.032<br>1.000 | 323.67<br>80.28 | 30.01<br>7.44 | 36.030<br>4.47 |

| | $Ag/NO_3^-$ | $Ag/H^+$ | $NO_3^-/H^+$ | $NO_3^-/NO$ | Ag/NO |
|---|---|---|---|---|---|
| mass ratio: | 5.22/1 | 80.28/1 | 15.38/1 | 2.066/1 | 10.78/1 |
| mole ratio: | 3/1 | 3/4 | 1/4 | 1/1 | 3/1 |

## SECTION 2-4: CALCULATIONS OF REACTION YIELDS

A balanced chemical equation can be used to predict the quantities of products formed in a reaction, or the amounts of reactants required to prepare a desired amount of product.

### Example 7

Aluminum metal reacts with aqueous hydroxide solutions to liberate hydrogen gas:

$$Al(s) + KOH(aq) + H_2O(l) \longrightarrow H_2(g) + K[Al(OH)_4](aq)$$

Is the equation balanced?

a. Theoretically, how many grams of hydrogen can be produced from the reaction of 40.5 g Al with sufficient water and potassium hydroxide?

Given: chemical equation (be sure it's balanced)
40.5 g Al

Find: mass $H_2$ theoretically obtainable, in grams

Solution: The balanced chemical equation is the key to solving most quantitative chemical problems. If you balanced correctly, you found that 2 moles Al produces 3 moles $H_2$, or that moles $H_2$/moles Al = 1.5. Since the known relationships among reactants and products are in terms of moles, information expressed as mass must be converted to moles before it can be used. A diagram illustrates this process.

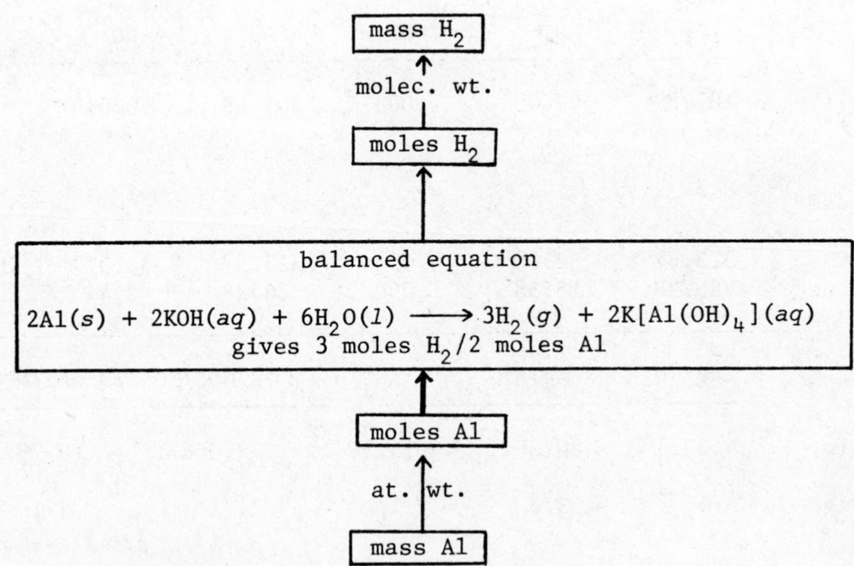

$$\text{moles Al} = \frac{40.5\ \text{g}}{26.98\ \text{g/mol}} = 1.501\ \text{mol}$$

(check: grams cancel)

$$\text{moles } H_2 = \frac{3\ \text{mol } H_2}{2\ \text{mol Al}}(1.501\ \text{mol Al}) = 2.252\ \text{mol}$$

(check: moles Al cancel and there should be more moles $H_2$ than moles Al since the equation gives a stoichiometric factor of 1.5 mole $H_2$ per mole Al.)

$$\text{mass } H_2 = (2.252\ \text{mol})(2.016\ \text{g/mol}) = 4.54\ \text{g}$$

(check: moles cancel)

(Note: Carry along an extra significant figure until the final step of the problem; this gives greater accuracy than rounding after each step. Since the datum in this problem, mass of Al, is given to three significant figures, and all arithmetic steps involve multiplication or division, only three significant figures may be used in the answer.)

b. How many moles of hydrogen would be produced in part a if the reaction yield were only 85%?

Given: 85% reaction yield
theoretical yield of 2.25 mol $H_2$

Find: moles $H_2$ if yield is 85%

The percent yield of a reaction is found by taking the ratio of the actual, or experimental, yield of product to the theoretical, i.e., that calculated from the balanced chemical equation:

$$\text{percent yield} = \frac{\text{actual yield}}{\text{theoretical yield}}$$

The actual and theoretical yields can be expressed as either mass or moles.

Solution: Actual yield = (% yield)(theoretical yield) = (0.85)(2.25 mol)
= 1.9 mol

(check: The actual yield can never be greater than the theoretical yield. If the actual yield equals the theoretical yield, this is a 100% yield or excellent experimental results!)

(Note: Most real reactions run at yields less than 100%, i.e., less than what is predicted by the balanced chemical equation. When working problems, you may assume that the theoretical yield is asked for, unless otherwise specified. You may be asked to calculate your percent yield when you do syntheses in the laboratory.)

Example 8

Oftentimes quantities of two or more reactants are specified in a problem. Before calculating the yield of product, a check must be made to determine if the reactants are present in the relative molar amounts required for reaction, given by the balanced equation. If one reactant is in excess, then the other one limits the amount of product that can be made. We'll begin with a nonchemical example, in which one counts single objects, rather than moles of them.

Imagine that you are working in the chemistry stockroom part-time to help pay your tuition. Your task is to determine how many students can be served with equipment that is available. Each student needs the following:

| | |
|---|---|
| 1 100 mL graduated cylinder | 2 400 mL beakers |
| 3 125 mL Erlenmeyer flasks | 1 150 mL beaker |
| 12 4 in. test tubes | 2 50 mL burets |

You have available:

| | |
|---|---|
| 125 100 mL graduated cylinders | 260 400 mL beakers |
| 370 125 mL Erlenmeyer flasks | 130 150 mL beakers |
| 1550 4 in. test tubes | 245 50 mL burets |

Given: collection of equipment listed above
equipment kit for one student

Find: number of student equipment kits

Solution: There are many different approaches to solving this problem. Some of them are diagrammed.

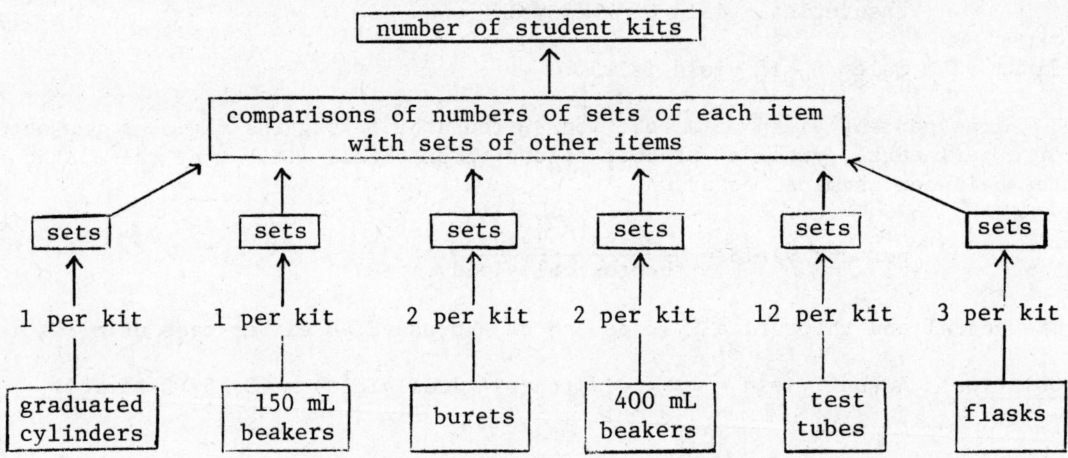


One of many avenues is worked out here:

step 1: Determine number of sets of each item, using the equipment data.

step 2: Determine item having smallest number of sets; this will be equal to the number of student kits.

$$\text{sets cylinders} = \frac{125 \text{ cyl}}{1 \text{ cyl/set}} = 125 \text{ sets}$$

$$\text{sets 150 mL beakers} = \frac{130 \text{ 150 mL beak}}{1 \text{ beak/set}} = 130 \text{ sets}$$

$$\text{sets burets} = \frac{245 \text{ burets}}{2 \text{ burets/set}} = 122\ 1/2 \text{ sets}$$

$$\text{sets 400 mL beakers} = \frac{260 \text{ 400 mL beak}}{2 \text{ beak/set}} = 130 \text{ sets}$$

$$\text{sets test tubes} = \frac{1550 \text{ t.t.}}{12 \text{ t.t./set}} = 129\ 1/6 \text{ sets}$$

$$\text{sets flasks} = \frac{370 \text{ flasks}}{3 \text{ flasks/set}} = 123\ 1/3 \text{ sets}$$

Smallest number of sets = 122 1/2 sets of burets. Therefore, the number of student kits = 122 kits.

Alternate solution:

step 1: Determine number of sets of one item.

step 2: Use equipment list to predict number of each of the other five items necessary for kits, based on number of sets of first item.

step 3: Compare items on hand with those calculated in step 2.

step 4: Repeat steps 1-3 until number of complete kits has been determined.

The flowchart illustrates this process.

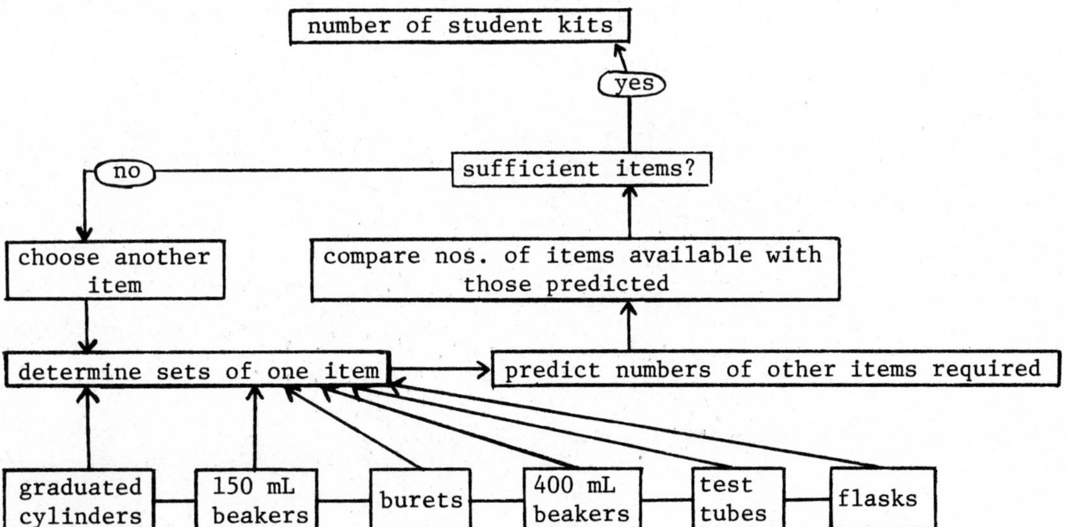

And now, a chemical problem:

Example 9

Nitrogen can be fixed by reaction with hot magnesium metal, forming magnesium nitride:

$$N_2(g) + 3Mg(s) \xrightarrow{\text{heat}} Mg_3N_2(s)$$

a. How many moles of magnesium nitride can be prepared from 35.0 g $N_2$ and 70.0 g Mg?

Given: balanced equation
35.0 g $N_2$ and 70.0 g Mg

Find: moles $Mg_3N_2$ produced

Solution: Since quantities of both reactants are given, one must determine whether they are present in the molar proportion specified by the equation for complete reaction. Two pathways to the unknown will be described. Read the flowcharts from the bottom.

method 1

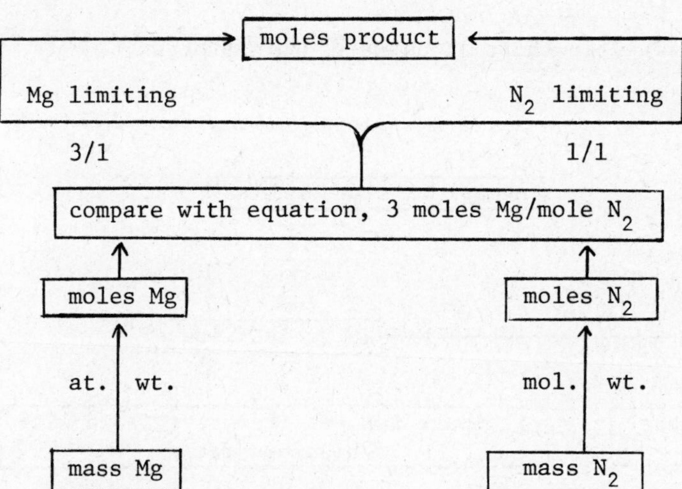

method 2

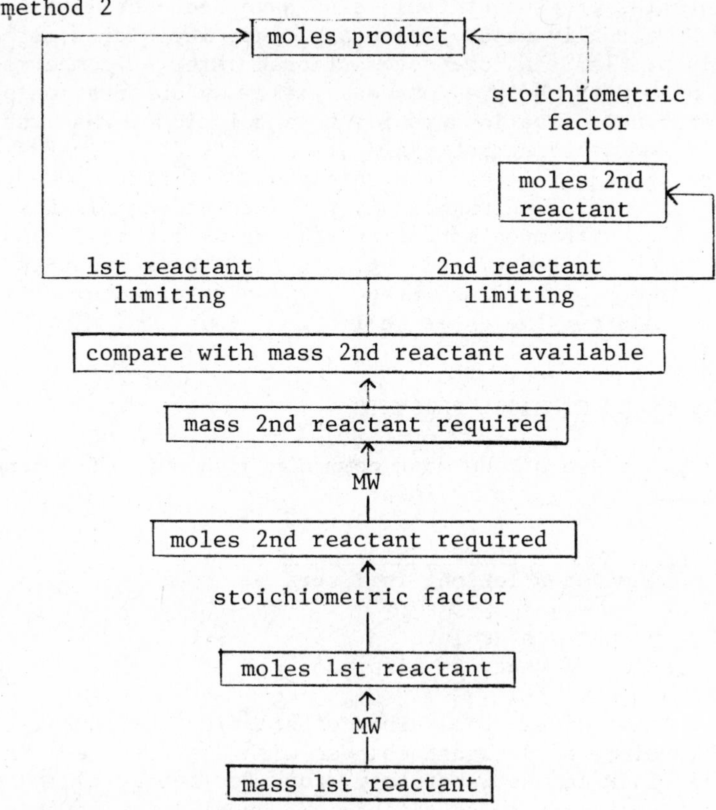


Calculations using method 1:

$$\text{moles Mg} = \frac{70.0 \text{ g}}{24.305 \text{ g/mol}} = 2.871 \text{ mol}$$

An extra significant figure is retained until the final answer is obtained.

$$\text{moles } N_2 = \frac{35.0 \text{ g}}{28.01 \text{ g/mol}} = 1.249 \text{ mol}$$

From the equation, 1 mole $N_2$ requires 3 moles Mg.

$$\text{available Mg}/N_2 = \frac{2.871 \text{ mol Mg}}{1.249 \text{ mol } N_2} = 2.379$$

Therefore, available Mg is insufficient to react with all the $N_2$, so Mg is the limiting reagent and $N_2$ is in excess.

From the equation

$$\text{moles } Mg_3N_2 = \text{mol Mg} \times \frac{1 \text{ mol } Mg_3N_2}{3 \text{ mol Mg}}$$

$$\text{moles } Mg_3N_2 = (1/3)(2.871) \text{ mol} = 0.957 \text{ mol}$$

The moles of product could also have been obtained from the moles of $N_2$ actually used. There are other legitimate methods for solving this problem that are not mentioned here. A comparison of this example with the previous one yields an observation of relative efficiency of various routes to a solution. When the amounts of only two starting materials are specified, as in Example 9, methods 1 and 2 require about the same amount of time. However, using method 2 to solve Example 8, the student equipment kit problem, would require much more time than using method 1. As you gain proficiency in problem solving, begin to think about the relative efficiency of various methods. Consideration of efficiency is important in other fields as well.

## SECTION 2-5: SOLUTIONS AS CHEMICAL REAGENTS

Molarity and molality are two of the most commonly used units for concentration of solutions. They are calculated as follows:

$$\text{molarity, M} = \frac{\text{moles of solute}}{\text{volume of solution, in liters}}$$

$$\text{molality, m} = \frac{\text{moles of solute}}{\text{mass of solvent, in kilograms}}$$

Notice that molarity incorporates the volume of solution and thus is temperature-dependent, since the volume of a liquid changes with temperature. The next time you see a volumetric flask in the laboratory, look for the label indicating the temperature at which the volume is specified. We usually ignore this parameter when doing ordinary laboratory work with aqueous solutions because volume changes very slowly with temperature (except near the boiling or freezing point). Molality, on the other hand, is independent of temperature since it involves only moles and mass.

Solutions with known molarity can be easily and quickly diluted when necessary, since the only equipment needed is volumetric glassware. Diluting a solution of a given molality to a lesser one requires a balance. The dilution process does not change the number of solute particles present in the solution; it just spreads them further apart.

moles solute, concentrated solution = moles solute, dilute solution

Rearranging the definition of molarity

$$M = \frac{\text{moles solute}}{\text{liter of solution}}$$

gives moles solute = M × V (in liters). Substituting in the expression above for dilution yields

$$M_{conc}V_{conc} = M_{dil}V_{dil}$$

Since volume appears on both sides of the equation, it can be expressed in any units, as long as they are consistent. It is not necessary to convert to liters from mL, for example.

Example 10

What mass of potassium chromate, $K_2CrO_4$, is required to prepare 250 mL of a 0.020 M solution?

Given: $K_2CrO_4$ as solute

Find: mass solute required

Solution: The definition of molarity employs moles of solute, not mass. Once moles are known, mass can be found using the molecular weight of $K_2CrO_4$. Thus

$$\text{moles } K_2CrO_4 = M \times V(L) = (0.020\ M)(250\ mL)(10^{-3}\ L/mL)$$

$$\text{moles } K_2CrO_4 = 5.0 \times 10^{-3}\ mol$$

$$MW = mass(g)/moles$$

$$\text{mass } K_2CrO_4 = (5.0 \times 10^{-3}\ mol)(194.2\ g/mol)$$

$$\text{mass } K_2CrO_4 = 0.97\ g$$

Example 11

An aqueous solution of nitric acid is 32.00% $HNO_3$ by weight, with density 1.1955 g/mL. Find the molarity and molality of this solution.

Given: aqueous solution of $HNO_3$, density = 1.1955 g/mL; wt % $HNO_3$ = 32.00%

Find: M and m

Solution: Several approaches to this problem are possible. The diagrams given show two of them. You may think of others.

Scheme 1

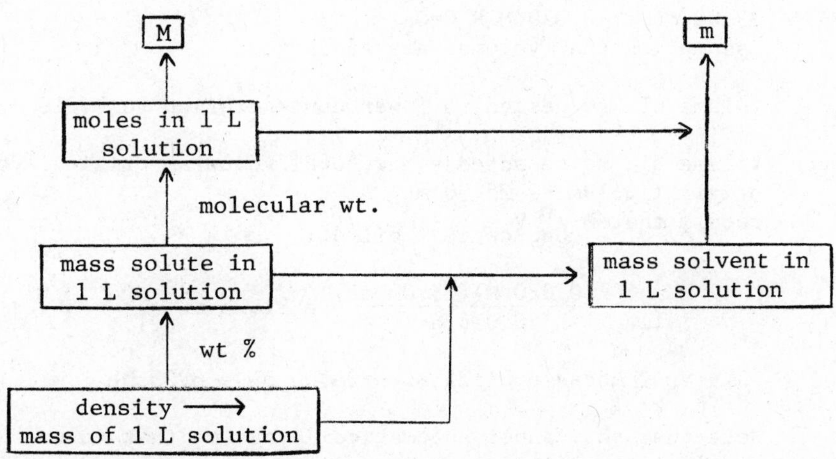

Scheme 2

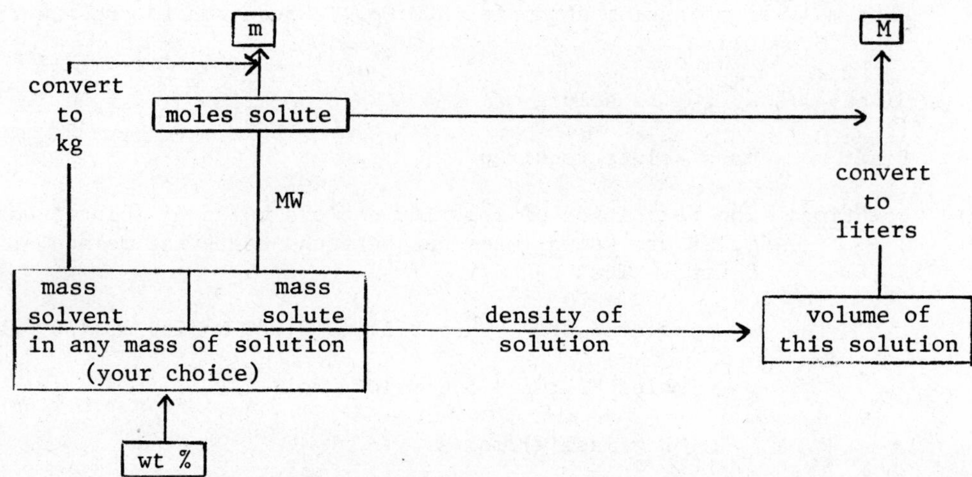


Here are the calculations using scheme 1. You should calculate M and m using scheme 2 yourself.

density = 1.1955 g/mL = (1.1955 g/mL)($10^3$ mL/L) = 1195.5 g/L

mass $HNO_3$/L = (32.00 %)(1195.5 g/L) = 382.56 g/L

moles $HNO_3$/L = (382.6 g/L)/(63.01 g/mol) = 6.071 mol/L = M

mass $H_2O$/L = 1195.5 g - 382.56 g = 812.9 g = 0.8129 kg

m = 6.071 mol/0.8129 kg = 7.469 m

Example 12

How much water must be added to 25.00 mL of the solution in Example 10 to dilute it from 0.020 M to 0.016 M, assuming that volumes are additive?

Given: 25.00 mL of 0.020 M $K_2CrO_4$
assumption that volumes are additive

Find: volume of $H_2O$ needed to lower concentration to 0.016 M

Solution: Volume $H_2O$ to be added = new total volume - original volume
original volume = 25.00 mL
recall that $M_{conc}V_{conc} = M_{dil}V_{dil}$

$$V_{dil} = \frac{(0.020\ M)(25.00\ mL)}{0.016\ M} = 31.25\ mL$$

$$V_{H_2O}\ \text{added} = 31.25\ mL - 25.00\ mL = 6.25\ mL$$

Note that you cannot automatically assume that volumes are additive, particularly if solute-solvent interactions are very strong relative to solvent-solvent interactions or if the original solution is very concentrated.

Example 13

Calcium carbonate is widespread in nature, being found in limestone, marble, and the shells of marine animals and birds' eggs. Acidic solutions, such as acid rain, decompose calcium carbonate:

$$CaCO_3(s) + 2HNO_3(aq) \longrightarrow CO_2(g) + H_2O(l) + Ca(NO_3)_2(aq)$$

a. How many moles of $CaCO_3$ can be decomposed by 50 mL of 0.35 mL of 0.35 M nitric acid?

Given: volume and molarity of $HNO_3$
balanced equation

Find: moles of $CaCO_3$

Solution: The balanced equation indicates a stoichiometric factor of 2 moles of $HNO_3$ reacting with each mole of $CaCO_3$. This combined with the available moles of $HNO_3$ will yield the desired result.

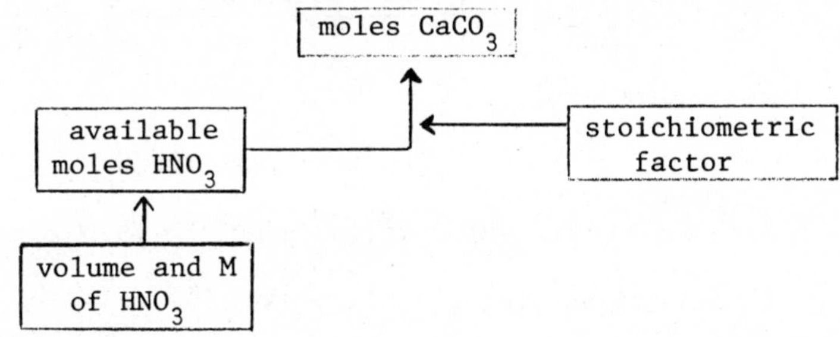


Notice that it is not necessary to use mass or molecular weight in this problem.

$$\text{moles } CaCO_3 = (1/2)(\text{moles } HNO_3)$$

$$\text{moles } HNO_3 = M \times V \text{ (liters)}$$

$$\text{moles } CaCO_3 = (1/2)(0.35\ M)(50\ mL)(10^{-3}\ L/mL)$$

$$\text{moles } CaCO_3 = 0.00875\ mol = 8.8 \times 10^{-3}\ mol$$

(2 significant figures allowed)

b. What volume of 6.0 M $HNO_3$ would be required to produce 35 g of $CO_2$? How many grams of $CaCO_3$ would be necessary for this reaction?

Given: 35 g $CO_3$ produced
6.0 M $HNO_3$

Find: volume of $HNO_3$
mass $CaCO_3$ required

Solution: Quantities of both reactants necessary to make a specified amount of product are asked for. As usual, the starting point is the balanced equation. The flowchart indicates several possible routes to the solution. Start at the bottom and read up. The calculations use only one of the paths. Check yourself by using an alternate one.

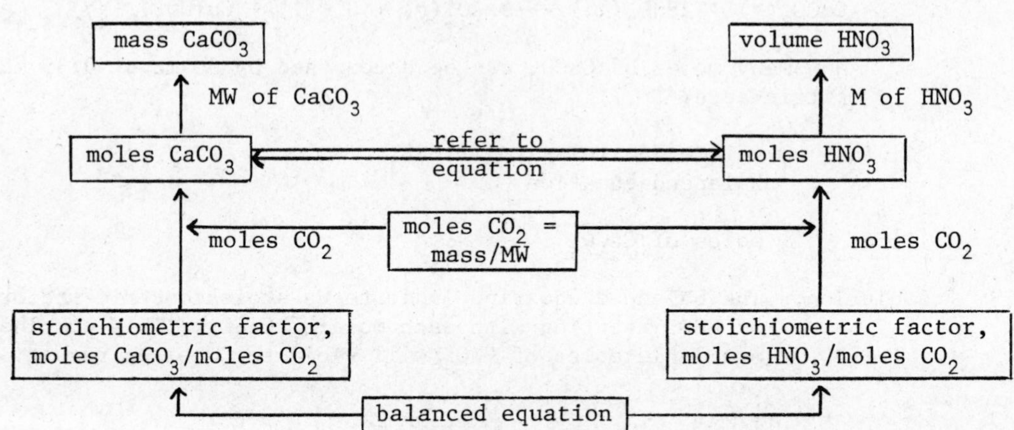


moles $CaCO_3$/moles $CO_2$ = 1/1

moles $CO_2$ = 35 g/(44.01 g/mol) = 0.795 mol

mass $CaCO_3$ = (0.795 mol)(100 g/mol) = 79.5 g = 80 g

(2 significant figures allowed)

moles $HNO_3$/moles $CaCO_3$ = 2/1

moles $HNO_3$ = 2(0.795 mol) = 1.59 mol

$$\text{volume } HNO_3 = \frac{1.59 \text{ mol}}{6.0 \text{ mol/L}} = 0.265 \text{ L} = 0.27 \text{ L}$$

c. A sample of $CaCO_3$ of mass 21.0 g was added to 250 mL of 1.50 M $HNO_3$. How many grams of $CO_2$ were generated?

Given: 21.0 g $CaCO_3$
250 mL of 1.50 M $HNO_3$
balanced chemical equation

Find: mass $CO_2$

Solution: Since quantities of two reagents are given, their molar amounts must be compared to the stoichiometric requirement of the reaction before the calculation of product yield can be carried out. The diagram illustrates this process.

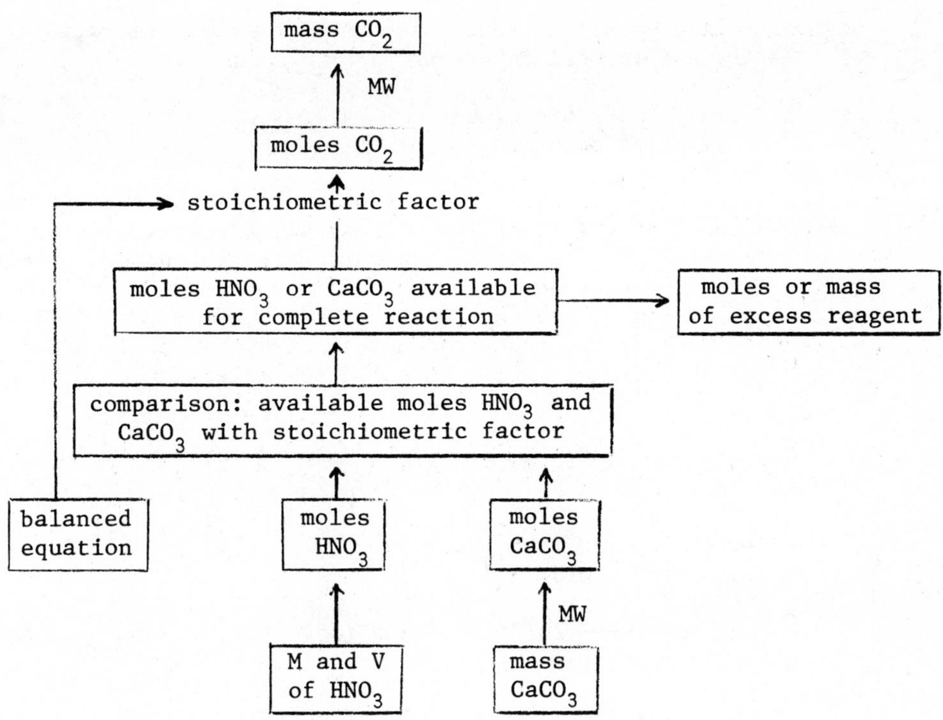


$$\text{moles } CaCO_3 = \frac{21.0 \text{ g}}{100 \text{ g/mol}} = 0.210 \text{ mol}$$

$$\text{moles } HNO_3 = (250 \text{ mL})(10^{-3} \text{ L/mL})(1.50 \text{ M}) = 0.375 \text{ mol}$$

balanced equation gives 2 mol $HNO_3$/mol $CaCO_3$

$$0.210 \text{ mole } CaCO_3 \text{ reacts with } \frac{2 \text{ mol } HNO_3}{1 \text{ mol } CaCO_3} \times 0.210 \text{ mol } CaCO_3$$

$$= 0.420 \text{ mol } HNO_3$$

Since only 0.375 mol $HNO_3$ is available, $HNO_3$ is the limiting reagent, and $CaCO_3$ is in excess. At this point, the yield of $CO_2$ can be calculated from either 0.375 mol $HNO_3$ or from (1/2)(0.375 mol $CaCO_3$).

$$\text{moles } CO_2 = 0.375 \text{ mol } HNO_3 \times \frac{1 \text{ mol } CO_2}{2 \text{ mol } HNO_3} = 0.188 \text{ mol}$$

$$\text{mass } CO_2 = (0.188 \text{ mol})(44.01 \text{ g/mol}) = 8.27 \text{ g}$$

Example 14

A titration can be used to analyze a sample of acid or base for such things as concentration or moles of solute, weight percent, or equivalent weight. You count hydrogen ions or hydroxide ions by converting them to water during the course of the titration:

$$H^+(aq) + OH^-(aq) \longrightarrow H_2O(l)$$

Normality is a useful concentration unit for these titrations. It is similar to molarity and is defined as

$$N = \frac{\text{equivalents of solute}}{\text{liter of solution}}$$

An equivalent is that quantity of acid which reacts to liberate one mole of hydrogen ions, or that quantity of base which reacts with one mole of hydrogen ions. The mass of acid or base corresponding to one equivalent is the equivalent weight. Operationally, one determines the number of equivalents in a mole of a particular acid by counting the number of acidic hydrogen atoms per molecule. With bases, count the number of hydroxide ions per formula unit or the number of hydrogen ions with which one molecule could react. Some examples follow:

$HBr(aq) \longrightarrow H^+(aq) + Br^-(aq)$ 1 equivalent/mole
hydrobromic acid

$H_2S(aq) \longrightarrow 2H^+(aq) + S^{2-}(aq)$ 2 equivalents/mole
hydrosulfuric acid

$Zn(OH)_2(s) \longrightarrow Zn^{2+}(aq) + 2OH^-(aq)$ 2 equivalents/mole
zinc(II) hydroxide

$CH_3NH_2(aq) + H_2O \longrightarrow CH_3NH_3^+(aq) + OH^-(aq)$ 1 equivalent/mole
methylamine

For HBr and $CH_3NH_2$, because there is one equivalent per mole, the equivalent weight equals the molecular weight. The equivalent weights of $H_2S$ and $Zn(OH)_2$ are one-half of their respective molecular weights, since there are two equivalents per mole for these materials.

Recall the acid-base titration reaction:

$$H^+(aq) + OH^-(aq) \longrightarrow H_2O(l)$$

When all the acid or base originally present has been converted to water, the equivalents of the reagent added will be equal to the equivalents of the one originally present. Or

$$\text{equivalents of acid} = \text{equivalents of base}$$

The point during the titration at which this is true is called the equivalence point. Rewriting this equation in solution parameters gives

$$N_{acid}V_{acid} = N_{base}V_{base}$$

Volume may be expressed in any convenient units.

Arsenic acid, $H_3AsO_4$, is an analog of phosphoric acid. The elements P and As are both found in group VA of the periodic table. Arsenic acid and arsenate salts are highly toxic.

a. What is the normality of a 0.10 M solution of arsenic acid?

Given: 0.10 M $H_3AsO_4$

Find: normality

Solution: Since $H_3AsO_4$ is an analog of $H_3PO_4$, it has three acidic hydrogen atoms. Thus there are three equivalents per mole, and

$$(0.10 \text{ mole/L})(3 \text{ equivalents/mole}) = 0.30 \text{ equivalents/L or } 0.30 \text{ N}$$

b. What is the equivalent weight of arsenic acid?

Solution: Since there are three equivalents per mole of $H_3AsO_4$,

$$\text{equivalent weight} = \frac{1 \text{ mole}}{3 \text{ equivalents}} \times \text{MW} \qquad \text{or}$$

$$\text{equivalent weight} = \frac{1 \text{ mole}}{3 \text{ equivalents}} \times \frac{141.94 \text{ g}}{\text{mol}} = \frac{47.31 \text{ g}}{\text{equivalent}}$$

c. How many moles of calcium hydroxide will just neutralize 250 mL of the 0.30 N arsenic acid solution in part a?

Given: 250 mL of 0.30 N $H_3AsO_4$

Find: moles of $Ca(OH)_2$ necessary to react completely with the acid

Solution: Method 1: Using equivalents and normality: The number of equivalents of acid will be equal to the number of equivalents of base required for neutralization:

$$\begin{aligned}\text{equivalents of acid} &= 250 \text{ mL} \times 10^{-3} \text{ L/mL} \times 0.30 \text{ N} \\ &= 7.5 \times 10^{-2} \text{ equivalents} \\ &= \text{equivalents of base}\end{aligned}$$

Each mole of $Ca(OH)_2$ will react with 2 moles of $H^+$, so there are 2 equivalents/mol of $Ca(OH)_2$. Then

$$\text{moles } Ca(OH)_2 = \frac{7.5 \times 10^{-2} \text{ equivalent}}{2 \text{ equivalents/mol}} = 3.8 \times 10^{-2} \text{ mol}$$

Method 2: Using the balanced equation: Write and balance the equation for the neutralization process:

$$2H_3AsO_4(aq) + 3Ca(OH)_2(aq) \longrightarrow Ca_3(AsO_4)_2(s) + 6H_2O(l)$$

The stoichiometric requirement is 3 mol $Ca(OH)_2$/2 mol $H_3AsO_4$. You need to calculate moles $H_3AsO_4$ in order to find moles of $Ca(OH)_2$. Recall that volume (liters) × molarity = moles. Since there are 3 equivalents/mol of $H_3AsO_4$, the molarity is

$$\frac{0.30 \text{ N}}{3 \text{ equiv/mol}} = 0.10 \text{ M}$$

Then moles $H_3AsO_4$ = 0.10 M × 250 mL × $10^{-3}$ L/mL = 2.5 × $10^{-2}$ mol

$$\begin{aligned}\text{moles } Ca(OH)_2 &= \frac{3 \text{ mol } Ca(OH)_2}{2 \text{ mol } H_3AsO_4} \times 2.5 \times 10^{-2} \text{ mol } H_3AsO_4 \\ &= 3.8 \times 10^{-2} \text{ mol}\end{aligned}$$

Notice that the use of normality and equivalents does not require that you balance the chemical equation, although it is necessary to convert from moles to equivalents.

Example 15

A solution of arsenic acid is being titrated with potassium hydroxide. A 25.00 mL aliquot (portion) of the acid requires 30.66 mL of 0.0225 N KOH to reach the equivalence point.

a. What is the normality of the acid?

Given: 25.00 mL of $H_3AsO_4$ solution
30.66 mL of 0.0225 N KOH solution added to reach the equivalence point

Find: normality of $H_3AsO_4$

Solution: At the equivalence point, equivalents of acid originally present equal equivalents of base added or

$$N_{acid}V_{acid} = N_{base}V_{base}$$

Recall that volumes may be expressed in any units as long as the units are the same on both sides of the equal sign. Thus

$$N_{acid}(25.00\text{ mL}) = (0.0225\text{ N})(30.66\text{ mL})$$

$$N_{acid} = \frac{(0.0225\text{ N})(30.66\text{ mL})}{25.00\text{ mL}} = 0.0276\text{ N}$$

b. What mass of arsenic acid is contained in the 25.00 mL aliquot?

Given: 25.00 mL of 0.0276 N $H_3AsO_4$

Find: mass of $H_3AsO_4$

Solution: To find the mass we need equivalents or moles, which can be combined with the equivalent weight or molecular weight.

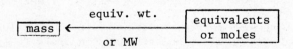

mass ← (equiv. wt. or MW) ← equivalents or moles

equivalents = N × V (liters)
moles = M × V (liters)

$$\text{equivalents of } H_3AsO_4 = (0.0276\text{ N})(25.00\text{ mL})(10^{-3}\text{ L/mL})$$
$$= 6.9 \times 10^{-4}\text{ equivalents}$$

Since there are 3 acidic hydrogen atoms per molecule of $H_3AsO_4$, the equivalent weight is one-third the molecular weight.

$$\text{mass } H_3AsO_4 = (1\text{ mol/3 equiv})(141.9\text{ g/mol})(6.9 \times 10^{-4}\text{ equiv})$$
$$= 3.3 \times 10^{-2}\text{ g}$$

An alternate method for solving this problem would be to convert normality to molarity and calculate moles, then mass.

$$\boxed{N} \xrightarrow{\text{equiv/mole}} \boxed{M} \xrightarrow{\text{V (liters)}} \boxed{\text{moles}} \xrightarrow{\text{MW}} \boxed{\text{mass}}$$

Example 16

Titrations can also be used to find the equivalent weight of an unknown acid. This information can be combined with other experimental data to find the molecular weight.

A newly synthesized acid is titrated with potassium hydroxide to determine its equivalent weight. A sample weighing 495 mg requires 23.64 mL of 0.185 N KOH to reach the equivalence point.

a. What is the equivalent weight of the acid?

Given: 495 mg of acid
23.64 mL of 0.185 N KOH for titration

$$\text{eq. wt.} = \frac{\text{mass (g)}}{\text{number of equivalents}}$$

Solution: Mass is given; the number of equivalents must be found. This can be calculated from the number of equivalents of base required for titration:

$$\begin{aligned} \text{original equivalents of acid} &= \text{equivalents of base added} \\ \text{milliequivalents base} &= (23.64\ \text{mL})(0.185\ \text{N}) \\ &= 4.37\ \text{meq} = \text{meq acid} \end{aligned}$$

$$\text{equivalent wt.} = \frac{495\ \text{mg}}{4.37\ \text{meq}} = 113\ \text{mg/meq} = 113\ \text{g/eq}$$

Milliequivalents (meq) and mL were used in this calculation for simplicity. These units, along with the millimole (mmol), are convenient ones to use when working with small quantities of material.

b. Additional experimental data indicates that this acid contains two acidic hydrogen atoms per molecule. What is its molecular weight?

Solution: Since $\text{eq. wt.} = \dfrac{\text{MW}}{\text{eq/mol}}$, and no. eq/mol = no. acidic H atoms,

$$\text{MW} = 2\ \text{eq/mol} \times 113\ \text{g/eq} = 226\ \text{g/mol}$$

## SECTION 2-6: HEATS OF REACTION, CONSERVATION OF ENERGY

Sections 1-5 of this chapter have dealt with the conservation of matter and charge during ordinary chemical reactions, and the consequences of those principles. This section treats the thermal changes that accompany these processes. The first part of the section examines kinetic and potential energy, heat, work, and mechanical force in a physical process -- the pitching of a baseball. The kinetic energy of the ball can be calculated via two different pathways: the first is stepwise, the second direct.

Under conditions of constant pressure, heat transfer occurring during chemical changes can be evaluated in a similar fashion. This is because the enthalpy, $H$, or "heat content" of a system is a state function. The value of $H$ depends solely on the current state of the system, e.g., its pressure, temperature, volume, and mass, as well as the kinds of atoms comprising it and the way they are bonded together. Enthalpy, or any other state function, for that matter, does not depend on how a system gets to be in a particular state. Enthalpy itself, $H$, cannot be measured; it only becomes apparent when the system undergoes some change. The value for the enthalpy change for a process, $\Delta H$, depends only on the initial and final states of the system and not on the path, or paths, between the states. When the initial and final states of the system have the same pressure, the change in enthalpy is numerically equal to the heat transferred into or away from the system, $q_p$:

$$\Delta H = q_p$$

These ideas are collected in Hess' law of heat summation, which allows one to calculate enthalpy changes that otherwise might be difficult or impossible to measure, by constructing an alternate pathway from the initial to the final state. Hess' law is one way of stating the principle of conservation of energy during ordinary chemical reactions.

Example 17

Nitrogen dioxide, a component of urban smog, is a reddish-brown toxic gas. It is formed very rapidly by oxidation of nitric oxide, NO, with oxygen. Calculate $\Delta H$ for the reaction

$$NO(g) + \tfrac{1}{2}O_2 \longrightarrow NO_2(g)$$

using the following data:

1. $2NO_2(g) \longrightarrow N_2O_4(g)$ $\qquad \Delta H = -58$ kJ

2. $2NO(g) + O_2(g) \longrightarrow N_2O_4(g)$ $\qquad \Delta H = -170$ kJ

Solution: The desired equation doubled can be obtained by combining equations 1 and 2.

2. $2NO(g) + O_2(g) \longrightarrow N_2O_4(g)$

1. $N_2O_4(g) \longrightarrow 2NO_2(g)$

---

3. $2NO(g) + O_2(g) + N_2O_4(g) \longrightarrow N_2O_4(g) + 2NO_2(g)$

3. $2NO(g) + O_2(g) \longrightarrow 2NO_2(g)$

The enthalpies of reaction can be combined in the same way as the equations, according to Hess' law. Several points must be kept in mind when applying Hess' law to a problem:

- Enthalpy is an extensive property, and thus depends on the amount of matter in the system.
- Enthalpy changes which are exothermic (negative sign) for reactions that run in one direction become endothermic (positive sign) if the reaction is run in the opposite direction.

- Physical states of all components of the system must be specified, as enthalpy depends on whether reactants and products are solids, liquids, or gases.

The two paths between the initial and final states are diagrammed as shown:

$$2NO(g) + O_2(g) \xrightarrow{\Delta H?} 2NO_2(g)$$

$-170$ kJ ($2NO(g) + O_2(g) \rightarrow N_2O_4(g)$); 58 kJ ($N_2O_4(g) \rightarrow 2NO_2(g)$)

For reaction 3, $\Delta H = -170 \text{ kJ} + 58 \text{ kJ} = -112 \text{ kJ}$

For the desired reaction,

$$NO(g) + \tfrac{1}{2}O_2(g) \longrightarrow NO_2(g)$$

$$\Delta H = \tfrac{1}{2}(-112 \text{ kJ}) = -56 \text{ kJ}$$

(Note that the sign of $\Delta H$ for reaction 1 is changed when the reaction is reversed. Furthermore, since equation 3 is exactly twice the desired equation, its enthalpy change is twice that of the desired one as well.)

Example 18

Another method for obtaining enthalpy changes for reactions uses the standard enthalpies of formation, $\Delta H_f^\circ$, of reactants and products. Recall that the standard enthalpy, or heat, of formation is $\Delta H$ for the reaction in which one mole of material is formed from its elements in their standard, or most commonly found, states at 1 atmosphere and a specified temperature, usually 25°C. It can be shown that, for any reaction,

$$\Delta H^\circ_{reaction} = \Sigma H_f^\circ \text{ (products)} - \Sigma H_f^\circ \text{ (reactants)}$$

Carbon disulfide is prepared commercially from methane and gaseous sulfur:

$$CH_4(g) + 4S(g) \longrightarrow CS_2(g) + 2H_2S(g)$$

Calculate the enthalpy change for this process at 25°C. The standard heats of formation at 25°C are

| substance | $\Delta H_f^\circ$(kJ mol$^{-1}$) |
|---|---|
| $CH_4(g)$ | -74.848 |
| $S(g)$ | 222.80 |
| $CS_2(g)$ | 115.27 |
| $H_2S(g)$ | -20.146 |

The equation of interest can be obtained by combining the equations representing the heats of formation of products and reactants:

$$2(H_2(g) + \frac{1}{8}S_8(s) \longrightarrow H_2S)$$

$$C(\text{graphite}) + \frac{1}{4}S_8(s) \longrightarrow CS_2(g)$$

$$CH_4(g) \longrightarrow C(\text{graphite}) + 2H_2(g)$$

$$4(S(g) \longrightarrow \frac{1}{8}S_8(s))$$

---

$$2H_2(g) + \frac{1}{4}S_8(s) + C(\text{graphite}) + \frac{1}{4}S_8(s) + CH_4(g) + 4S(g) \longrightarrow$$

$$2H_2S(g) + CS_2(g) + C(\text{graphite}) + 2H_2(g) + \frac{1}{2}S_8(s)$$

$$CH_4 + 4S(g) \longrightarrow 2H_2S(g) + CS_2(g)$$

$$\Delta H^\circ_{\text{reaction}} = (2\text{ mol})(-20.146\text{ kJ/mol}) + (1\text{ mol})(115.27\text{ kJ/mol})$$

$$- (1\text{ mol})(-74.848\text{ kJ/mol}) - (4\text{ mol})(222.80\text{ kJ/mol})$$

$$\Delta H^\circ_{\text{reaction}} = -741.37\text{ kJ}$$

(Note that heats of formation are defined and listed for one mole of material. Note also that heats of formation of elements in their standard states at one atmosphere and 25°C are assigned values of zero by international convention. The heat of formation of an element in a non-standard state, e.g., $S(g)$, has a nonzero value.

Terms to Know

acid
base
chemical analysis
conservation of energy
conservation of mass
dilute
empirical formula
enthalpy
equivalence point
equivalent
heat of formation
Hess' law of heat summation
molality
molarity
normality
solute
solvent
standard state
strong acid
titration
weak acid

## Test Yourself

1. Calcium phosphate is a major constituent of bones and teeth. For a 10.0 g sample of calcium phosphate, calculate the following:

   a. moles $Ca_3(PO_4)_2$

   b. moles O

   c. number of P atoms

   d. mass of Ca

   e. number of $Ca_3(PO_4)_2$ formula units

2. White elemental phosphorus, $P_4$, is manufactured by heating calcium phosphate, sand ($SiO_2$), and graphite in an electric furnace. Balance the equation for this process.

$$Ca_3(PO_4)_2 + SiO_2 + C \longrightarrow P_4 + CaSiO_3 + CO$$

3. When zinc metal reacts with aqueous hydrogen ion, as from hydrochloric acid, hydrogen gas is evolved and aqueous zinc(II) ion is produced. Write a balanced equation for this process, including the physical states of all species involved.

4. Oxygen can be generated as follows:

$$5H_2O_2 + 2KMnO_4 + 3H_2SO_4 \longrightarrow 5O_2 + 2MnSO_4 + K_2SO_4 + 8H_2O$$

   How many grams of potassium permanganate are required for production of 64.0 g of $O_2$, if sufficient quantities of hydrogen peroxide and sulfuric acid are available?

5. Acrylonitrile, the starting material for synthesis of the acrylic polymers used in clothing, is produced from propylene and nitric oxide.

$$\underset{\text{propylene}}{4C_3H_6} + 6NO \longrightarrow \underset{\text{acrylonitrile}}{4C_3H_3N} + 6H_2O + N_2$$

   How many kilograms of acrylonitrile can be made from 10.0 kg each of propylene and nitric oxide?

6. Cyanide salts can be rendered nonpoisonous by reaction with iron(II) nitrate (ferrous nitrate).

   a. Balance the equation for this reaction:

$$CN^-(aq) + Fe(NO_3)_2(aq) \longrightarrow [Fe(CN)_6]^{4-}(aq) + NO_3^-(aq)$$

   b. What is the minimum volume of 0.100 M $Fe(NO_3)_2$ solution that would be required to react completely with 5.50 g of potassium cyanide?

7. A sample of an organic acid weighing 225.2 mg was dissolved in water and titrated with aqueous potassium hydroxide. Neutralization of the entire sample of acid required 24.73 mL of 0.1011 M KOH.

   a. What is the equivalent weight of the acid?

b. This acid contains one acidic proton. What is its molecular weight?

8. Joseph Priestley generated oxygen by heating the red calx of mercury, HgO:

$$HgO(s) \longrightarrow Hg(l) + \tfrac{1}{2}O_2(g), \qquad \Delta H° = 90.8 \text{ kJ}$$

How many kilojoules of heat would be required to decompose 10.0 g of this calx?

9. One method for the manufacture of methanol, $CH_3OH$, utilizes carbon monoxide and hydrogen:

$$CO(g) + 2H_2(g) \longrightarrow CH_3OH(g)$$

Calculate the enthalpy change for this process from the information given:

| | $\Delta H°$ (kJ) |
|---|---|
| $C(s) + H_2O(g) \longrightarrow CO(g) + H_2(g)$ | 130 |
| $C(s) + 2H_2(g) + \tfrac{1}{2}O_2(g) \longrightarrow CH_3OH(g)$ | -239 |
| $H_2(g) + \tfrac{1}{2}O_2(g) \longrightarrow H_2O(g)$ | -286 |
| $H_2O(l) \longrightarrow H_2O(g)$ | 44 |

10. How much heat would be generated if a model airplane of mass 1500 g, traveling at 35 mph, crashed into a stone wall? How much work is done on the wall?

# 3 Gas Laws and the Kinetic Theory

CHAPTER OVERVIEW AND OBJECTIVES

The physical behavior of gases and the theory devised to explain their behavior provide the subject matter for this chapter.

When you finish the chapter you should be able to:

1. Judge which problems can be solved by application of the appropriate gas law:

   - o Avogadro's principle
   - o Boyle's law
   - o Charles' law
   - o ideal gas law; combined gas law
   - o Dalton's law of partial pressures
   - o Graham's law of effusion

2. Make qualitative predictions of gas behavior, as described by P, V, T, and n, using a suitable gas law, and perform the related calculations;

3. Understand the postulates of the kinetic molecular theory of gases and the implications of the result K.E. = $(3/2)RT = (\frac{1}{2})M\overline{v^2}$;

4. Explain how real gases differ from ideal ones and be able to give a physical interpretation of the van der Waals constants, a and b;

5. Understand the concept of pressure and how it is measured.

SECTION 3-1: AVOGADRO'S LAW

The quantitative study of gases and their reactions in the nineteenth century played a tremendously important role in supporting atomic theory, elucidating the molecular formulas of many common gases, and establishing the atomic weight scale. The centerpiece of this work was the interpretation of the results of Gay-Lussac's work with gaseous reactions given by Amadeo Avogadro in 1811. Gay-Lussac concluded that gases react in simple whole-number ratios of their volumes. According to Avogadro, this was because equal volumes of gases, measured at the same temperature and pressure, contain equal numbers of molecules. Mathematically, this can be written as:

$V \propto n$ (constant $P$ and $T$)
$V = kn$ (constant $P$ and $T$)
where $n$ = number of moles of gas and $k$ is a constant of proportionality

Unfortunately Dalton, the father of atomic theory, did not believe Avogadro. Neither did other famous chemists of that time, such as Berthollet and Berzelius. So fifty years of turmoil in the chemical world ensued, until Cannizzaro succeeded in getting proper recognition of Avogadro's hypothesis in 1860, four years after the latter's death. Once Avogadro's hypothesis was accepted, a great deal of apparently conflicting data began to make sense.

Example 1

Cannizzaro showed that, if Avogadro's hypothesis were true, gas density should be proportional to molecular weight. Derive this relationship.

Given: Avogadro's law, $V = kn$ at $T$, $P$ constant

Find: $\rho = cM$

where $\rho$ = density, $M$ = molecular weight, and $c$ is a constant of proportionality

Solution: Density is mass per unit volume, or

$$\rho = m/V$$

Also $n = m/M$

$$n = V/k \quad \text{(Avogadro's law)}$$

$$m/M = V/k$$

$$\rho = m/V = M/k$$

Let $1/k = c$

Then $\rho = cM$

## SECTIONS 3-2 AND 3-3: PRESSURE AND BOYLE'S LAW

These sections deal with the concept of pressure, its measurement, and the relationship between pressure and volume of gases. You should understand how a barometer works. Note particularly that pressure is a ratio, force per unit area. It is because $P = F/A$ that the size of a barometer tube doesn't matter, nor does the total amount of liquid inside the barometer.

Robert Boyle published his studies of the spring of the air in The Sceptical Chymist, 1661. Be sure to study carefully Figure 3-3 and the accompanying discussion of data analysis. Keep in mind that Boyle's law applies only to fixed amounts of gases at constant temperature.

Example 2

Suppose one wants to design a barometer using a fluid other than mercury, for safety reasons. Calculate the height of a column of aqueous sodium chloride solution, 26.00% by mass, density 1.1972 g/mL, corresponding to 1.00 atm pressure. Comment on the advantages and disadvantages of using this barometer.

Given: barometer containing aqueous sodium chloride
26.00% NaCl by mass, $\rho$ = 1.1972 g/mL

Find: height equivalent to 1 atm pressure
advantages and disadvantages of the instrument

Solution: Method 1: Comparison with a mercury barometer

Since mercury is denser than the salt solution, the pressure exerted by a mercury column will be greater than that exerted by a column of salt solution of the same height. Or, a mercury column would have to be shorter than a salt solution one for both to exert the same pressure. This relationship can be derived as follows:

$$P = F/A = mg/A \quad \text{where } g \text{ is acceleration due to gravity}$$

$$\rho = m/V = m/A \cdot h$$

$$m/A = \rho h$$

Substituting for $m/A$ in the first equation,

$$P = \rho g h$$

For the two barometers, $P$ = constant

$$\rho_{Hg} g h_{Hg} = \rho_{NaCl} g h_{NaCl}$$

$$\rho_{Hg} h_{Hg} = \rho_{NaCl} h_{NaCl}$$

The density of Hg is given in the <u>Handbook of Chemistry and Physics</u> as 13.5939 $g/cm^3$.

$$h_{NaCl} = \frac{(13.5939\ g/cm^3)(760\ mm)}{1.1972\ g/mL} = 8.63\ m$$

Method 2: Direct calculation

The height of the column can be calculated directly from

$$P = \rho g h$$

if pressure is expressed in pascals.

$$1\ atm = 101{,}323\ Pa$$

$$\rho = 1.1972\ g/mL = 1.1972\ kg/dm^3$$

$$h = P/\rho g = (101{,}323\ Pa)/[(1.1972\ kg/dm^3)(10\ dm/m)^3(9.806\ m/s^2)]$$

$$h = 8.631\ m$$

While the salt solution is certainly cheaper and less toxic than mercury, these advantages are offset by the inconvenient height of the barometer.

The following example illustrates some situations in which Boyle's law is applicable.

Example 3

Consider a sample of gas at constant temperature trapped in the apparatus in Figure 3-2 (c).

a. How would the volume change if the pressure were decreased to 1/3 of its original value?

Given: gas at constant $n$, $T$; pressure drop to 1/3 original pressure

Find: change in volume

Solution: The unknown is the new volume relative to the initial volume, i.e., $V_2/V_1$ or $V_2 - V_1$. At constant $n$ and $T$,

$$PV = \text{constant} \qquad \text{(Boyle's law)}$$

$$P_1V_1 = P_2V_2$$

No value is given for $P_1$ or $V_1$, but we can write, however,

$$P_2 = 1/3P_1$$

Since $PV$ is constant, if $P$ decreases $V$ must increase. Thus we can write immediately

$$V_2 > V_1$$

This will provide a check on the final answer. Substituting into Boyle's law

$$P_1V_1 = 1/3P_1V_2$$

Canceling $P_1$,

$$V_1 = 1/3V_2$$

or $V_2/V_1 = 3$

or $V_2 - V_1 = 3V_1 - V_1 = 2V_1$

Thus the volume increases by a factor of three, or the difference between initial and final volume is twice the original volume. This agrees with the original estimate, that $V_2 > V_1$.

b. If the pressure of the gas in part a is 752 torr and the volume is 525 mL, what will the pressure be after the volume is decreased by 50 mL?

Given: sample of gas at constant $n$, $T$
$P_{initial}$ = 752 torr
$V_{initial}$ = 525 mL
$V$ decreases by 50 mL

Find: $P_{final}$

Solution: At constant $n$ and $T$

$$P_1V_1 = P_2V_2$$

Since $V$ is decreasing, $P$ must increase, so

$$P_2 > P_1$$

Then

$$(752\ \text{torr})(525\ \text{mL}) = P_2(525\ \text{mL} - 50\ \text{mL})$$

$$P_2 = (752\ \text{torr})(525\ \text{mL})/475\ \text{mL} = 831\ \text{torr}$$

This agrees with the original estimate, that $P_2 > P_1$. Note that pressure and volume can be expressed in any convenient units, as long as they are consistent. This is possible because pressure and volume appear on both sides of the equation, and conversion between units uses multiplicative factors.

c. Express the final pressure in part b in atmospheres and pascals.

Given: $P$ = 831 torr

Find: $P$ in units of atmospheres and pascals

Solution: All that is necessary are the conversion units:

760 torr = 1 atmosphere

101,325 pascals = 1 atmosphere

Then

$$831\ \text{torr}/(760\ \text{torr/atm}) = 1.09\ \text{atm}$$

$$(1.09\ \text{atm})(101{,}325\ \text{Pa/atm}) = 110{,}791\ \text{Pa} = 111\ \text{kPa}$$

One can see why the pascal hasn't caught on with chemists as a practical unit of pressure.

## SECTION 3-4: CHARLES' LAW RELATING VOLUME AND TEMPERATURE

Although Charles determined the relationship between volume and temperature of fixed amounts of gases at constant pressure in 1787, he did not publish his work. Gay-Lussac rediscovered the relationship and published it in 1802. When their data is plotted up as V vs. T in °C, it gives a straight line of positive slope that does not pass through the origin. Extrapolation to V = 0 gives an intercept on the T axis of -273.15°C, which is the zero of temperature on the Kelvin, or absolute, scale. This is why temperature must be expressed in Kelvins when using the gas laws:

$$V = \text{constant} \times T(\text{Kelvin})$$

$$V = \text{constant} \times (T(°\text{C}) + 273)$$

Keep in mind also that Charles' law only applies to systems at constant pressure and moles of gas.

Example 4

A balloon is partially inflated with air to a volume of 1 $dm^3$ (1 liter) at room temperature. By what factor can the temperature of the air in the balloon be changed before the 2.5-liter capacity of the balloon is exceeded and the balloon explodes?

Given: balloon containing 1 L of air at 25°C
maximum volume of 2.5 L

Find: factor to change temperature such that volume does not exceed 2.5 L

Solution: Since nothing is mentioned about pressure in the problem, assume that the balloon is flexible enough that pressure remains constant during expansion. According to Charles' law, the volume of a gas sample is directly proportional to temperature at constant pressure:

$$V \propto T \qquad \text{(at constant } P\text{)}$$

$$V = \text{constant} \times T \qquad \text{(at constant } P\text{)}$$

$$V/T = \text{constant}$$

Thus for $V$ to increase, $T$ must increase. For two states, 1 and 2, of a gas at constant pressure

$$V_1/T_1 = V_2/T_2$$

$$T_2/T_1 = V_2/V_1$$

Since $V_2 > V_1$ in this problem, $T_2$ will be larger than $T_1$.

$$T_2/T_1 = 2.5 \text{ L}/1 \text{ L} = 2.5$$

So temperature can be increased by a factor of 2.5 before the maximum capacity of the balloon is reached.

$$T_2 = 2.5(298 \text{ K}) = 745 \text{ K or } 472°\text{C}$$

Remember that temperature must be in Kelvin to use the gas laws.

Jacques Charles was a ballooning enthusiast and made the second recorded human balloon ascent, in 1783. Balloons get their lift from the fact that the gas within them is less dense than the surrounding air.

$$\text{lift} = \Delta m = m_{air} - m_{gas}$$

where $m_{gas}$ = mass of gas in the balloon

$m_{air}$ = mass of air that could occupy the balloon

The balloon can lift anything lighter than $\Delta m$.

Example 5

A helium-filled balloon has volume of 30,000 L when the air temperature is 10°C.

a. How much mass can this balloon lift?

Given: $V$ = 30,000 L at 10°C

Find: lift of the balloon, $\Delta m = m_{air} - m_{gas}$

Solution: In order to find the masses of air and helium that can fill this balloon, one needs the densities at 10°C ($\rho$ = mass/volume).

$$\rho_{air\ (moist)} = 1.1487\ g/L \qquad (10°C,\ 700\ torr)$$

$$\rho_{He} = 0.1586\ g/L \qquad (10°C,\ 700\ torr)$$

$$\rho = m/V$$

$$\Delta m = V(\rho_{air} - \rho_{He})$$

$$\Delta m = 30{,}000\ L\ (1.1487\ g/L - 0.1586\ g/L)$$

$$\Delta m = 30{,}000\ L\ (0.9901\ g/L) = 29{,}703\ g = 29.70\ kg$$

Expressing the lift in English units,

$$\Delta m = 29.70\ kg \times 2.2\ lb/kg = 65\ lb$$

This balloon is large enough to carry lightweight objects, such as meteorological equipment, but it is too small to carry a person.

## SECTION 3-5: THE COMBINED GAS LAW

The laws of Avogadro, Boyle, and Charles can be combined into one equation describing the relationship among $T$, $V$, $P$, and $n$ of an ideal gas. This ideal gas law can be written two ways:

$$PV = nRT$$

where $R$ is a constant, 0.08205 L•atm/mol•K

and for a fixed quantity (moles or mass) of gas

$$P_1V_1/T_1 = P_2V_2/T_2$$

where the subscripts 1 and 2 refer to initial and final states of the gas, respectively.

Both forms of the ideal, or combined, gas law should be memorized, along with the value of the gas constant, $R$. You will find $R$ given in other units, such as J/mol•K, in the appendix, but when using the ideal gas law, the units of $R$ must be L•atm/mol•K.

The examples that follow describe various situations to which the ideal gas law can be applied. Often one form is easier to use than another, and in some cases the combined law simplifies to one of the other laws, i.e., those of Avogadro, Boyle, Charles, or Gay-Lussac.

Example 6

Consider a 0.50-mol sample of sulfur dioxide trapped in a container with a movable wall. The gas occupies 12.2 L at 22°C and 755 torr.

a. What will the volume be if the pressure is halved?

Given: 0.50 mol of $SO_2$
$V_1 = 12.2$ L, $P_1 = 755$ torr, $T_1 = 22°C$
$P_2 = \frac{1}{2}P_1$

Find: $V_2$

Solution: Method 1: Begin by analyzing the physical situation and estimating the answer. Notice that $n$, the number of moles of gas, and $T_1$, the temperature, do not change. Thus the combined gas law simplifies to Boyle's law, $PV$ = constant. Since $P$ is decreasing, $V$ must increase.

$$P_1V_1 = P_2V_2$$

$$P_1 > P_2$$

$$V_2 > V_1$$

Given that

$$P_2 = (\tfrac{1}{2})P_1$$

$$P_1V_1 = (\tfrac{1}{2})P_1V_2$$

$$V_1 = (\tfrac{1}{2})V_2$$

So the volume doubles, and

$$V_2 = 2V_1 = 2(12.2 \text{ L}) = 24.4 \text{ L}$$

Note that $P$ and $V$ can be expressed in any units, so long as they are consistent. It is not necessary to use atmospheres and liters.

Method 2: Alternately, you could use the combined gas law,

$$P_1V_1/T_1 = P_2V_2/T_2$$

substituting in the appropriate values of $P_1$, $V_1$, $T_1$, $T_2$, and $P_2$. As in method 1, any units can be used for $P$ and $V$. However, $T$ must be in Kelvins.

Method 3: You can use the ideal gas law,

$$PV = nRT$$

substituting in the values

$P = \frac{1}{2}(755 \text{ torr})/(760 \text{ torr/atm})$

$n = 0.50$ mol

$T = (22 + 273)$K

$R = 0.08205$ L•atm/mol•K

Note that units of atmospheres, liters, and Kelvins must be used.
Any of these methods are acceptable ones for solving the problem. Some, however, are less efficient and more prone to error than others.

b. What will the volume be if the temperature is raised by 10%, following the pressure change in part a?

Given: 0.50 mol $SO_2$

$P = 378$ torr

$T_1 = 295$ K

$V_1 = 24.4$ L

$T_2 = 110\%\ T_1 = 324.5$ K (The phrase "is raised by 10%" means that $T_2$ is 10% larger than $T_1$, or 110% × $T_1$.)

Find: $V_2$

Solution: Method 1: In this situation, $n$ is constant, as is $P$. Thus Charles' law is applicable:

$$V/T = \text{constant}$$

$$V_2/T_2 = V_1/T_1$$

$$V_2/V_1 = T_2/T_1$$

Since $T_2 > T_1$, $V_2$ will be larger than $V_1$.

$$V_2/24.4 \text{ L} = 110\%\ T_1/T_1$$

$$V_2 = (24.4 \text{ L})(1.10) = 26.8 \text{ L}$$

or

$$V_2 = (24.4 \text{ L})(324.5 \text{ K})/(295 \text{ K}) = 26.8 \text{ L}$$

Method 2: Use the combined gas law,

$$P_1V_1/T_1 = P_2V_2/T_2$$

Method 3: Use the ideal gas law,

$$PV = nRT$$

with

$P$ = 377.5 torr/(760 torr/atm)

$n$ = 0.50 mol

$T$ = 110%(295 K)

$R$ = 0.08205 L•atm/mol•K

c. What will the pressure of this gas be if the temperature is decreased by one-third and the volume is decreased by 15% from the final values given in part b?

Given: 0.50 mol $SO_2$

$P_1$ = 378 torr

$T_1$ = 324 K

$V_1$ = 26.8 L

$V_2$ decreased by 15% from $V_1$, or $\Delta V = 15\%V_1$, or

$V_2 = 85\%V_1$

$T_2$ decreased by 1/3 from $T_1$, or $T_2 = (2/3)T_1$

Find: $P_2$

Solution: In this situation, the only constant parameter is $n$.

Method 1: Combined gas law, $n$ constant:

$$P_1V_1/T_1 = P_2V_2/T_2$$

$$P_2 = P_1V_1T_2/V_2T_1 = P_1V_1(2/3)T_1/(.85)V_1T_1$$

Alternately,

$$P_2(\text{torr}) = (378\text{ torr})(26.8\text{ L})(2/3)(324\text{ K})/(0.85)(26.8\text{ L})(324\text{ K})$$

Cancel like factors where possible to simplify calculations:

$$P_2(\text{torr}) = (378\text{ torr})(2/3)/(0.85) = 296\text{ torr}$$

Method 2: Ideal gas law

$$PV = nRT$$

$$P = (0.50\text{ mol})(0.08205\text{ L•atm/mol•K})(2/3)(324\text{ K})/(0.85)(26.8\text{ L})$$

$$P = 0.389\text{ atm}$$

$$P = (0.389\text{ atm})(760\text{ torr/atm}) = 296\text{ torr}$$

As you can see, both methods yield the same answer, but method 1 involves fewer calculations, and thus is less prone to error than method 2.

d. Write and solve a problem which can be solved using the relationship $P \propto T$ at constant $V$ and $n$, verified by Gay-Lussac.

Solution: Your problem must include a closed system, one that cannot change volume or number of moles of gas, that is heated or cooled. Examples are soda-pop or champagne bottles, and, within certain limits, automobile tires, pressure cookers, and steamboilers.

The next example combines skills from Chapter 2 with the gas laws.

Example 7

Hydrogen sulfide reacts with nitric acid to produce nitric oxide and elemental sulfur:

$$3H_2S(aq) + 2H^+(aq) + 2NO_3^-(aq) \longrightarrow 2NO(g) + 4H_2O(l) + 3S(s)$$

What volume of NO, measured at STP, can be formed from 25.0 mL of 5.00 M $HNO_3$ and 3.74 g $H_2S$?

Given: balanced chemical equation
3.74 g $H_2S$
25.0 mL of 5.00 M $HNO_3$

Find: $V$ of NO generated, measured at STP

Solution: To find the volume of NO produced, measured at standard temperature and pressure (STP), one must know how many moles NO result. That information comes from solving the stoichiometry problem of $H_2S$ reacting with NO. A flowchart can be helpful here.

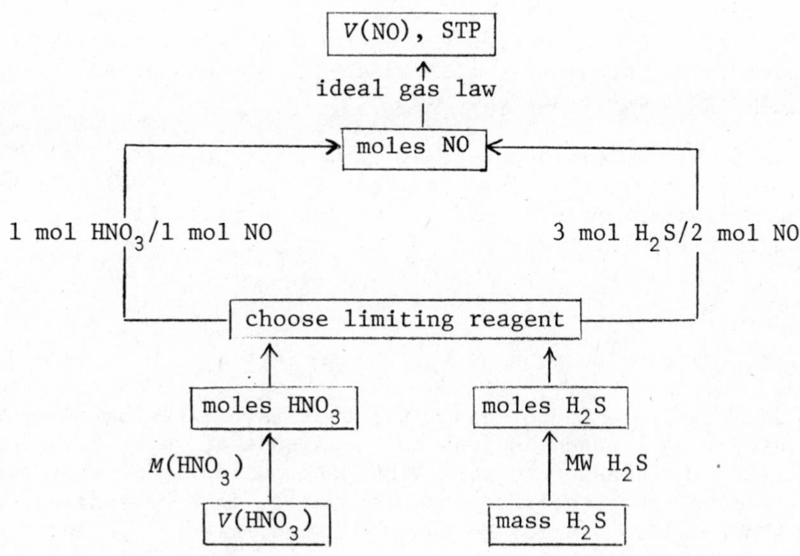


moles $HNO_3$ = (25.0 mL)(5.0 M)($10^{-3}$ L/mL) = 0.7500 mol

moles $H_2S$ = 3.74 g/(34.0 g/mol) = 0.110 mol

0.0750 mol $HNO_3$ requires (3/2)(0.0750 mol) = 0.112 mol $H_2S$

∴ $H_2S$ is limiting

$$\text{moles NO} = (2 \text{ mol NO}/3 \text{ mol } H_2S)(0.110 \text{ mol } H_2S) = 0.0733 \text{ mol}$$

$$V = nRT/P$$

STP means 1 atm, 0°C (not 25°C).

$$V = (0.0733 \text{ mol})(0.08205 \text{ L·atm/mol·K})(273 \text{ K})/1 \text{ atm}$$

$$V = 1.64 \text{ L}$$

Alternately, since 1 mole of ideal gas occupies 22.4 L at STP,

$$V = (0.0733 \text{ mol}/1 \text{ mol})(22.4 \text{ L}) = 1.64 \text{ L}$$

## SECTION 3-6: THE KINETIC MOLECULAR THEORY

One of the activities of chemists is to relate observed macroscopic properties of materials to the behavior of their constituent atoms or molecules. Chemists seek to answer the question, "What is happening at the atomic level that causes particular observable phenomena on a macroscopic scale?" We have just studied the gas laws, which describe the behavior of bulk quantities of gases. To try to explain this behavior, one first constructs a conceptual model of gases, then uses the model to make predictions. The test of the model is agreement between prediction and observation. The model of an ideal gas, the kinetic molecular theory, features three postulates:

- a gas is mostly empty space; the molecules themselves are point masses;
- gas molecules are in constant random motion, except when colliding with each other and the walls of the container;
- all collisions of gas molecules are perfectly elastic because there are no forces between the molecules, i.e., there is no loss of energy due to friction and momentum is conserved.

One way to test this model is to use it to predict gas pressure. Since Boyle's law says that $PV$ is constant at a given temperature, a good model will predict Boyle's law. The following examples expand on certain parts of the derivation of Boyle's law given in the text.

Example 8

How can velocity $v$ have components $v_x$, $v_y$, and $v_z$?

Solution: Velocity is a vector quantity; that is, it has both magnitude and direction. Speed is just the magnitude of velocity. Vector quantities are easier to work with mathematically if they have been resolved into their components, which, in a cartesian coordinate system, lie parallel to the $x$, $y$, and $z$ axes. Be sure to study Figure 3-9 in the text.

Example 9

Show that force is the rate of change of momentum.

Solution: Force is mass times acceleration. Momentum is mass times velocity.

$$F = ma$$

momentum = $mv$

$$F = \Delta mv/\Delta t$$

but for a nonreacting gas, mass is constant:

$$F = m\Delta v/\Delta t$$

Example 10

Why is the change in momentum 2 $mv$ per collision?

Solution 1: Using vector notation, one sees in Figure 3-9 that the momentum of the molecule approaching the wall is $-mv_x$. The momentum of the molecule leaving the wall is $+mv_x$ and $\Delta mv_x = +mv_x - (-mv_x) = 2mv_x$.

Solution 2: Alternately, you can view the collision of a molecule with the wall in this way. The molecule moves toward the wall with momentum $mv_x$. Upon collision, momentum becomes zero. The molecule then bounces off the wall in the opposite direction, its momentum going from zero to $mv_x$. As a result of the collision, the momentum of the molecule has thus changed from $mv_x$ to zero and back to $mv_x$, for a total change of 2 $mv_x$.

Example 11

Why is the time between collisions 2 $1/v_x$?

Solution: We are talking about a molecule starting out at one end of the box, moving distance 1 to collide with the wall, then moving back to the other end of the box, where the process starts all over. Because

$$v = \text{distance/time}$$

$$v_x = \Delta 1/\Delta t$$

$$\Delta t = \Delta 1/v_x = 2\ 1/v_x$$

Combining this result with that of the previous example we have

$$F_x = 2\ mv_x/(2\ 1/v_x) = mv_x^2/1$$

The foregoing derivation of Boyle's law shows that the kinetic molecular theory is an excellent model for ideal gas behavior. Moreover, it gives the interesting and useful result that kinetic energy, KE, of a gas depends solely on its temperature, and thus temperature is a measure of molecular motion.

$$\text{KE} = (3/2)RT$$

This statement is true for all gases, no matter what their identity. This leads to an interesting conclusion, which you can discover by considering a large number of gas molecules, e.g., a mole.

$$(3/2)RT = (1/2)\text{N}m\overline{v^2}$$

For one mole, Nm = molecular weight, $M$.

$$3RT = M\overline{v^2}$$

Thus, the heavier the molecules, the more slowly they move at a given temperature; light molecules have the highest velocities.

## SECTION 3-7: PREDICTIONS OF THE KINETIC MOLECULAR THEORY

Molecular speeds can be readily calculated if molecular weight and temperature are known. This speed is the root-mean-square speed (rms), the square root of the average of the squares of speeds of individual molecules in a gas used in the previous derivations. It is close in value to the average speed.

$$3RT = M\overline{v^2}$$

$$\sqrt{\overline{v^2}} = \sqrt{3RT/M} = v_{rms}$$

Take the average of 3, 5, and 7 and compare it with the square root of the average of $3^2$, $5^2$, and $7^2$ to get a feel for the difference between the average and rms speeds. Speeds of individual molecules in a gas range, of course, above and below $v_{rms}$. Be sure to study Figure 3-11, a plot of the Maxwell-Boltzmann distribution of molecular speeds at various temperatures.

### Example 12

You have most likely observed a helium-filled balloon lose its lift over a period of time due to diffusion of helium out of the balloon. As He diffuses out, air diffuses in, at least initially. After a short period of time, say about one hour, will the ratio of $O_2$ to $N_2$ be less than, equal to, or greater than it is in the atmosphere?

Solution: Consider the relative speeds of $O_2$ and $N_2$ at the same temperature.

$$v_{O_2} = \sqrt{3RT/M_{O_2}}$$

$$v_{N_2} = \sqrt{3RT/M_{N_2}}$$

$$v_{O_2}/v_{N_2} = \sqrt{M_{N_2}/M_{O_2}} = \sqrt{(28\text{ g mol}^{-1})/(32\text{ g mol}^{-1})}$$

$$v_{O_2}/v_{N_2} = 0.94$$

$O_2$ is a little heavier than $N_2$ and diffuses into the balloon more slowly. Thus, there will be fewer $O_2$ molecules relative to $N_2$ molecules inside the balloon than in the atmosphere.

Because ideal gas molecules exert no forces on each other, the total energy of a gas is just the sum of the energies of its constituent molecules, and the same is true of pressure. The partial pressure of a particular gas in a mixture is directly proportional to the number of moles of that gas present.

Example 13

The mole fraction of hydrogen in a mixture of hydrogen and oxygen is 0.85 and the total pressure is 1.50 atm. What are the partial pressures of $H_2$ and $O_2$? Do not be concerned about reaction between the gases to form water; no sparks or other means of igniting the mixture are present!

Solution: Mole fraction is a concentration unit which compares the moles of a component of a mixture to the total moles of all the components.

$$X_{H_2} = n_{H_2}/(n_{H_2} + n_{O_2}) = 0.85$$

Since there are only two components in this mixture, the mole fraction of oxygen is 1.00 - 0.85 or 0.15. The sum of the mole fractions of all components is one. Since $X_{H_2} > X_{O_2}$, we can expect $p_{H_2}$ to be greater than $p_{O_2}$.

$$p_{H_2} = X_{H_2} P = 0.85(1.50 \text{ atm}) = 1.275 \text{ atm} = 1.28 \text{ atm}$$

$$p_{O_2} = P - p_{H_2} = 1.50 \text{ atm} - 1.28 \text{ atm} = 0.22 \text{ atm}$$

$$p_{O_2} = X_{O_2} P = 0.15(1.50 \text{ atm}) = 0.225 \text{ atm} = 0.22 \text{ atm}$$

As predicted, the partial pressure of $O_2$ is smaller than that of $H_2$. Notice that Dalton's law can be written in two different ways:

$$P = p_1 + p_2 + p_3 \ldots$$

$$P = X_1 P + X_2 P + X_3 P + \ldots$$

## SECTION 3-8: REAL GASES AND DEVIATIONS FROM THE IDEAL GAS LAW

Two assumptions of the kinetic molecular theory are only approximately true for real gases:

- o the molecules are point masses;
- o there are no intermolecular forces between the molecules, except upon collision.

Because real gas molecules do have small, but finite, volumes, and because there are long-range attractive forces between molecules, real gas behavior deviates from ideal gas behavior, especially at high pressures and low temperatures. A low temperature is one near the condensation point of a gas, and high pressure is extremely high, so that molecules are very close to each other. Under most conditions, however, deviations from ideal behavior are very small, and the ideal gas equation of state is quite adequate. An equation of state describes the behavior of a material in terms of relationships among bulk parameters such as $P$, $V$, $T$, and $n$.

The van der Waals equation is one of several equations of state that accurately describe real gas behavior.

$$(P + a/\overline{V}^2)(\overline{V} - b) = RT$$

where $\overline{V}$ is molar volume, $V/n$; $a$ and $b$ are empirically determined constants.

The van der Waals constant $b$ corrects the observed real gas volume to ideal volume by accounting for the space occupied by the molecules themselves. The other constant, $a$, provides a correction to the observed pressure by accounting for intermolecular attractive forces, which tend to decrease pressure below its ideal value. Values of $a$ and $b$ vary with the gas in question; the larger they are, the less ideal the gas. Van der Waals constants are measured experimentally.

The compressibility factor, $Z$, is another measure of deviation from ideality:

$$Z = P\overline{V}/RT$$

$Z$ equals one for ideal gases. Values of $Z$ less than one indicate the presence of intermolecular attractive forces. When $Z$ is greater than one, usually at high pressures, repulsions due to finite molecular size predominate over attractions. Notice in Figure 3-15 in the text that $Z$ is always greater than one for $H_2$, indicating that intermolecular forces are very small. The same is true for helium. Be sure to study Figures 3-15, 3-16, and 3-17 carefully.

## Terms to Know

Avogadro's law
Boyle's law
Celcius temperature scale
Charles' law
combined gas law
Dalton's law of partial pressures
elastic collision
force
Graham's law of effusion
ideal gas law
Kelvin temperature scale
kinetic molecular theory
mole fraction
momentum
pressure
STP

## Test Yourself

1. For a fixed sample of gas at 20°C, what change in pressure will produce a volume decrease of 25%?

2. Why must the skins of whole potatoes be pricked before they are baked in a microwave oven?

3. A hydrogen gas thermometer is calibrated such that its volume is exactly 1 L at 100°C. To what temperature does a volume of 655.0 mL correspond?

4. Ammonia is synthesized from hydrogen and nitrogen.

   a. Balance the equation for the synthesis:

   $$N_2(g) + H_2(g) \longrightarrow NH_3(g)$$

   b. How many liters of ammonia can be prepared from 75 L of hydrogen and 28 L of nitrogen, if all volumes are measured at the same temperature and pressure?

c. Which gas law did you use to solve this problem?

5. A sample of gas weighing 5.75 g occupies 2.80 L at STP. What is its molecular weight?

6. A material containing bicarbonate ion is to be analyzed by decomposing it with acid and measuring the carbon dioxide evolved:

$$HCO_3^- + H^+ \longrightarrow CO_2 + H_2O$$

The carbon dioxide is collected over an aqueous solution that is saturated with carbon dioxide. The pressure inside the collection apparatus is equal to atmospheric pressure at the time of measurement of volume. A sample of the material weighing 0.2742 g evolves 41.63 mL of $CO_2$ at 23.0°C and 756.8 torr atmospheric pressure.

a. How many moles of $CO_2$ were evolved?

b. What is the mass percent $HCO_3^-$ in the sample?

7. A quantity of argon gas requires 1.0 hour to effuse through the orifice of an apparatus. The same volume of an unknown gas, measured at the same temperature and pressure, requires only 19 minutes to effuse.

a. What is the molecular weight of the unknown gas?

b. If this gas were an element, which would it be?

# 4 Will it React? An Introduction to Chemical Equilibrium

## CHAPTER OVERVIEW AND OBJECTIVES

Two themes emerge in this chapter. One is the need for a criterion of spontaneity: to be able to predict whether a proposed reaction will, in fact, take place. The other is quantitative treatment of chemical systems that are in, or approaching, a state of dynamic equilibrium.

When you finish this chapter you should be able to:

1. Understand the concept of chemical equilibrium and the equilibrium constant:

   o Write the equilibrium constant expression for any chemical equation;
   o Calculate $K_{eq}$ for an equation derived from other equations, given $K$'s for the constituent equations;
   o Convert from $K_p$ to $K_c$ and vice versa;

2. Apply the concept of equilibrium quantitatively:

   o Calculate $K_{eq}$ given data for a system at equilibrium;
   o Use $K_{eq}$ and the reaction quotient, $Q$, to predict the direction of spontaneous reaction;
   o Use $K_{eq}$ to calculate equilibrium concentrations or partial pressures;

3. Understand and apply LeChatelier's principle to equilibrium systems, both qualitatively and quantitatively.

## SECTIONS 4-1, 4-2, AND 4-3: SPONTANEOUS REACTION, EQUILIBRIUM, AND THE LAW OF MASS ACTION

A question of central concern to anyone studying the physical world is, "Will a particular combination of materials react together chemically or not?" Great pains are taken to ensure that many of the materials we use every day do not undergo chemical reactions. For example, iron and steel surfaces are coated to prevent reaction with oxygen and water to form rust. Many foods are refrigerated or frozen to retard possible reactions. Items such as baking powder, Alka-Seltzer, and Drano are stored in closed containers to prevent their reaction with water in the air. Being able to predict whether a reaction will occur spontaneously, that is, voluntarily, allows one to efficiently design both processes which require chemical reaction and materials that must be chemically inert in ordinary use.

A system capable of reaction is said to be at equilibrium if both the reaction in the forward direction and the reverse of that reaction are occurring at equal rates. This equilibrium is dynamic; changes occur at the molecular level, but the overall composition of the system is constant. An equilibrium state can be achieved by starting from either direction, that is, with the reactants of the forward reaction, or its products, which, of course, are the reactants for the reverse process.

Dynamic equilibrium can be expressed quantitatively by the equilibrium constant, $K_{eq}$. The mathematical form of $K_{eq}$ can be derived directly from the balanced equation describing the system, using the law of mass action. For a general equation

$$lL + mM \rightleftharpoons qQ + rR$$

one can write

$$K_{eq} = \frac{[Q]^q[R]^r}{[M]^m[L]^l}$$

The fraction on the right-hand side is called the equilibrium constant expression.

Example 1

a. The equilibrium constant expression for the equation

$$2NH_3(g) + (3/2)O_2(g) \rightleftharpoons N_2(g) + 3H_2O(g)$$

is

$$K_{eq} = \frac{[N_2][H_2O]^3}{[NH_3]^2[O_3]^{3/2}}$$

Things to note:

1. The symbol $[A]$ means molar concentration of $A$.

2. Product concentrations are multiplied together and written in the numerator of the expression; reactants are in the denominator.

3. The concentration of each species is raised to a power equal to its stoichiometric coefficient in the balanced equation.

4. The numerical value of $K_{eq}$ for a system varies only with temperature.

b. For the equation

$$6H_2O(g) + 2N_2(g) \rightleftharpoons 3O_2(g) + 4NH_3(g)$$

the equilibrium constant expression is

$$K_{eq} = \frac{[NH_3]^4[O_2]^3}{[N_2]^2[H_2O]^6}$$

Notice that equation b is twice the reverse of equation a and that the equilibrium constant expression for b is the square of the reciprocal of that for a.

$$(1/K(a))^2 \quad \left[\frac{[O_2]^{3/2}[NH_3]^2}{[N_2][H_2O]^3}\right]^2 = \frac{[O_2]^3[NH_3]^4}{[N_2]^2[H_2O]^6} = K(b)$$

The theoretical underpinnings of the law of mass action will be studied in Chapter 15. For the present, note that the form of the equilibrium constant expression depends only on the balanced chemical equation describing the system. Even though equilibrium is defined as the state of a system in which the rates of the forward and reverse reactions are equal, the reaction mechanism and the rate laws need not be known in order to write the equilibrium constant expression. Reaction rate laws and mechanisms can only be determined by experimentation, and cannot be deduced from chemical equations, balanced or not. It is fortunate that the law of mass action can be applied without having any more information than the balanced chemical equation; many chemical processes have been utilized for years before their step-by-step mechanisms were elucidated by persistent experimentors.

## SECTIONS 4-4 AND 4-5: USING EQUILIBRIUM CONSTANTS

Equilibrium constants are useful in two ways:

- o to provide a criterion of spontaneity, that is, to predict whether a reaction is possible;
- o to allow a quantitative description of the composition of a system at equilibrium.

Reactions for which $K_{eq}$ is greater than one are classified as spontaneous. However, $K_{eq}$ values do not give any information about how fast a reaction will occur and an equilibrium state will be achieved. The answer to the question: "How fast up in Chapter 20. The equilibrium constant expression for reactions involving gases can be written using partial pressures instead of concentrations. For example, for the equation

$$4NH_3(g) + 3O_2(g) \rightleftharpoons 2N_2(g) + 6H_2O(g)$$

the equilibrium constant using concentrations is

$$K_c = \frac{[N_2]^2[H_2O]^6}{[NH_3]^4[O_2]^3}$$

and using partial pressures of the gases is

$$K_p = \frac{p_{N_2}^{\,2}\,p_{H_2O}^{\,6}}{p_{NH_3}^{\,4}\,p_{O_2}^{\,3}}$$

The relationship between $K_c$ and $K_p$ for any reaction can be easily derived using the ideal gas law.

$$p = (n/V)RT = RT\ (\text{molarity})$$

$$\text{molarity} = n/V = p/RT$$

Using the reaction above as an example, and substituting $p/RT$ for concentrations,

$$K_c = \frac{(p_{N_2}/RT)^2(p_{H_2O}/RT)^6}{(p_{NH_3}/RT)^4(p_{O_2}/RT)^3} = \frac{p_{N_2}^2 p_{H_2O}^6/(RT)^8}{p_{NH_3}^4 p_{O_2}^3/(RT)^7}$$

$$K_c = \frac{p_{N_2}^2 p_{H_2O}^6}{p_{NH_3}^4 p_{O_2}^3 (RT)} = K_p/RT$$

This agrees with the expression derived in the text,

$$K_p = K_c(RT)^{\Delta n}$$

Here, $\Delta n$, the difference between moles of products and moles of reactants, is equal to +1. While this equation relating $K_p$ to $K_c$ is a handy one, if you should forget it, you can always derive $K_p$ from $K_c$, or vice versa, by using the ideal gas law.

When the conventions $K_p$ and $K_c$ are used, units are sometimes attached to equilibrium constants. Such units follow the mathematical forms of the particular equilibrium constant expression. For the reaction we have just been discussing, units for $K_c$ would be mol liter$^{-1}$ and for $K_p$, atm. Strictly speaking, equilibrium constants do not have units. You will see why this is true in Chapter 17.

Example 2

The shift reaction can be used to produce hydrogen, an important industrial reagent, from carbon monoxide and steam:

$$CO(g) + H_2O(g) \rightleftharpoons CO_2(g) + H_2(g)$$

At 100°C, an equilibrium mixture of CO, $CO_2$, $H_2$ and $H_2O$ contains 0.696 atm $H_2O$, $1.00 \times 10^{-2}$ atm CO, and 5.00 atm each $H_2$ and $CO_2$. Calculate $K_p$ for this reaction at 100°C.

Solution: The equilibrium constant expression is

$$K_p = \frac{p_{CO_2} p_{H_2}}{p_{H_2O} p_{CO}}$$

Substituting in the equilibrium partial pressures of the four gases in the system gives

$$K_p = \frac{(5.00)^2}{(1.00 \times 10^{-2})(0.696)} = 3.59 \times 10^3$$

The next example demonstrates the use of the reaction quotient $Q$ to judge whether a system is at equilibrium and, if not, in what direction net reaction will occur until equilibrium is achieved. The form of $Q$ is identical to that of the equilibrium constant expression.

Example 3

When the water-gas shift reaction,

$$CO(g) + H_2O(g) \rightleftharpoons CO_2(g) + H_2(g)$$

is run at 25°C, $K_p$ is $1.03 \times 10^5$, almost two orders of magnitude larger than it is at 100°C. Consider the following reaction mixtures, and predict whether further net reaction in either direction will occur.

a. The partial pressures of $CO_2$ and $H_2$ are 5 atm each, the partial pressure of $H_2O$ is 1 atm, and that of CO is $10^{-2}$ atm.

Solution: If the reaction quotient, $Q$, is less than the equilibrium constant, then products will continue to form until equilibrium is reached. If $Q$ is greater than $K$, there will be spontaneous net decomposition of products until equilibrium is attained.

$$Q = \frac{p_{CO_2} p_{H_2}}{p_{CO} p_{H_2O}}$$

$$Q = (5)^2/(1)(10^{-2}) = 25 \times 10^2 \cong 3 \times 10^2$$

Since $Q < K$, the reaction will proceed further to the right, yielding more $CO_2$ and $H_2$ net. This will continue until equilibrium is reached, i.e., when $Q = K$.

b. The partial pressures of CO and $H_2O$ are $10^{-2}$ atm each, while those of $CO_2$ and $H_2$ are both 7 atm.

Solution: Compare $Q$ with $K$.

$$Q = (7)^2/(10^{-2})^2 = 49 \times 10^4 = 5 \times 10^5$$

Since $Q > K$, there will be net decomposition of $CO_2$ and $H_2$, until $Q = K$.

Equilibrium constants, in combination with reaction stoichiometry, are useful in predicting the concentrations of components of a reaction mixture at equilibrium.

Example 4

Methyl alcohol, $CH_3OH$, can be synthesized from carbon monoxide and hydrogen:

$$CO(g) + 2H_2(g) \rightleftharpoons CH_3OH(g)$$

At 100°C, $K_p$ for this reaction is 10.84. If equimolar amounts of CO and $H_2$ were mixed together at 100°C such that the total initial pressure was 2.00 atm, what would be the partial pressures of $CH_3OH$, CO, and $H_2$ at equilibrium?

Given: reaction at 100°C, $K_p = 10.84$

$$CO + 2H_2 \rightleftharpoons CH_3OH$$

1:1 mole ratio of CO and $H_2$ initially;

total initial pressure of 2.00 atm

Find: equilibrium partial pressures of $CH_3OH$, CO, $H_2$

Solution: The equilibrium expression for the reaction of interest is

$$K_p = \frac{p_{CH_3OH}}{p_{CO}p^2_{H_2}} = 10.84$$

Since $K > 1$, the position of equilibrium will lie to the right. Appreciable conversion of reactants to products is predicted. In cases such as this one, calculations are simplified by imagining that the reaction first goes to completion and that some of the product then dissociates. The chart illustrates this thought process. Let $x$ be the partial pressure of $CH_3OH$ that dissociates after the imaginary completion step. The initial pressures of CO and $H_2$ are 1.00 atm by Avogadro's law, because they are present in equimolar amounts.

| | CO | $H_2$ | $CH_3OH$ |
|---|---|---|---|
| start | 1.00 | 1.00 | 0 |
| completion | 0.50 | 0 | 0.50 |
| change | $+x$ | $+2x$ | $-x$ |
| equilibrium | $0.50 + x$ | $2x$ | $0.50 - x$ |

The reaction stoichiometry tells us that $H_2$ is the limiting reagent and CO is in excess by 0.50 atm. The maximum quantity of $CH_3OH$ that could form is 0.50 atm. Substituting the equilibrium values of partial pressure into the expression for $K_p$ gives

$$K_p = \frac{0.50 - x}{(0.50 + x)(2x)^2} = 10.84$$

Inspection of this expression shows that it is cubic in $x$. The method of successive approximations is a good one to use for such problems. First, estimate a value for $x$, and solve the equation using this value in the factors $0.50 + x$ and $0.50 - x$. The value of $x$ obtained from this calculation is used to solve the equation a second time. This process is repeated until two succeeding values of $x$ are identical. Choose $x = 0$ for the first value. This is equivalent to neglecting $x$ with respect to 0.50.

$$\frac{0.50 - 0}{(0.50 + 0)(2x)^2} = 10.84$$

$$x^2 = 0.02306$$

$$x = 0.15$$

Repeat the calculation with $x = 0.15$

$$\frac{0.50 - 0.15}{(0.50 + 0.15)(2x)^2} = 10.84 \qquad x = 0.11$$

Repeat, using $x = 0.11$

$$\frac{0.50 - 0.11}{(0.50 + 0.11)(2x)^2} = 10.84 \qquad x = 0.12$$

Repeat, using $x = 0.12$

$$\frac{0.50 - 0.12}{(0.50 + 0.12)(2x)^2} = 10.84 \qquad x = 0.12$$

Since the last two calculations give the same result, the equation has been solved. Equilibrium pressures are

$$p_{CH_3OH} = 0.50 - x = 0.38 \text{ atm}$$

$$p_{CO} = 0.50 + x = 0.62 \text{ atm}$$

$$p_{H_2} = 2x = 0.24 \text{ atm}$$

As we predicted before doing the calculations, much of the hydrogen and a substantial portion of the carbon monoxide have been converted to methyl alcohol. The position of equilibrium is to the right.

## SECTION 4-6: EQUILIBRIA INVOLVING GASES WITH LIQUIDS OR SOLIDS

Systems containing more than one phase are called heterogeneous. Examples of reactions in such systems are the production of "water gas" from coke and steam:

1. $C(s) + H_2O(g) \rightleftharpoons CO(g) + H_2(g)$

the reduction of bunsenite to metallic nickel:

2. $NiO(s) + CO(g) \rightleftharpoons Ni(s) + CO_2(g)$

and the vaporization of liquid mercury, a health hazard:

3. $Hg(l) \rightleftharpoons Hg(g)$

When writing equilibrium constant expressions for heterogeneous equilibria, concentrations of pure liquid and pure solid phases are not included. Detailed reasons for this convention are given in Chapter 15. For such a system to be in equilibrium, some amount of the solid or liquid must be present, of course, else there would be no chemical reaction. However, it makes no difference how much solid or liquid there is in contact with the gaseous components.

Equilibrium constant expressions for the three reactions just mentioned are

1. $K_c = \dfrac{[CO][H_2]}{[H_2O]}$ 2. $K_c = \dfrac{[CO_2]}{[CO]}$ 3. $K_c = [Hg(g)]$

You should write out the expressions for $K_p$. These expressions are used in the same way as those for homogeneous, or one-phase, equilibria:

- to predict whether a reaction will occur spontaneously;
- to calculate concentrations, or partial pressures of gases, of the components of a system at equilibrium.

Note that $K_p$ for system 3,

$$Hg(l) \rightleftharpoons Hg(g)$$

is just the equilibrium vapor pressure of mercury, expressed in atmospheres. Solids also have equilibrium vapor pressures, which are equal to the $K_p$ values for the process of sublimation. For example, the sublimation of ice,

$$H_2O(s) \rightleftharpoons H_2O(g)$$

accounts for the gradual disappearance of snow at temperatures below the freezing point of water. While snow cannot melt unless the temperature reaches 0°C, it does sublime. At -5°C, the vapor pressure of ice is 3 torr.

Equilibrium vapor pressures depend on only two parameters:

- temperature, with which all equilibrium constants vary, and
- the nature of the solid or liquid.

Liquids and solids having strong intermolecular attractive forces will have relatively low vapor pressures, since these attractive forces must be overcome in order for molecules to enter the gas phase. One final point to keep in mind: there is no equilibrium, and hence no equilibrium vapor pressure, unless some solid or liquid is present in contact with its vapor.

## SECTION 4-7: FACTORS AFFECTING EQUILIBRIUM

This section considers how systems that are initially at equilibrium behave when perturbed in some way. Four kinds of perturbations are discussed:

- removal or addition of one of the components of the system at constant temperature;
- a change in the temperature;
- a change in the pressure at constant temperature;
- addition of a catalyst.

The effects of the first three disturbances can be predicted by using Le Chatelier's principle: a system at equilibrium that is stressed in some way will react to relieve the stress by changing its position of equilibrium. The examples which follow illustrate the effects of these stresses.

### Example 5

The equilibrium constant for the reaction

$$CO(g) + 2H_2(g) \rightleftharpoons CH_3OH(g)$$

is 10.84 at 100°C. What would happen to an equilibrium mixture of CO, $H_2$, and gaseous $CH_3OH$ if some methanol ($CH_3OH$) were removed from the system, for instance by condensing it to liquid? The temperature of the gaseous mixture remains constant.

Solution: The equilibrium constant expression for this process is

$$K_p = \frac{p_{CH_3OH}}{p_{CO}p_{H_2}^2}$$

As long as the temperature remains constant, the numerical value of $K_p$ will not change. Therefore, if some gaseous methanol were removed from the system, $p_{CH_3OH}$ would be lowered and the reaction quotient would no longer be equal to $K$. In order to reestablish equilibrium, that is, make $Q = K$, the numerator of $Q$ must increase, or the denominator must decrease, or both. Since the numerator and denominator of any reaction quotient are interdependent, increasing $p_{CH_3OH}$ through the formation of more $CH_3OH(g)$ from CO and $H_2$ necessarily decreases $p_{CO}$ and $p_{H_2}$. Stated another way, one says that the position of equilibrium has shifted to the right, increasing the yield of product. The yield of $CH_3OH$ can also be increased by adding more reactant: CO or $H_2$.

Example 6

The production of water gas is an endothermic process:

$$C(s) + H_2O(g) + \text{heat} \rightleftharpoons CO(g) + H_2(g)$$

$$\Delta H = 130 \text{ kJ}$$

Would raising the temperature of an equilibrium reaction mixture favor formation of products, i.e., hydrogen and carbon monoxide, or reactants?

Solution: Energy in the form of heat can be thought of as a reactant necessary for the production of CO and $H_2$. Thus raising the temperature makes more heat available for the forward reaction, increasing the yield of products. The position of equilibrium shifts to the right at higher temperatures, and the value of $K$ increases as well. The value of $K$ changes only if the temperature changes.

Example 7

The synthesis of methanol from carbon monoxide and hydrogen is an exothermic reaction:

$$CO(g) + 2H_2(g) \rightleftharpoons CH_3OH(g) + \text{heat}$$

$$\Delta H° = -92 \text{ kJ mol}^{-1}$$

How would the position of equilibrium be affected by an increase in temperature?

Solution: In exothermic processes, heat is a product. To increase yield, one wants to remove heat generated by the forward reaction, which will shift the position of equilibrium to the right. Lowering the temperature will increase *K*. Adding heat to the system by raising the temperature accomplishes just the opposite: the forward reaction will be inhibited and the reverse one favored, the position of equilibrium will shift to the left, and *K* will decrease. Dramatic evidence for this conclusion is provided by the values of $K_p$ for this reaction at various temperatures, displayed in Table 4-1.

*Table 4-1*

| T(°C) | 0 | 25 | 100 | 200 | 300 | 400 |
|---|---|---|---|---|---|---|
| $K_p$ | $5.27 \times 10^5$ | $2.12 \times 10^4$ | 10.84 | $1.695 \times 10^{-2}$ | $2.316 \times 10^{-4}$ | $1.091 \times 10^{-5}$ |

Example 8

Consider again the synthesis of methanol from CO:

$$CO(g) + 2H_2(g) \rightleftharpoons CH_3OH(g)$$

How would an equilibrium reaction mixture be affected if the volume of the container were decreased to 2/3 its original value, at constant temperature?

Solution: Decreasing *V* at constant *T* will cause an increase in pressure. Le Chatelier's principle applied to this situation predicts that net reaction will occur to decrease the total number of molecules in the system, thus helping to alleviate the stress. Thus net formation of $CH_3OH$ is predicted.

Calculating *Q*, the reaction quotient, immediately after the pressure has increased, but before equilibrium has been reestablished, provides a check on the prediction. Since *T* is constant and net reaction has not yet occurred, Boyle's law applies:

$$P_1V_1 = P_2V_2$$

$$P_2 = P_1V_1/V_2$$

$$V_2 = (2/3)V_1$$

$$P_2 = P_1V_1/(2/3)V_1 = (3/2)P_1$$

$$Q = \frac{p_{CH_3OH}}{p_{CO}p_{H_2}^2}$$

$$Q' = \frac{(3/2)p_{CH_3OH}}{(3/2)p_{CO}(3/2)p_{H_2}^2}$$

$$Q' = \frac{(4/9)p_{CH_3OH}}{p_{CO}p_{H_2}^2} = (4/9)Q$$

For equilibrium to be reestablished, $Q$ must equal $K$, thus the value of $Q'$ must increase. There will be net formation of $CH_3OH$, in agreement with the prediction from Le Chatelier's principle.

Note: If there are equal numbers of moles of gaseous reactants and products, then a volume, or pressure, change will have no effect on the position of equilibrium. Using the shift reaction as an example,

$$CO(g) + H_2O(g) \rightleftharpoons CO_2(g) + H_2(g)$$

$$K_p = \frac{p_{CO_2}p_{H_2}}{p_{CO}p_{H_2O}}$$

Let's decrease the volume of an equilibrium mixture by one-half. Then each partial pressure will double, that is, $p' = 2p$.

$$Q' = \frac{p'_{CO_2}p'_{H_2}}{p'_{CO}p'_{H_2O}} = \frac{2p_{CO_2}2p_{H_2}}{2p_{CO}2p_{H_2O}}$$

Since all the factors of 2 cancel,

$$Q' = K_p$$

The final perturbation on equilibrium systems to be examined is catalysis. A catalyst functions by allowing a reaction to occur via a path that is lower in energy than the uncatalyzed one. However, both the forward and the reverse reactions are catalyzed. Thus, the function served by catalysis is to achieve equilibrium more quickly than would occur without the catalyst. The position of equilibrium, and the value of $K$, are unaffected. Catalysis will be considered in more detail in Chapter 20.

In summary, the position of equilibrium in a system can be affected by changes in temperature, pressure or volume, or composition, but not by catalysis. The direction that the position of equilibrium will shift when a system is stressed can be predicted qualitatively by Le Chatelier's principle. This provides a convenient method for estimating solutions to problems involving equilibrium systems.

## Terms to Know

catalyst
chemical equilibrium
equilibrium constant
equilibrium constant expression
equilibrium vapor pressure
$K_c$
$K_p$
law of mass action
Le Chatelier's principle

reaction quotient
spontaneous reaction

## Test Yourself

1. Mercury (II) oxide can be decomposed to its elements:

$$HgO(s) \rightleftharpoons Hg(l) + \tfrac{1}{2}O_2(g)$$

   a. Write the equilibrium constant expression for this reaction.

   b. The standard enthalpy change for this process is 91 kJ $mol^{-1}$ at 25°C. Suggest two ways to increase the yield of the reaction, i.e., to decompose more HgO.

2. Write the equilibrium constant expressions for the following equations:

   a. $2H_2S(g) + 3O_2(g) \rightleftharpoons 2H_2O(g) + 2SO_2(g)$

   b. $2PbS(s) + 3O_2(g) \rightleftharpoons 2PbO(s) + 2SO_2(g)$

   c. $O_2(g) + 2Hg(l) \rightleftharpoons HgO(s)$

   d. $SO_2(g) + H_2O(g) \rightleftharpoons \frac{3}{2}O_2(g) + H_2S(g)$

3. Find the relationship between $K_c$ and $K_p$ for each of the equations in question 2.

4. Find the relationship between the equilibrium constants for equations a and d in question 2.

5. For which of the following processes is there nearly complete conversion of reactants to products at equilibrium?

   a. $COCl_2(g) \rightleftharpoons CO(g) + Cl_2(g)$ $K_c = 8.05 \times 10^{-4}$ at 400°C

   b. $CO(g) + 2H_2(g) \rightleftharpoons CH_3OH(g)$ $K_c = 1.27 \times 10^{7}$ at 25°C

   c. $CO_2(g) + C(s) \rightleftharpoons 2CO(g)$ $K_c = 14.0$ at 800°C

   d. $N_2O_4(g) \rightleftharpoons 2NO_2(g)$ $K_c = 0.125$ at 25°C

6. Phosgene, $COCl_2$, is a highly poisonous gas used in the manufacture of polyurethanes. It is synthesized from chlorine and carbon monoxide:

$$CO(g) + Cl_2(g) \rightleftharpoons COCl_2(g)$$

$K_p = 71.3$ for this reaction at 400°C

   a. If the partial pressures of CO and $Cl_2$ in an equilibrium mixture are 375 torr and 200 torr respectively, what is the partial pressure of phosgene?

   b. If 1.00 mol of pure phosgene were placed in an evacuated 10.0-L vessel at 400°C, what would be the partial pressures of carbon monoxide and chlorine at equilibrium? How many moles of each would have formed?

c. What would be the partial pressure of phosgene at equilibrium if 0.100 mol carbon monoxide and 0.200 mol chlorine were mixed in an evacutated 5.0-L vessel at 400°C?

7. The equilibrium constant for the reaction in question varies with temperature as follows:

| T(°C): | 25 | 100 | 400 |
|---|---|---|---|
| $K_p$: | $6.81 \times 10^{12}$ | $7.48 \times 10^{8}$ | 71.3 |

a. Is this reaction exothermic or endothermic?

b. What effect, if any, will removal of chlorine from an equilibrium mixture have?

c. What effect, if any, will decreasing the size of the reaction vessel containing an equilibrium mixture produce?

d. What will be the effect on equilibrium, if any, of adding a catalyst to a mixture of CO and $Cl_2$ at 100°C?

# 5 Solution Equilibria: Acids and Bases

## CHAPTER OVERVIEW AND OBJECTIVES

Aqueous solutions of acids, bases, and sparingly soluble salts are examined qualitatively and quantitatively. Equilibria involving acid-base and solution-precipitation reactions are often combined with stoichiometry, so you may wish to review appropriate sections of Chapter 2.

When you finish this chapter you should be able to:

1. Understand the pH scale and perform pH calculations;
2. Define acids and bases according to the Arrhenius and Brønsted-Lowry formalisms, and relate values of $K_a$ and $K_b$ to acid and base strength;
3. Solve qualitative and quantitative problems involving mixtures of strong acids and bases;
4. Solve qualitative and quantitative problems involving weak acids and bases and their salts, both singly and in combination, using the principles of chemical equilibrium and stoichiometry;
5. Understand the phenomena of precipitation and dissolution of sparingly soluble salts and describe them quantitatively.

## SECTION 5-1: EQUILIBRIA IN AQUEOUS SOLUTIONS

The most important concept that emerges in this section is that water, because it is a polar substance, is an excellent solvent for other polar and ionic materials. A molecule is polar if its electrons are unevenly distributed, so that there is a partial negative charge in one part of the molecule and a corresponding partial positive charge in another part of the molecule. The electrostatic interaction between water molecules and solute molecules or ions is called hydration. Figure 5-1 in the textbook illustrates this nicely. In some aqueous solution processes water is a reactant in addition to being the solvent; these are hydrolysis reactions.

## SECTION 5-2: IONIZATION OF WATER AND THE pH SCALE

Before considering the autoionization of water and pH, we will spend some time on the mathematical topic of logarithms. If you are not familiar with logarithms, you should study this section very carefully, and do many practice problems.

## Logarithms

Logarithms are exponents. The expression log $x = a$ means $x = 10^a$.

The logarithm of $x$, or $a$, is the exponent to which 10, the base, is raised to equal $x$. Logarithms come in two varieties. Common logarithms have base 10; that is, 10 raised to a power, the logarithm, equals a given number. There are also natural logarithms, abbreviated ln, that have $e = 2.71828...$ as the base. One writes $\ln x = b$ meaning $x = e^b$.

The two bases are related by $\ln x = 2.303 \log x$, which is sometimes written as $\log_e x = 2.303 \log_{10} x$.

Common logarithms are very convenient to use when working with numbers having very large or very small powers of 10.

The pH scale is a logarithmic scale for expressing hydrogen ion concentration in aqueous solution. It uses common logarithms. Later in the course you will use natural logarithms.

When using common logarithms, you can do part of the calculation mentally, and thus get an estimate to within one order of magnitude. (An order of magnitude is a factor of 10.)

### Example 1

What is log 45?

Solution: To find the log of a number, first write the number in scientific notation, with one nonzero digit to the left of the decimal point.

$$45 = 4.5 \times 10^1 = 10^a \times 10^1 = 10^{a+1}$$

The log of 45 is then $a + 1$. You look up the value of $a$, the log of 4.5, using a calculator or a table of logarithms. Doing so we find

$$\log 4.5 = 0.653 = a$$

Combining the two parts of the logarithm we have

$$\log 4.5 \times 10^1 = 0.653 + 1 = 1.653$$

### Example 2

What is $\log 2.78 \times 10^{15}$?

Solution: The log of $10^{15}$ is just 15. Looking up the log of 2.78 we find 0.444, so

$$\log 2.78 \times 10^{15} = 15.444, \text{ or}$$

$$2.78 \times 10^{15} = 10^{0.444} \times 10^{15}$$

Notice that a common logarithm can always be estimated. This is because part of it can be done in your head, as long as the number is written in exponential notation.

### Example 3

What is $\log 6.5 \times 10^{-8}$?

Solution: The log of $10^{-8}$ is -8. Looking up the log of 6.5 reveals it to be 0.813. Thus, log $6.5 \times 10^{-8} = 0.813 - 8$. We can write this more compactly, because $0.813 - 8 = -7.187$.

Example 4

The reverse process, finding a number for which a logarithm is given, is called taking the antilog. What number has logarithm 3.066?

Solution: This says log $x = 3.066$. Since logarithms are exponents,

$$x = 10^3 \times 10^{0.066}$$

So $x$ is some number between 1 and 10, multiplied by $10^3$, i.e., a number between 1000 and 10,000. Consulting a calculator or log table reveals that

$$0.066 = \log 1.16$$

Thus, $x = 1.16 \times 10^3$.

Example 5

Log $x = -5.325$. What is $x$?

Solution: To find $x$, we must first rewrite the log in the form

$$-5.325 = 0.675 - 6$$

Then we know that $x$ is some number between 1 and 10 multiplied by $10^{-6}$, because

$$-6 = \log 10^{-6}$$

The log table gives 0.675 as log 4.73. Then,

$$x = 4.73 \times 10^{-6}.$$

Here are some important facts about common logarithms to keep in mind:

1. The log of a number between 1 and 10 will lie between 0 and 1.
2. The log of 1 is zero, because $1 = 10^0$.
3. The log of a number between 0 and 1 is negative.
4. The log of zero is $-\infty$ and logarithms of negative numbers are undefined.
5. Three useful properties of logs are:
   a. $\log x \cdot y = \log x + \log y$
   b. $\log (x/y) = \log x - \log y$
   c. $\log x^a = a \log x$

pH and pOH

The pH scale, as was stated earlier, is a means of expressing hydrogen ion concentration in aqueous solution in logarithmic form. This scale was invented for convenience, because $[H^+]$ can vary over many orders of magnitude. The pH scale is only defined for aqueous solutions.

Example 6

a. What is the pH of a $1.4 \times 10^{-5}$ M solution of HI, a strong acid?

$$pH = -\log [H^+]$$

Solution: Since HI is a strong acid it is completely dissociated, and $[H^+] = 1.4 \times 10^{-5}$.

$$pH = -\log (1.4 \times 10^{-5})$$

$$pH = -(\log 1.4 - 5) = -(0.15 - 5)$$

$$pH = 4.85$$

The slight dissociation of water molecules into $H^+$ and $OH^-$ occurs, to one degree or another, in all aqueous solutions. The relative concentrations of $H^+$ and $OH^-$ in any aqueous solution are controlled by this equilibrium.

$$H_2O(l) \rightleftharpoons H^+(aq) + OH^-(aq)$$

$$K_w = [H^+][OH^-] = 1.00 \times 10^{-14} \text{ at } 25°C$$

Thus, you can always calculate $[H^+]$ if $[OH^-]$ is known, and vice versa. You should memorize the value of $K_w$ at 25°C. You will use it often.

Example 7

What is the hydroxide ion concentration and pOH in the HI solution in the previous example?

Given: $1.4 \times 10^{-5}$ M HI($aq$)
pH = 4.85

Find: $[OH^-]$, pOH

Solution: There are two possible routes to the unknowns. The first route uses the relationship

$$[H^+][OH^-] = 1.00 \times 10^{-14}$$

$$[OH^-] = 1.00 \times 10^{-14}/[H^+]$$

$$= 1.00 \times 10^{-14}/(1.4 \times 10^{-5})$$

$$[OH^-] = 7.1 \times 10^{-10}$$

$$pOH = -\log [OH^-] = -(0.85 - 10) = 9.15$$

The second route takes advantage of the fact that

$$pH + pOH = 14.00$$

Thus,

$$pOH = 14.00 - pH = 14.00 - 4.85$$

$$pOH = 9.15 = -\log [OH^-] = -(0.85 - 10)$$

$$[OH^-] = 7.1 \times 10^{-10}$$

## SECTIONS 5-3 and 5-4: STRONG AND WEAK ACIDS AND BASES

These two sections can be considered together, because they are interrelated. The answer to the question, "What are acids and bases?" can be given in various ways. The Brønsted-Lowry formalism is very commonly used: acids donate protons, or hydrogen ions, while bases accept protons. This definition is true for any solvent, but in water it is equivalent to the Arrhenius one.

Acids and bases are classified as strong or weak, depending on the extent to which they ionize. Do not confuse the terms strong and weak with concentrated and dilute. They are not related. Strong acids and bases are completely dissociated into ions in solution, while weak ones are only partially dissociated. "Concentrated" and "dilute" refer to relative amounts of solute in a solution, whether dissociated or not. The value of the dissociation constant for an acid or a base, $K_a$ or $K_b$, is a measure of its strength. Consider for example, uric acid, which plays a role in the arthritic disease gout:

$$C_5H_3N_4O_3H(aq) \rightleftharpoons H^+(aq) + C_5H_3N_4O_3^-(aq)$$

$$K_a = \frac{[H^+][C_5H_3N_4O_3^-]}{[C_5H_3N_4O_3H]} = 1.3 \times 10^{-4}$$

Uric acid is classified as weak because its dissociation constant, $K_a$, is less than one. Recall that equilibrium constants are dimensionless. Some commonly encountered strong acids are:

| | |
|---|---|
| hydrochloric | $HCl$ |
| hydrobromic | $HBr$ |
| hydroiodic | $HI$ |
| perchloric | $HClO_4$ |
| nitric | $HNO_3$ |
| sulfuric (1st proton only) | $H_2SO_4$ |
| chloric | $HClO_3$ |
| permanganic | $HMnO_4$ |

When a Brønsted-Lowry acid loses a proton, the ion remaining is that acid's conjugate base. Thus, urate ion, $C_5H_3N_4O_3^-$, is the conjugate base of uric acid. Hydroxide ion is the conjugate base of water:

$$H_2O \rightleftharpoons H^+ + OH^-$$

However, water can also act as a base, accepting protons from acids:

$$\underset{\text{base}}{H_2O} + \underset{\text{acid}}{HCOOH} \rightleftharpoons \underset{\text{conjugate acid}}{H_3O^+} + \underset{\text{conjugate base}}{HCOO^-}$$

Substances that can behave either as Brønsted-Lowry acids or bases, depending on their environment, are called amphiprotic.

An acid is classified as strong if its conjugate base readily gives up a proton. Thus, the conjugate base of a strong acid is very weak. Conversely, very weak acids have strong conjugate bases.

Example 8

Arrange the acids in the list in order of increasing acid strength.

| Acid | | $pK_a$ |
|---|---|---|
| Chloric acid | $HClO_3$ | -3 |
| Hypoiodous acid | HIO | 10.64 |
| Butyric acid | $C_3H_7COOH$ | 4.812 |
| Lactic acid | $C_2H_5OCOOH$ | 3.863 |
| Phenol | $C_6H_5OH$ | 9.893 |

Solution: The greater the value of $K_a$, the stronger an acid is. The information given here is in the form of $pK_a$ values, i.e., the negative logarithms of the $K_a$'s. Thus, the smaller $K_a$ itself is, the larger will be its $pK_a$. The weakest acid is thus hypoiodous acid, with $K_a$ of the order of magnitude $10^{-11}$. The strongest acid in the list is chloric acid, with $K_a$ of the order of magnitude $10^3$. $HClO_3$ is classified as a strong acid, since its $K_a > 1$.

HIO < phenol < butyric acid < lactic acid < $HClO_3$

weakest acid ⟶ strongest acid

Example 9

Arrange the acids in the previous example in order of increasing strength of their conjugate bases. Write formulas for the conjugate bases.

Solution: The stronger an acid, the weaker its conjugate base, and vice versa. Thus, the weakest conjugate base is that of chloric acid; the strongest conjugate base is that of hypoiodous acid. Notice that the larger $K_a$, the stronger the conjugate base is.

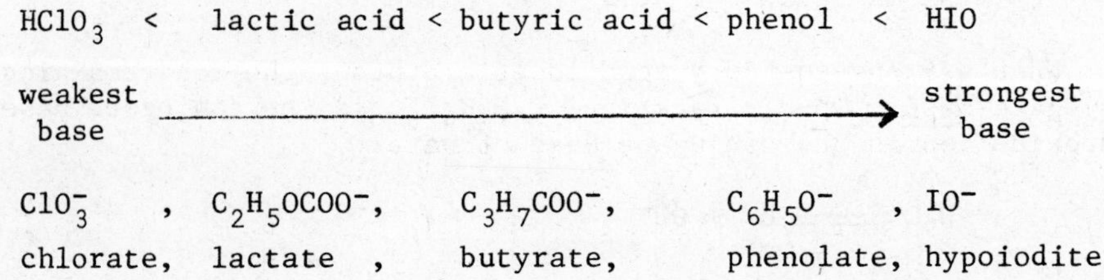

Acids whose conjugate bases are weaker than water, that is, strong acids, all appear to be of equal strength in aqueous solution. Water binds protons better than do the conjugate bases of these acids, a phenomenon known as the leveling effect. These acids often are of very different strengths in other solvents, however.

Metal hydroxides which completely dissociate in water to give the Brønsted-Lowry base $OH^-$ are classified as strong. The most frequently encountered hydroxides that are strong bases are as follows:

- Those of the alkali metals, periodic Group I:

  LiOH, NaOH, KOH, RbOH, CsOH, FrOH

- Those of the heavier alkaline earth metals, Group II:

  $Ca(OH)_2$, $Sr(OH)_2$, $Ba(OH)_2$, $Ra(OH)_2$

Almost all other bases, whether they are inorganic or organic, can be assumed to be weak ones. Organic bases usually have nitrogen atoms that act as proton acceptors.

$$HONH_2(aq) + H_2O(l) \rightleftharpoons HONH_3^+(aq) + OH^-(aq)$$

hydroxylamine — hydroxylammonium

$$K_b = \frac{[HONH_3^+][OH^-]}{[HONH_2]} = 1.1 \times 10^{-8}$$

Recall that pure liquids and solids are not included in equilibrium constant expressions.

Dissociation constants for conjugate acids and bases are related to those of the parent bases and acids. For example, urate ion is the conjugate base of uric acid:

$$C_5H_3N_4O_3^- + H_2O \rightleftharpoons C_5H_3N_4O_3H + OH^-$$

$$K_b = \frac{[C_5H_3N_4O_3H][OH^-]}{[C_5H_3N_4O_3^-]}$$

Part of the equilibrium constant expression for $K_a$ of uric acid is contained in $K_b$ for urate, but inverted. What is missing is $[H^+]$ in the denominator. In order to introduce $[H^+]$, both numerator and denominator must be multiplied by this factor, else the value of the fraction is changed. Thus:

$$K_b = \frac{[C_5H_3N_4O_3H][OH^-][H^+]}{[C_5H_3N_4O_3^-][H^+]}$$

$$K_b = \frac{[C_5H_3N_4O_3H]}{[C_5H_3N_4O_3^-][H^+]} \cdot [OH^-][H^+] = \frac{1}{K_a} \cdot K_w$$

$$K_b = K_w/K_a$$

Demonstrate for yourself that a similar relationship can be derived which relates $K_b$ for a weak base to $K_a$ for its conjugate acid. The relationship

$$K_a = K_w/K_b$$

or $$K_aK_b = K_w$$

is only true for conjugate acid-base pairs. It is a very convenient one, since the dissociation constant for one member of a conjugate acid-base pair may be calculated if that for the other member is known.

## SECTION 5-5: SOLUTIONS OF STRONG ACIDS AND BASES

Classifying an acid or base as strong implies that the concentration of hydrogen or hydroxide ion in solution will be equal to the concentration of the acid or base itself, ignoring the dissociation of water. Thus a 0.1 M solution of HBr is 0.1 M in hydrogen ion, and a 0.05 M solution of $Ba(OH)_2$ is 0.1 M in hydroxide ion. Problems involving only strong acids or bases or mixtures of them are thus very easily solved, since the only equilibrium to be considered is the auto-ionization of water, summarized by $K_w$.

In most cases, however, this dissociation, already small in neutral solution, is sufficiently depressed by the addition of acid or base that it can be ignored in all but the most dilute solutions. Keep in mind, though, that solutions of acids, no matter how dilute, will have pH values of less than 7. Similarly, even extremely dilute solutions of bases have pH greater than 7, e.g., a $10^{-10}$ M solution of KOH has pH slightly greater than 7, not pH of 4, or 10!

Example 10

What are the pH and pOH of a solution prepared by mixing 35 mL of 0.055 M barium hydroxide with 25 mL of 0.12 M hydrobromic acid?

Given: 35 mL of 0.055 M $Ba(OH)_2$, a strong base

25 mL of 0.12 M HBr, a strong acid

Find: pH and pOH after the two solutions are mixed

Solution: Mixing these two solutions will result in an acid-base reaction to produce water and the salt barium bromide. To find the final pH, you must first determine if either acid or base is in excess.

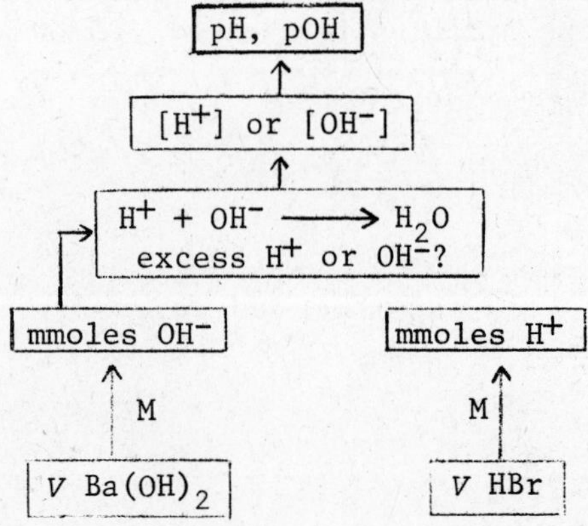

When working with small quantities of materials, it is often more convenient to use the units millimole (mmol) and milligram (mg). Molarity can have units of mmol $mL^{-1}$ as well as mol $liter^{-1}$. Similarly, units for formula weight can be mg $mmol^{-1}$ as well as the more familiar g $mol^{-1}$.

$$\text{mmol } H^+ = (0.12 \text{ M})(25 \text{ mL}) = 3.0 \text{ mmol}$$

$$\text{mmol } OH^- = (0.055 \text{ M})(35 \text{ mL})(2 \text{ mol } OH^-/\text{mol } Ba(OH)_2)$$

$$\text{mmol } OH^- = 3.9 \text{ mmol}$$

Therefore, $OH^-$ is in excess, by 0.9 mmol, and 3.0 mmol water are produced.

$$[OH^-] = 0.9 \text{ mmol}/(25 + 35) \text{ mL} = 0.015 \text{ M}$$

$$\text{pOH} = -\log 0.015 = -\log 1.5 \times 10^{-2}$$

$$\text{pOH} = -(0.18 - 2) = 1.8$$

$$\text{pH} = 14.0 - \text{pOH} = 14.0 - 1.8 = 12.2$$

Example 11

Hydrobromic acid is to be titrated with sodium hydroxide. If a 25.00 mL aliquot of the acid required 32.06 mL of 0.1525 M NaOH to reach the equivalence point, how many mL of base had been added when the pH was 3.00?

Given: HBr, a strong acid, titrated with NaOH, a strong base
32.06 mL of 0.1525 M NaOH to neutralize 25.00 mL HBr

Find: mL base added to reach pH 3.00

Solution: At pH 3.00, part of the acid has been neutralized, so the moles of $H^+$ have decreased by an amount equal to the moles of base added. Also, the volume has increased from its initial value, $V_0$, to $V_0$ + mL base added. Thus, at pH 3.00,

$$[H^+] = \frac{\text{mmol } H^+}{V} = \frac{\text{mmol } H^+\text{, initial} - \text{mmol } OH^-}{V_0 + V_{base}}$$

The unknown we are looking for is $V_{base}$. Values are needed for the initial mmol of $H^+$ and the mmol of base added. The equivalence point data gives the initial mmol of $H^+$. The mmol of $OH^-$ added can be expressed as $(M \times V)_{base}$. Substituting this information into the equation above gives one unknown, $V_{base}$.

$$\text{mmol } H^+\text{, initial} = (32.06 \text{ mL})(0.1525 \text{ M}) = 4.889 \text{ mmol}$$

$$[H^+] = \text{antilog}(-3.00) = 1.00 \times 10^{-3}$$

$$[H^+] = 1.00 \times 10^{-3} = \frac{4.889 \text{ mmol} - (0.1525 \text{ M})(V_{base})}{25.00 \text{ mL} + V_{base}}$$

$$(1.00 \times 10^{-3})(25.00 + V_{base}) = 4.889 - 0.1525\ V_{base}$$

$$2.50 \times 10^{-2} + 1.00 \times 10^{-3}\ V_{base} = 4.889 - 0.1525\ V_{base}$$

$$V_{base}(0.00100 + 0.1525) = 4.889 - 2.50 \times 10^{-2} = 4.889 - 0.0250$$

$$V_{base} = 4.867/0.1535$$

$$V_{base} = 31.71 \text{ mL}$$

Since only 32.06 mL of base are needed to reach the equivalence point, much of the acid has already been neutralized at pH 3.00.

## GENERAL NOTES CONCERNING SECTIONS 5-6 - 5-9

There are two broad classes of equilibria involving weak acids and bases:

- o simple solutions of weak acids, weak bases, or their salts;
- o solutions of two or more solutes.

In dealing with these equilibria, you may find the following series of steps helpful:

1. Identify the physical situation. Are you dealing with a single substance, or with a mixture? Draw a picture, if this helps.

2. Write the appropriate chemical equation.

3. Identify the unknown.

4. Write the equilibrium expression.

5. Write down initial conditions, changes and equilibrium conditions.

6. Rewrite the equilibrium expression in terms of the equilibrium conditions in step 5.

7. Estimate the answer.

8. Do the arithmetic.

9. Check the answer against the estimate from step 7. Is the answer reasonable?

Example 12

Coniine is a weak base found in hemlock. This is the poison that killed Socrates.

a. Calculate pH and pOH for a 0.070 M solution of coniine, $pK_b = 3.125$.

Given: 0.070 M solution of a weak base, coniine, abbreviate Con
$pK_b = 3.125$

Find: pH and pOH of this solution

Solution: There is one solute, coniine, a weak base, dissolved in water. The appropriate chemical equation is then

$$Con + H_2O \rightleftharpoons ConH^+ + OH^-$$

$$K_b = \frac{[ConH^+][OH^-]}{[Con]}$$

$$pK_b = 3.125 = -(0.875 - 4)$$

$$K_b = 7.5 \times 10^{-4}$$

Conditions before and after equilibrium has been established are summarized as shown. Let $x$ be the concentration of coniine that ionizes.

| | [Con] | $[ConH^+]$ | $[OH^-]$ |
|---|---|---|---|
| initial | 0.070 | 0 | 0 |
| change | $-x$ | $+x$ | $+x$ |
| equilibrium | $0.070 - x$ | $x$ | $x$ |

Since coniine is a base, the pH of the solution must be > 7 at equilibrium, or $x$ must be $> 10^{-7}$. Substituting appropriate values in the equilibrium expression gives

$$\frac{x^2}{0.070 - x} = 7.5 \times 10^{-4}$$

If $x \ll 0.070$ then it can be neglected in the denominator, simplifying the solution to the equation. The rule of thumb to be followed in cases such as this is that the simplifying assumption is valid if

$$K/\text{concentration of solute} \lesssim 10^{-3}$$

In the problem here, $K/0.070\ M = 1.1 \times 10^{-2}$. Since $1.1 \times 10^{-2} > 10^{-3}$, the equation must be solved exactly. Two methods can be used.

Method 1: Successive approximations

In this method, an initial value of $x$ is estimated, and the equation is solved using this value in the factor $0.070 - x$. The known value of $x$ so calculated is used to solve the equation a second time, and the process is repeated until two succeeding values of $x$ are identical.

Let us choose $x = 0$ for the initial value. This is equivalent to neglecting $x$ with respect to 0.070.

$$x^2 = (0.070 - 0)(7.5 \times 10^{-4})$$

$$x = 7.2 \times 10^{-3} = 0.0072$$

Use this value of $x$ in the $0.070 - x$ factor and solve again.

$$x^2 = (0.070 - 0.0072)(7.5 \times 10^{-4}) = (0.0678)(7.5 \times 10^{-4})$$

$$x = 7.13 \times 10^{-3} = 0.00713$$

Solve again.

$$x^2 = (0.070 - 0.00713)(7.5 \times 10^{-4}) = (0.0629)(7.5 \times 10^{-4})$$

$$x = 6.87 \times 10^{-3} = 0.00687$$

Solve again.

$$x^2 = (0.070 - 0.00687)(7.5 \times 10^{-4}) = (0.0631)(7.5 \times 10^{-4})$$

$$x = 6.88 \times 10^{-3}$$

Rounding to the appropriate number of significant figures, i.e., 2, gives

$$x = 6.9 \times 10^{-3}$$

This is identical to the preceding value, so no further calculation is required.

$$[OH^-] = 6.9 \times 10^{-3}$$

$$pOH = -\log 6.9 \times 10^{-3} = -(0.839 - 3)$$

$$pOH = 2.16$$

$$pH = 14.00 - 2.16 = 11.84$$

As we predicted initially, $pH > 7$ and $pOH < 7$.

Method 2: Quadratic formula

$$y^2 = (7.5 \times 10^{-4})(0.070 - y) = 0.525 \times 10^{-4} - 7.5 \times 10^{-4}y$$

$$y^2 + 7.5 \times 10^{-4}y - 5.25 \times 10^{-5} = 0$$

The quadratic formula is

$$x = \frac{-b \pm\sqrt{b^2 - 4ac}}{2a}$$

Substituting $a = 1$, $b = 7.5 \times 10^{-4}$, and $c = -5.25 \times 10^{-5}$

$$y = \frac{-7.5 \times 10^{-4} \pm\sqrt{(7.5 \times 10^{-4})^2 - 4(-5.25 \times 10^{-5})}}{2(1)}$$

$$y = \frac{-7.5 \times 10^{-4} \pm\sqrt{56.25 \times 10^{-8} + 21.00 \times 10^{-5}}}{2}$$

$$y = \frac{-7.5 \times 10^{-4} \pm\sqrt{0.5625 \times 10^{-6} + 210.0 \times 10^{-6}}}{2}$$

$$y = \frac{-7.5 \times 10^{-4} \pm\sqrt{210.6 \times 10^{-6}}}{2} = \frac{-7.5 \times 10^{-4} \pm 14.5 \times 10^{-3}}{2}$$

Only the positive root will give a physically real solution:

$$y = \frac{(145 - 7.5) \times 10^{-4}}{2} = \frac{138 \times 10^{-4}}{2}$$

$$y = 6.9 \times 10^{-3}$$

This gives the same answer as the first method. Choose the quadratic formula if $K$/(concentration of solute) is much greater than $10^{-3}$. Otherwise, the method of successive approximations will be faster and easier.

b. What is the percent ionization of coniine in this solution?

Solution: Percent ionization is just the ratio of the moles of substance ionizing to the original moles of substance. It can be found using the ratio of appropriate concentrations. In this case,

original [coniine] = 0.070 M

$[ConH^+] = 6.9 \times 10^{-3}$, the concentration of coniine ionized

% ionization = $6.9 \times 10^{-3}/7.0 \times 10^{-2} = 0.099 = 9.9\%$

Example 13

The analgesic morphine is a weak organic base. Because of its very limited solubility in water, it is often dispensed as a salt, e.g., morphine hydrochloride.

a. What are the pH and pOH of a 0.15 M solution of morphine hydrochloride? $K_b$ for morphine is $1.62 \times 10^{-6}$.

Given: a 0.15 M solution of morphine hydrochloride
a salt of the weak base morphine
$K_b$ for morphine, $1.62 \times 10^{-6}$

Find: pH and pOH of this solution

Solution: We have here an aqueous solution of a single solute, the salt of the weak base morphine. The cation of this salt is the conjugate acid of morphine, which dissociates in water to give an acidic solution. We can write an equation for this process, using Mor = morphine and $MorH^+$ for its conjugate acid.

$$MorH^+ \rightleftharpoons Mor + H^+$$

$$K_a = \frac{[Mor][H^+]}{[MorH^+]}$$

An estimation of the answer will be that pH < 7 and pOH > 7, values for an acidic solution. The equilibrium constant we are given is $K_b$ for morphine, i.e., for the reaction:

$$Mor + H_2O \rightleftharpoons MorH^+ + OH^-$$

$$K_b = \frac{[MorH^+][OH^-]}{[Mor]}$$

One can see that the equilibrium expression for $K_a$ of $MorH^+$ and $K_b$ of Mor contain similar factors. They are related as follows:

$$K_a = \frac{[Mor][H^+]}{[MorH^+]}$$

contains part of the inverse of $K_b$, i.e., $[Mor]/[MorH^+]$. The factor $[OH^-]$, however, is missing. It can be introduced by multiplying the expression by 1 in the form of $[OH^-]/[OH^-]$, which won't change its value.

$$K_a = \frac{[Mor][H^+]}{[MorH^+]} \times \frac{[OH^-]}{[OH^-]}$$

Now the expression contains $K_w$ and the inverse of $K_b$.

$$K_a = \frac{[Mor]}{[MorH^+][OH^-]} \times [H^+][OH^-] = K_w/K_b$$

Thus, $K_a = (1.0 \times 10^{-14})/(1.62 \times 10^{-6}) = 6.16 \times 10^{-9}$

$$6.16 \times 10^{-9} = \frac{[Mor][H^+]}{[MorH^+]}$$

Since this solution contains a single solute, the conditions in the table apply. Let $x$ be the concentration of $MorH^+$ that dissociates.

| | [Con] | [Mor] | $[H^+]$ |
|---|---|---|---|
| initial | 0.15 | 0 | 0 |
| change | $-x$ | $+x$ | $+x$ |
| equilibrium | $0.15 - x$ | $x$ | $x$ |

$$6.16 \times 10^{-9} = \frac{x^2}{0.15 - x}$$

Applying the rule of thumb for approximations, $K$/concentration of solute $\leq 10^{-3}$, we find $6.16 \times 10^{-9}/0.15 = 4.11 \times 10^{-8}$, and so $x$ may be neglected with respect to 0.15. (Note: Approximations such as this one can only be made for addition and subtraction, not for multiplication or division.)

$$x^2 = (6.16 \times 10^{-9})(0.15) = 9.24 \times 10^{-10}$$

$$x = 3.04 \times 10^{-5}$$

$$pH = -\log [H^+] = -\log 3.04 \times 10^{-5}$$

$$pH = -(0.48 - 5) = 4.52$$

$$pOH = 14 - pH$$

pOH = 9.48

As we predicted before calculating the answers above, the solution is acidic: pH < 7, pOH > 7.

b. How many mL of this solution contain the average dose, 10 mg? The formula weight of morphine hydrochloride is 375.84.

Given: 10 mg dose of morphine hydrochloride
formula wt = 375.84 g $mol^{-1}$

Find: mL of a 0.15 M solution containing 10 mg morphine hydrochloride

Solution: Recall similar problems in Chapter 2.

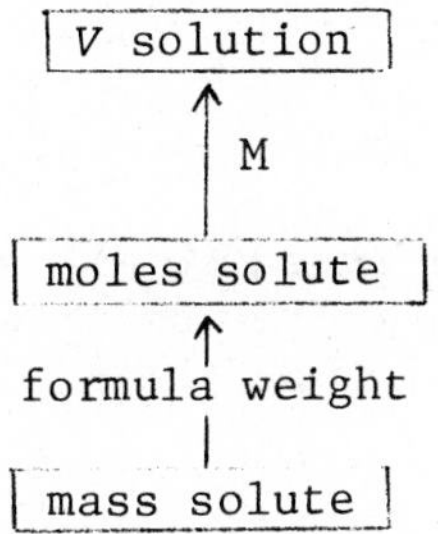


mmol MorHCl = 10 mg/375.84 mg/mmol

mol solute = $2.66 \times 10^{-2}$ mmol

volume solution = $2.66 \times 10^{-2}$ mmol/0.15 M

volume solution = 0.18 mL

Equipment for measuring very small volumes would be required to dispense this solution accurately. The alternative is to make up a more dilute solution of the medication, so that a larger, more easily measurable, volume would be needed.

Example 14

A buffer is to be prepared from methylamine, $CH_3NH_2$, and methylammonium chloride, $CH_3NH_3^+Cl^-$. How many grams of the salt should be added to 4.0 L of a 1.5 M solution of the free base to make 5.0 L of buffer of pH 10.0? $K_b = 3.7 \times 10^{-4}$ for methylamine.

Given: 4.0 L of 1.5 M methylamine
5.0 L of pH 10.0 buffer
$K_b = 3.7 \times 10^{-4}$ for methylamine

Find: grams of methylammonium chloride needed to prepare buffer

Solution: A buffer solution contains two solutes; here, the weak base methylamine and its conjugate acid. The appropriate equation is that for reaction of a weak base with water.

$$CH_3NH_2 + H_2O \rightleftharpoons CH_3NH_3^+ + OH^-$$

$$K_b = \frac{[CH_3NH_3^+][OH^-]}{[CH_3NH_2]} = 3.7 \times 10^{-4}$$

Since the pH of the buffer is specified, you can calculate the ratio of conjugate acid to free base present at equilibrium.

$$pH = 10.0 \longrightarrow pOH = 14.0 - 10.0 = 4.0$$

$$[OH^-] = 1.0 \times 10^{-4}$$

$$\frac{[CH_3NH_3^+](1.0 \times 10^{-4})}{[CH_3NH_2]} = 3.7 \times 10^{-4}$$

$$[CH_3NH_3^+]/[CH_3NH_2] = (3.7 \times 10^{-4})/(1.0 \times 10^{-4}) = 3.7$$

So 3.7 times as many moles of salt as free base are required to prepare this buffer.

The presence of added $CH_3NH_3^+$ shifts the equilibrium to the left. Therefore, most of the free base originally present will remain as $CH_3NH_2$ at equilibrium. So the equilibrium concentrations of base and salt are

$$[CH_3NH_2] = (4.0 \text{ L})(1.5 \text{ M})/(5.0 \text{ L}) = 1.2 \text{ M}$$

$$[CH_3NH_3^+] = 3.7[CH_3NH_2] = (3.7)(1.2 \text{ M})$$

$$[CH_3NH_3^+] = 4.4 \text{ M}$$

We are asked for the mass of $CH_3NH_3^+Cl^-$ needed to prepare 5.0 L of 4.4 M solution.

[molarity] → [moles solute] —formula weight→ [mass solute]

$$\text{mol } CH_3NH_3^+Cl^- = (4.4 \text{ M})(5.0 \text{ L}) = 22 \text{ mol}$$

$$\text{mass } CH_3NH_3^+Cl^- = (22 \text{ mol})(67.52 \text{ g mol}^{-1}) = 1485 \text{ g} = 1.5 \text{ kg}$$

Example 15

A buffer often used in clinical laboratories and biochemical research is the base tris(hydroxymethyl)aminomethane (THAM) and its conjugate acid ($THAMH^+$). These buffers are prepared by adding hydrochloric acid to a solution of THAM until the desired pH is obtained. How many mL of concentrated (11.6 M) HCl should be added to 7.0 L of 1.25 M THAM to prepare 10.0 L of buffer at pH 7.90? $K_b = 1.2 \times 10^{-6}$.

Given: 7.0 L of 1.25 M THAM, a weak base
$K_b = 1.2 \times 10^{-6}$ for THAM
10.0 L of pH 7.90 buffer, to contain THAM and $THAMH^+$
11.6 M of HCl, for converting THAM to $THAMH^+$

Find: volume, in mL, of 11.6 M HCl required

Solution: This problem is similar to the previous one, in that a basic buffer, containing a weak base and its conjugate acid, is to be prepared. The difference is that the weak base is to be partially neutralized with hydrochloric acid, which will produce the necessary mixture. The appropriate equilibrium is:

$$THAM + H_2O \rightleftharpoons THAMH^+ + OH^-$$

$$K_b = \frac{[THAMH^+][OH^-]}{[THAM]} = 1.2 \times 10^{-6}$$

The ratio $[THAMH^+]/[THAM]$ can be obtained using the specified pH, 7.90. This buffer is only slightly basic.

$$pH = 7.90 \longrightarrow pOH = 14.00 - 7.90 = 6.10$$

$$6.10 = -\log [OH^-] = -(0.90 - 7)$$

$$[OH^-] = 7.9 \times 10^{-7}$$

$$\frac{[THAMH^+](7.9 \times 10^{-7})}{[THAM]} = 1.2 \times 10^{-6}$$

$$[THAMH^+]/[THAM] = 1.5$$

We have one equation with two unknowns. A second equation can be written from the information that all $THAMH^+$ and THAM present at equilibrium originated from the 7.0 L of 1.25 M THAM that was given.

$$\text{total moles } THAMH^+ + THAM = (7.0\ L)(1.25\ M) = 8.75\ mol = 8.8\ mol$$

The concentration ratio, $[THAMH^+]/[THAM]$, is also a mole ratio, since volume is the same for numerator and denominator. So,

$$\text{mol } THAMH^+ = 1.5 \times \text{mol THAM}$$

We now have two equations and two unknowns.

$$\text{mol } THAMH^+ = 1.5 \times \text{mol THAM} = 8.75\ mol - \text{mol THAM}$$

$$1.5 \times \text{mol THAM} + \text{mol THAM} = 8.75\ mol$$

$$2.5 \times \text{mol THAM} = 8.75\ mol$$

$$\text{mol THAM} = 8.75\ mol/2.5 = 3.5\ mol$$

$$\text{mol } THAMH^+ = (8.75 - 3.5)\ mol = 5.3\ mol$$

Now $THAM^+$ is generated by adding HCl to THAM:

$$THAM + HCl \longrightarrow THAMH^+ + Cl^-$$

Thus mol $THAMH^+$ = mol HCl. The volume of 11.6 M HCl needed is:

$$V = \text{mol HCl}/M$$

$$V = 5.25\ mol/11.6\ M = 0.452\ L = 450\ mL$$

The buffer is prepared by adding 450 mL of the hydrochloric acid to the 7.0 L of THAM solution, along with sufficient water to bring the volume up to 10.0 L.

Example 16

Nicotine is a weak diprotic base with $K_{b_1} = 6.9 \times 10^{-7}$ and $K_{b_2} = 1.3 \times 10^{-11}$. It is used as an insecticide, either as a solution of the base or its sulfate salt. An oral dose of 40 mg of the free base can be fatal to humans.

a. What are the concentrations of nicotine (Nic), $NicH^+$, $NicH_2^{2+}$, and $OH^-$ in a 0.050 M solution of nicotine? $NicH^+$ and $NicH_2^{2+}$ are the mono- and diprotonated ions, respectively. What is the pH of this solution?

Given: 0.050 M solution of nicotine, a weak diprotic base
$K_1 = 6.9 \times 10^{-7}$
$K_2 = 1.3 \times 10^{-11}$

Find: concentrations of species Nic, $NicH^+$, $NicH_2^{2+}$, and $OH^-$ present at equilibrium; pH

Solution: Polyprotic bases ionize in stepwise fashion. The same is true for polyprotic acids. In this example, the first step is

$$Nic + H_2O \rightleftharpoons NicH^+ + OH^-$$

$$K_1 = \frac{[NicH^+][OH^-]}{[Nic]} = 6.9 \times 10^{-7}$$

$K_1$ is fairly small, so some $OH^-$ is produced in this step, but not a large amount. The second step is

$$NicH^+ + H_2O \rightleftharpoons NicH_2^{2+} + OH^-$$

$$K_2 = \frac{[NicH_2^{2+}][OH^-]}{[NicH^+]} = 1.3 \times 10^{-11}$$

$K_2$ is extremely small, so very little $NicH_2^{2+}$ and additional $OH^-$ are formed. One can predict, then, that most $OH^-$ will come from the first step, and that the concentration of $NicH_2^{2+}$ will be miniscule. The pH of the solution, since this is a base, will be > 7.

| Step 1: | [Nic] | [NicH$^+$] | [OH$^-$] |
|---|---|---|---|
| initial | 0.050 | 0 | 0 |
| change | $-x$ | $+x$ | $+x$ |
| equilibrium | $0.050 - x$ | $x$ | $x$ |

$$K_1 = 6.9 \times 10^{-7} = \frac{x^2}{0.050 - x}$$

Since $6.9 \times 10^{-7}/(0.050) = 1.4 \times 10^{-5}$, which is $< 10^{-3}$, $x$ can be neglected with respect to 0.050.

$$(6.9 \times 10^{-7})(0.050) = x^2 = 3.45 \times 10^{-8}$$

$x = 1.86 \times 10^{-4} = 1.9 \times 10^{-4}$

| Step 2: | $[NicH^+]$ | $[NicH_2^{2+}]$ | $[OH^-]$ |
|---|---|---|---|
| initial | $1.9 \times 10^{-4}$ | 0 | $1.9 \times 10^{-4}$ |
| change | $-y$ | $+y$ | $+y$ |
| equilibrium | $1.9 \times 10^{-4} - y$ | $y$ | $1.9 \times 10^{-4} + y$ |

Note that in this second step there is $OH^-$ already present from step 1.

$$K_2 = 1.3 \times 10^{-11} = \frac{y(y + 1.9 \times 10^{-4})}{1.9 \times 10^{-4} - y}$$

Since $1.3 \times 10^{-11}/1.9 \times 10^{-4} < 10^{-3}$, $y$ may be neglected with respect to $1.9 \times 10^{-4}$.

$$1.3 \times 10^{-11} = \frac{y(1.9 \times 10^{-4})}{1.9 \times 10^{-4}} = \quad = [NicH_2^{2+}]$$

Thus, $[NicH_2^{2+}]$ is just the value of $K_2$, as is the $[OH^-]$ produced in this step. Our initial estimate of total $[OH^-]$ was correct since

$$1.9 \times 10^{-4} + 1.3 \times 10^{-11} = 1.9 \times 10^{-4}$$

$$pOH = -\log 1.9 \times 10^{-4}$$

$$pOH = -(0.27 - 4) = 3.73$$

$$pH = 14.00 - 3.73 = 10.27$$

b. What will be the concentrations of Nic, $NicH^+$, and $NicH_2^{2+}$ in a solution originally 0.050 M in nicotine, if the pH is adjust to 11.50?

Given: nicotine solution, originally 0.050 M
adjustment of pH to 11.50

Find: [Nic], $[NicH^+]$, $[NicH_2^{2+}]$

Solution: Since the pH of a 0.050 M solution of pure nicotine is 10.27, $OH^-$ from a second source, such as KOH or NaOH, must be added to bring the pH up to 11.50. According to Le Chatelier's principle, this will depress the ionization of nicotine.

$$Nic + H_2O \rightleftharpoons NicH^+ + OH^-$$

$$NicH^+ + H_2O \rightleftharpoons NicH_2^{2+} + OH^-$$

Thus, concentrations of $NicH^+$ and $NicH_2^{2+}$ will be smaller in this solution than in a 0.050 M solution of pure nicotine.

| Step 1: | [Nic] | $[NicH^+]$ | $[OH^-]$ |
|---|---|---|---|
| initial | 0.050 | 0 | $< 3.2 \times 10^{-3}$ |
| change | $-x$ | $+x$ | |
| equilibrium | $0.050 - x$ | $x$ | $3.2 \times 10^{-3}$ (pH = 11.50) |

$$K_1 = \frac{x(3.2 \times 10^{-3})}{0.050 - x} = 6.9 \times 10^{-7}$$

Since $6.9 \times 10^{-7}/0.050 < 10^{-3}$, $x$ can be neglected with respect to 0.050.

$$6.9 \times 10^{-7} = \frac{x(3.2 \times 10^{-3})}{0.050}$$

$$x = (6.9 \times 10^{-7})(5.0 \times 10^{-2})/3.2 \times 10^{-3} = 10.8 \times 10^{-6}$$

$$x = 1.1 \times 10^{-5} = [\text{NicH}^+]$$

| Step 2: | $[\text{NicH}^+]$ | $[\text{NicH}_2^{2+}]$ | $[\text{OH}^-]$ |
|---|---|---|---|
| initial | $1.1 \times 10^{-5}$ | 0 | $3.2 \times 10^{-3}$ |
| change | $-x$ | $+x$ | none, pH = 11.50 |
| equilibrium | $1.1 \times 10^{-5} - x$ | $x$ | $3.2 \times 10^{-3}$ |

$$K_2 = \frac{x(3.2 \times 10^{-3})}{1.1 \times 10^{-5} - x} = 1.3 \times 10^{-11}$$

Since $1.3 \times 10^{-11}/1.1 \times 10^{-5} < 10^{-3}$, $x$ can be neglected with respect to $1.1 \times 10^{-5}$.

$$1.3 \times 10^{-11} = \frac{x(3.2 \times 10^{-3})}{1.1 \times 10^{-5}}$$

$$x = (1.3 \times 10^{-11})(1.1 \times 10^{-5})/3.2 \times 10^{-3}$$

$$x = 4.5 \times 10^{-14} = [\text{NicH}_2^{2+}]$$

As predicted, both $[\text{NicH}^+]$ and $[\text{NicH}_2^{2+}]$ are significantly smaller than in the solution of pure nicotine. The predominant species in the pH 11.50 solution are unionized nicotine and hydroxide ion.

c. What will be the concentration of Nic, $\text{NicH}^+$, and $\text{NicH}_2^{2+}$ in a solution originally 0.050 M in nicotine if the pH is adjusted to 7.0?

Given: nicotine solution, originally 0.050 M
adjustment of pH to 7.0

Find: [Nic], $[\text{NicH}^+]$, and $[\text{NicH}_2^{2+}]$

Solution: Recall that a 0.050 M solution of nicotine is pH 10.27. Therefore, acid has been added to the nicotine in this solution to bring the pH down to 7.0. We can predict, then, that the concentration of nicotine will be smaller, and those of its protonated ions, $\text{NicH}^+$ and $\text{NicH}_2^{2+}$, larger relative to the pure solution. It is useful to begin to solve problems such as this one by first calculating the ratios of various nicotine species. Consider the first ionization step:

$$\text{Nic} + H_2O \rightleftharpoons \text{NicH}^+ + \text{OH}^-$$

Addition of acid shifts this equilibrium to the right. To find out how far to the right the shift is, you calculate the ratio $[NicH^+]/[Nic]$.

$$K_1 = 6.9 \times 10^{-7} = \frac{[NicH^+][OH^-]}{[Nic]}$$

$$6.9 \times 10^{-7} = 10^{-7}\frac{[NicH^+]}{[Nic]}$$

$$[NicH^+]/[Nic] = 6.9$$

So while there is seven times as much $NicH^+$ as Nic in the solution, significant amounts of both are present. Now you examine the relative amounts of $NicH_2^{2+}$ and $NicH^+$.

$$NicH^+ + H_2O \rightleftharpoons NicH_2^{2+} + OH^-$$

$$K_2 = 1.3 \times 10^{-11} = \frac{[NicH_2^{2+}][OH^-]}{[NicH^+]}$$

$$1.3 \times 10^{-11} = \frac{[NicH_2^{2+}](10^{-7})}{[NicH^+]}$$

$$[NicH_2^{2+}]/[NicH^+] = 1.3 \times 10^{-4}$$

Thus there is very little $NicH_2^{2+}$ in solution. The predominant species are $NicH^+$ and Nic.

The concentrations of Nic, $NicH^+$, and $NicH_2^{2+}$ are obtained from the ratios just calculated, combined with the fact that the total concentration of all the nicotine species must equal 0.050 M, the initial nicotine concentration.

$$[Nic] + [NicH^+] + [NicH_2^{2+}] = 0.050\text{ M}$$

Assume there was negligible change in volume upon addition of the acid.

$$[NicH^+] = 6.9[Nic]$$

$$[NicH_2^{2+}] = 1.3 \times 10^{-4}[NicH^+]$$

Substituting these values in the equation above gives

$$[Nic] + 6.9[Nic] + 1.3 \times 10^{-4}[NicH^+] = 0.050\text{ M}$$

Since $1.3 \times 10^{-4}[NicH^+] << [Nic]$, it can be neglected.

$$[Nic] + 6.9[Nic] = 0.050\text{ M}$$

$$[Nic] = 0.050\text{ M}/7.9 = 6.3 \times 10^{-3}$$

$$[NicH^+] = 6.9(6.3 \times 10^{-3}\text{ M}) = 4.3 \times 10^{-2}\text{ M}$$

$$[NicH_2^{2+}] = (1.3 \times 10^{-4})(4.3 \times 10^{-2}) = 5.6 \times 10^{-6}\text{ M}$$

(Neglecting $[NicH_2^{2+}]$ above was, in fact, justified.)

Thus the predominant species in this solution are Nic and $NicH^+$. The ratio of their concentrations, $0.1 < 6.9 < 10$, indicates that this solution is a buffer.

## SECTION 5-10: EQUILIBRIA WITH SLIGHTLY SOLUBLE SALTS

Two classes of phenomena are considered here: dissolving a solid in a liquid, either pure water or a solution; and mixing two or more solutions from which a solid precipitates. Both of these physical situations are described by the same equilibrium, quantitatively expressed as the solubility product, $K_{sp}$. Precipitation and dissolution reactions approach equilibrium from opposite directions.

Review the nine steps in solving acid-base equilibria in the General Notes preceding Example 12.

### Example 17

Calcium phosphate is the primary constituent of bones and teeth.

a. Will a solution of $Ca_3(PO_4)_2$ be acidic, basic, or neutral?

Solution: The equation describing the dissolution of $Ca_3(PO_4)_2$ in water is

$$Ca_3(PO_4)_2(s) \rightleftharpoons 3Ca^{2+}(aq) + 2PO_4^{3-}(aq)$$

Phosphate ion is the conjugate base of phosphoric acid, a weak triprotic acid. Thus, the solution will be basic, due to hydrolysis of $PO_4^{3-}$.

b. What is the solubility of calcium phosphate in water at 25°C?

Given: $Ca_3(PO_4)_2$, a sparingly soluble salt

Find: solubility in $H_2O$

Solution: The solubility product of $Ca_3(PO_4)_2$ must be looked up. It is $1.3 \times 10^{-32}$ at 25°C. The units of solubility are mol liter$^{-1}$ of solution. "Mol" refers to moles of solute, here $Ca_3(PO_4)_2$. Inspection of the chemical formula indicates that each mole of $Ca_3(PO_4)_2$ that dissolves produces three moles of $Ca^{2+}$ and two of $PO_4^{3-}$. The solubility then is equal to $1/3[Ca^{2+}]$ or $1/2[PO_4^{3-}]$. Referring to the equation in part a, we can write:

$$K_{sp} = [Ca^{2+}]^3[PO_4^{3-}]^2 = 1.3 \times 10^{-32}$$

Recall that pure solid phases are not included in equilibrium expressions. Since the solvent is pure water, all $Ca^{2+}$ and $PO_4^{3-}$ ions in solution come from $Ca_3(PO_4)_2$ that dissolves. The stoichiometry of the formula gives,

$$[Ca^{2+}]/[PO_4^{3-}] = 3/2 \quad \text{and}$$

$$K_{sp} = (1.5[PO_4^{3-}])^3[PO_4^{3-}]^2 = 1.3 \times 10^{-32}$$

$$3.375[PO_4^{3-}]^5 = 1.3 \times 10^{-32}$$

$$[PO_4^{3-}]^5 = 3.85 \times 10^{-33}$$

Using a calculator to take the 5th root:

$$[PO_4^{3-}]^5 = 385 \times 10^{-35}$$

$$[PO_4^{3-}] = 385^{1/5} \times 10^{-7} = 3.29 \times 10^{-7}$$

$$\text{solubility} = 1/2[PO_4^{3-}] = 1.6 \times 10^{-7} \text{ mol liter}^{-1}$$

Alternately, you can calculate $[PO_4^{3-}]$ using logarithms:

$$[PO_4^{3-}]^5 = 3.85 \times 10^{-33}$$

Take the log of both sides of the equation:

$$\log[PO_4^{3-}]^5 = 5 \log[PO_4^{3-}] = \log 3.85 \times 10^{-33}$$

$$5 \log[PO_4^{3-}] = (0.585 - 33) = -32.415$$

$$\log[PO_4^{3-}] = -6.483 = 0.517 - 7$$

$$[PO_4^{3-}] = 3.29 \times 10^{-7}$$

c. What is the solubility of calcium phosphate in 0.10 M calcium nitrate solution at 25°C?

Given: $Ca_3(PO_4)_2$, $K_{sp} = 1.3 \times 10^{-32}$ at 25°C
0.10 M $Ca(NO_3)_2$, aqueous

Find: solubility of $Ca_3(PO_4)_2$

<u>Solution:</u> By Le Chatelier's principle, adding product to an equilibrium system shifts the position of equilibrium to the left. In this situation,

$$Ca_3(PO_4)_2(s) \rightleftharpoons 3Ca^{2+}(aq) + 2PO_4^{3-}(aq)$$

adding $Ca^{2+}$ from a second source shifts the position of equilibrium toward solid $Ca_3(PO_4)_2$. Thus, the solubility will be less than its value in pure water, $1.6 \times 10^{-7}$ M.

$$K_{sp} = [Ca^{2+}]^3[PO_4^{3-}]^2 = 1.3 \times 10^{-32}$$

Let $s$ = solubility. $Ca^{2+}(aq)$ comes from two sources, $Ca_3(PO_4)_2$ and $Ca(NO_3)_2$, which is a strong electrolyte.

$$[Ca^{2+}]^3[PO_4^{3-}]^2 = (3s + 0.10)^3(2s)^2 = 1.3 \times 10^{-32}$$

Since we have estimated that $s$ will be less than $1.6 \times 10^{-7}$ M, $s \lll 0.10$.

$$[Ca^{2+}] \approx 0.10$$

$$(0.10)^3(2s)^2 = 1.3 \times 10^{-32} = 4.0 \times 10^{-3}s^2$$

(2 here is an exact number)

$$s^2 = 1.3 \times 10^{-32}/(4.0 \times 10^{-3}) = 3.2 \times 10^{-30}$$

$$s = 1.8 \times 10^{-15} \text{ mol } Ca_3(PO_4)_2 \text{ per L of } 0.10 \text{ M } Ca(NO_3)_2 \text{ solution}$$

The solubility is eight orders of magnitude less than it is in pure water.

d. Will the solubility of calcium phosphate in 0.010 M HCl solution be less than, greater than, or about the same as it is in pure water?

Given: 0.010 M HCl solution
$Ca_3(PO_4)_2$, $K_{sp} = 1.3 \times 10^{-32}$

Find: solubility relative to that in pure $H_2O$

Solution: Since phosphate ion is a base, it reacts with acid:

$$PO_4^{3-}(aq) + H^+(aq) \rightleftharpoons HPO_4^{2-}(aq)$$

$K_{eq}$ for this reaction is $[HPO_4^{2-}]/([PO_4^{3-}][H^+])$, the reciprocal of $K_{a_3}$ for phosphoric acid.

$$K_{eq} = 1/(2.2 \times 10^{-13}) = 4.5 \times 10^{12}$$

The large value of $K_{eq}$ indicates that this reaction goes to completion. Therefore, calcium phosphate will be much more soluble in acid than in pure water.

e. What volume of water is required to dissolve 0.0010 mol $Ca_3(PO_4)_2$?

Given: 0.0010 mol $Ca_3(PO_4)_2$

Find: volume $H_2O$ to dissolve completely

Solution: The solubility of $Ca_3(PO_4)_2$ in water is $1.6 \times 10^{-7}$ mol liter$^{-1}$, as calculated in part b. Thus, only $1.6 \times 10^{-7}$ mol $Ca_3(PO_4)_2$ will dissolve in each liter of water. To dissolve 0.0010 mol requires:

$$0.0010 \text{ mol}/(1.6 \times 10^{-7} \text{ mol liter}^{-1}) = 6.3 \times 10^4 \text{ L of water}$$

This volume would fill a cube 4 m on a side.

f. The calcium ion in 25.0 mL of 0.010 M $Ca(NO_3)_2$ is to be completely precipitated as $Ca_3(PO_4)_2$. What volume of 0.10 M $Na_3PO_4$ (the cleaning compound TSP) must be added to the $Ca^{2+}$ solution such that the equilibrium concentration of $Ca^{2+}$ will be no greater than $10^{-3}$ times its original value?

Given: 25.0 mL of 0.010 M $Ca(NO_3)_2$
0.10 M $Na_3PO_4$

Find: volume $Na_3PO_4$ to ppt $Ca^{2+}$ such that final $[Ca^{2+}]$ is no greater than $10^{-3}$ of original value

Solution: The equation describing the precipitation process is:

$$3Ca^{2+}(aq) + 2PO_4^{3-}(aq) \rightleftharpoons Ca_3(PO_4)_2(s)$$

Complete precipitation of one ion by another is facilitated by employing Le Chatelier's principle: addition of an excess of the precipitating reagent, $PO_4^{3-}$(*aq*) here, will drive the equilibrium to the right. To precipitate all the $Ca^{2+}$, then, the stoichiometric amount of $PO_4^{3-}$ must be added, plus extra phosphate that remains in solution. The equilibrium concentration of $Ca^{2+}$ is to be

$$(10^{-3})(0.010\ M) = 1.0 \times 10^{-5}\ M$$

The equilibrium constant for the reaction is

$$1/([Ca^{2+}]^3[PO_4^{3-}]^2) = 1/K_{sp}$$

This is inconvenient to work with; the solubility product will serve as well. To find phosphate still in solution at equilibrium (the extra phosphate), use $K_{sp}$:

$$(1.0 \times 10^{-5})^3[PO_4^{3-}]^2 = 1.3 \times 10^{-32}$$

$$[PO_4^{3-}]^2 = 1.3 \times 10^{-17} = 13 \times 10^{-18}$$

$$[PO_4^{3-}] = 3.6 \times 10^{-9}\ \text{mol liter}^{-1}$$

The amount of phosphate necessary to form $Ca_3(PO_4)_2$ must be added to that which remains in solution to find the total amount of $Na_3PO_4$ to be mixed with the $Ca^{2+}$ solution. From the formula of $Ca_3(PO_4)_2$, it is seen that each mol of $Ca^{2+}$ requires 2/3 mol $PO_4^{3-}$.

$$\text{mmol } Ca^{2+} = (25.0\ mL)(0.010\ M) = 0.25\ \text{mmol}$$

$$\text{mmol } PO_4^{3-} = (2\ \text{mol } PO_4^{3-}/3\ \text{mol } Ca^{2+})(0.25\ \text{mmol } Ca^{2+})$$

$$\text{mmol } PO_4^{3-} = 0.17\ \text{mmol}$$

$$\text{volume } Na_3PO_4 \text{ solution} = 0.17\ \text{mmol}/0.10\ M = 1.7\ mL$$

$$\text{total volume } Na_3PO_4 = 1.7\ mL + \text{extra } PO_4^{3-}$$

The extra $PO_4^{3-}$ is to be $3.6 \times 10^{-9}$ M. The volume of the mixture will be about (25.0 + 1.7) mL = 26.7 mL. Thus, some quantity of 0.10 M $PO_4^{3-}$ solution is to be diluted to 26.7 mL such that $[PO_4^{3-}]$ is $3.6 \times 10^{-9}$ M.

$$V\ (mL) \times 0.10\ M = (26.7\ mL)(3.6 \times 10^{-9}\ M)$$

$$V = 9.6 \times 10^{-7}\ mL$$

This is such a small amount that it can't be measured.

$$\text{total volume } Na_3PO_4 = (1.7 + 9.6 \times 10^{-7})\ mL = 1.7\ mL$$

Calculate how many drops of solution this is, using 20 drops/mL.

## Terms to Know

acid dissociation constant
aliquot
amphiprotic
antilog
Arrhenius acid, base
autoionization
base dissociation constant
Brønsted-Lowry acid, base
buffer
common ion effect
concentrated
conjugate acid, base
dilute
endpoint
equivalence point
hydration
hydrolysis
ion product of water, $K_w$
leveling effect
neutralize
pH, pOH
polyprotic acid
selective precipitation
solubility
solubility product
sparingly soluble salt
strong acid, base
titrate
weak acid, base

## Test Yourself

1. Arrange the acids below in order of decreasing strength of their conjugate bases.

| acid | $K_a$ |
|---|---|
| n-caproic a. | $1.43 \times 10^{-5}$ |
| 3,6-dinitrophenol | $7.1 \times 10^{-6}$ |
| benzosulfonic a. | $2 \times 10^{-1}$ |
| cacodylic a. | $6.4 \times 10^{-7}$ |
| o-boric a. | $7.3 \times 10^{-10}$ |

2. Lead(II) ion can be precipitated from aqueous solutions as the sulfate:

$$Pb^{2+}(aq) + SO_4^{2-}(aq) + PbSO_4(s)$$

The object is to precipitate as much lead sulfate as possible, by adding excess $SO_4^{2-}$. Why would it be better to add potassium sulfate to the lead(II) solution rather than sulfuric acid, since both reagents contain sulfate ion?

3. Gout is a disease caused by deposit of salts of uric acid in the joints. The pH of a 0.100 M solution of uric acid, $C_5H_4N_4O_3$, is 2.44. Calculate $K_a$ for uric acid.

4. Imidazol is a constituent of Vitamin $B_{12}$. It is a weak organic base, $pK_b = 7.05$. What is the pH of a 0.015 M solution of imidazol?

5. What is the pH of a 0.18 M solution of hydroxylammonium chloride, $HONH_3{}^+Cl^-$? $K_b = 1.1 \times 10^{-8}$ for hydroxylamine, $HONH_2$.

6. What mass of solid potassium hydroxide should be added to 6.00 L of 0.115 M lactic acid to produce a buffer of pH 3.70?

7. The solubility product of lead(II) chloride is $1.6 \times 10^{-5}$ at 25°C and $6 \times 10^{-3}$ at 95°C. What volume of hot water would be required to dissolve 25.0 mg $PbCl_2$?

8. Citric acid, found in fruits, is a weak triprotic acid, with $K_{a_1} = 8.4 \times 10^{-4}$, $K_{a_2} = 1.8 \times 10^{-5}$, and $K_{a_3} = 5.0 \times 10^{-7}$.

   a. What is the pH of a 0.15 M solution of citric acid? Abbreviate citric acid as $H_3Cit$, and its ions as $H_2Cit^-$, $HCit^{2-}$, and $Cit^{3-}$.

   b. What would be the ratios $[H_3Cit]/[H_2Cit^-]$, $[H_2Cit^-]/[HCit^{2-}]$, and $[HCit^{2-}]/[Cit^{3-}]$ at pH 6.0?

# 6 Periodic Behavior of the Elements: Oxidation-Reduction Chemistry

## CHAPTER OVERVIEW AND OBJECTIVES

The recurring, or periodic, behavior of the elements allows us to organize them in the periodic table. Prediction of chemical properties, which can be tested by experimentation, is facilitated by this organizational structure. In this chapter, a brief history of the modern periodic table is followed by a discussion of binary oxides and oxidation-reduction chemistry, which exemplify chemical periodicity.

When you finish this chapter you should be able to:

1. Briefly describe the development of the modern periodic table;

2. Locate various named categories of elements and predict properties of an element in a group, or column in the periodic table, from the properties of the other members of that group;

3. Use the periodic table to predict properties of binary oxides;

4. Assign oxidation numbers to the elements in any compound;

5. Balance oxidation-reduction equations and use them quantitatively.

## SECTION 6-1: THE BASIS FOR THE PERIODIC CLASSIFICATION

This section examines Mendeleev's and Meyer's periodic table and the refinements of Moseley and others which have produced the table in use today. Mendeleev devised the periodic table by organizing the known elements according to their physical and chemical properties. His statement of the periodic law correlated variations of properties of the elements with their atomic weights in a systematic fashion. He left spaces for elements yet undiscovered, and used the periodic law to accurately predict properties of these elements. Study Table 6-1 carefully to get an idea of how this is done.

As Mendeleev began to bring order out of chaos, chemists were inspired to make careful redeterminations of many atomic weights. Some discrepancies were found which led to a modification of the original statement of the periodic law; atomic numbers were invented. Atomic numbers were put on a firm footing by the experimental work of Moseley. He obtained a beautiful linear correlation between the frequency of X rays emitted by the elements and their atomic number. These experiments were crucial to the development of the model of the atom that we currently use.

Example 1

Predict values for the following properties of astatine (At), the heaviest halogen. Consult the Handbook of Chemistry and Physics or Lange's Handbook for corresponding properties of the other halogens. (These books will be found at the reference desk in the library.)

a. physical state at 25°C
b. melting point
c. formula of hydride

Solution: Look for trends in the properties of the other halogens.

| halogen | F | Cl | Br | I | At |
|---|---|---|---|---|---|
| atomic wt. | 19.0 | 35.45 | 79.9 | 126.9 | 210 |
| physical state, 25°C | gas | gas | liquid | solid | |
| melting pt. (°C) | -219.62 | -100.98 | -7.2 | 113.5 | |

a. Since the physical state of the other halogens becomes more condensed as atomic weight increases down the group, one can safely predict that At will be a solid at room temperature.

b. The melting points of the halogens show a definite trend, increasing by about 100°C per halogen. One might be tempted to predict a melting point of 215°C as a first approximation. However, notice the large difference in the atomic weights of I and At -- 83 units. Compare this to a difference of only 47 units between the atomic weights of Br and I, and similar differences between Br, Cl and F. The lanthanides, elements 58-71, fall between I and At, which accounts for their relatively large atomic-weight difference. This will have some effect on astatine's melting point. Since 83 is almost two times 47, one could predict nearly a doubling in the melting-point difference between I and At, compared to the other halogens. This would make astatine's melting point about 300°C. In fact, it is 302°C.

c. The general formula for hydrides of the other halogens is HX. One might reasonably expect astatine to follow this pattern, forming HAt, which it does. HAt is probably a strong acid, but astatine chemistry is difficult to study, since the longest-lived of its 20 isotopes has only an 8.2-hour half-life, and is usually prepared in a cyclotron!

## SECTION 6-2: THE PERIODIC TABLE

Finding your way around the periodic table is the subject of this section. Moseley's refinement of the periodic law states that various chemical properties of the elements, arranged according to increasing atomic number, repeat at regular intervals. The arrangement of electrons in the elements, which will be taken up in Chapter 8, accounts nicely for these observations.

You should become familiar with the locations of the following collections of elements:

a. representative elements, both metals and nonmetals, as well as the following:

1. alkali metals
2. alkaline earth metals
3. halogens

4. rare (or noble, i.e., unreactive) gases
5. semimetals (metalloids)

b. transition metals: four series -- elements 21-30, 39-48, 57-80, 89-109 -- and counting;

c. inner transition metals: lanthanides and actinides.

You should learn the names of the elements specified in points 1-5 under a. Other terms to know are period and group. Note also the A and B labels on group numbers. Reference will be made to the periodic table often in your study of chemistry and related sciences. It can provide you with much information, and is, as one teacher puts it, a "legal crib sheet." So use it!

## SECTION 6-3: PERIODICITY OF CHEMICAL PROPERTIES AS ILLUSTRATED BY BINARY OXIDES

The chemical behavior of oxides provides one of the clearest illustrations of periodic trends and of the differences between metals, nonmetals, and metalloids. A binary oxide is a compound between oxygen and one other element. Nearly all the elements, except the lighter noble gases, form oxides. The following are key points pertaining to oxides:

- Formulas can be predicted from group numbers;
- Bonding types range from ionic oxides of metals on the left side of the periodic table to covalent oxides of nonmetals on the right side of the table;
- Melting points vary with bonding type, the highest-melting oxides being the ionic ones, and the lowest-melting, covalently bonded ones of nonmetals such as C, N, S and the halogens;
- Acid-base properties vary with position in the periodic table, with most metals having basic oxides, metalloids and a few metals having amphoteric ones, and those of nonmetals being acidic.

Example 2

Predict the products of the reaction between water and the compounds listed below. Write a balanced equation describing each process.

a. $RaO$
b. $P_4O_{10}$
c. $SnO_2$

Solution: a. Radium is an alkaline earth metal, and thus is expected to form ionic compounds. Its oxide is a basic anhydride, that is, it reacts with water (hydrolyzes) to form a basic solution.

$$RaO(s) + H_2O(l) \rightarrow Ra^{2+}(aq) + 2OH^-(aq)$$

b. Phosphorus is a nonmetal; thus, its oxide is an acid anhydride. Hydrolysis of $P_4O_{10}$ produces phosphoric acid, a weak acid. $P_4O_{10}$ is used in the laboratory as a drying agent, because it readily reacts with both water vapor and liquid water.

$$P_4O_{10}(s) + 6H_2O(l) \rightarrow 4H_3PO_4(aq)$$

c. The oxides of Be, Al, Ga, Ge, Sn, Pb and some transition metals are amphoteric. They are generally only slightly soluble in water, but dissolve in both acidic and basic solutions to give complex ions. These oxides can act either as acids or bases.

$$SnO_2(s) + 2OH^-(aq) + 2H_2O(l) \rightarrow [Sn(OH)_6]^{2-}$$

$$SnO_2(s) + 2H^+(aq) + 4H_2O(l) \rightarrow [Sn(H_2O)_6]^{2+}$$

## SECTION 6-4: OXIDATION NUMBERS

First and foremost, bear in mind that oxidation numbers are an electron bookkeeping system. They are not meant to indicate charges on individual atoms, except for monatomic ions such as $Sr^{2+}$ or $Br^-$. Chemical reactions are characterized by the shifting of electrons from one atom or group of atoms to another; oxidation numbers are an aid to keeping track of electrons. They are invaluable for balancing oxidation-reduction equations.

Recall from Chapter 1 that oxidation is a process in which an atom loses electrons. The oxidation number of such an atom thus becomes more positive. The electrons lost by the atom which is oxidized are gained by another atom in the system, which is reduced.

Another term you need to remember from Chapter 1 is electronegativity. It is the ability of an atom to attract the electrons in a covalent bond to itself. Fluorine is the most electronegative of the elements; electronegativity decreases as one moves from right to left across periods, and down groups in the periodic table, i.e., away from fluorine.

Learn the nine rules given in the text for assigning oxidation numbers, and practice until you can make assignments with facility. Becoming familiar with the way oxidation numbers correlate to the position of elements in the periodic table will expedite this process.

### Example 3

Assign oxidation numbers to all atoms in the following compounds:

a. $Rb_2O_2$

Solution: In most instances, oxygen's oxidation number is -2. However, Rb is an alkali metal, Group IA, and can have only the +1 oxidation number. Therefore, oxygen must have a -1 oxidation number; the compound is a peroxide.

b. $HBrO_3$

Solution: There are no metals in this compound, bromic acid, so the oxidation number of hydrogen is +1. Bromine can have many oxidation numbers, so its number must be deduced from those of H and O. There is no reason not to assign -2 to oxygen. Thus, the oxidation number of bromine is positive:

$$-(3 \text{ O atoms})(-2/\text{O atom}) + (1 \text{ H atom})(+1/\text{H atom}) = 6 - 1 = 5$$

$$\overset{+1}{H}\ \overset{+5}{Br}\ \overset{-2}{O_3}$$

c. $Na_2S_4O_6$, sodium tetrathionate

Solution: Sodium can only be +1 in oxidation number. Assigning -2 to oxygen leaves sulfur with the following positive oxidation number:

$$-(6\ \text{O atoms})(-2/\text{O atom}) + (2\ \text{Na atoms})(+1/\text{Na atom}) =$$

$$+12 - 2 = +10 \text{ for 4 S atoms, or } +2\tfrac{1}{2} \text{ per S atom}$$

Oxidation numbers can, and sometimes do, have fractional values.

$$\overset{+1}{Na_2}\ \overset{+2\frac{1}{2}}{S_4}\ \overset{-2}{O_6}$$

## SECTION 6-5: OXIDATION-REDUCTION REACTIONS

Terms in this section which may be new to you are:

- o redox reaction: a synonym for oxidation-reduction reaction, one in which some atoms are oxidized and other reduced;
- o reducing agent or reductant: species that provides electrons to reduce another atom. Reducing agents are oxidized during the reaction; their oxidation numbers increase;
- o oxidizing agent or oxidant: species that accepts electrons from other atoms, and thus is reduced. Oxidation numbers of oxidants decrease.
- o disproportionate: process whereby the same species acts as both oxidizing and reducing agent; some of the atoms of a given element are reduced, while the rest are oxidized.

Example 4

Identify the oxidizing agent, reducing agent, species oxidized, and species reduced in the following reactions:

a. $I_2 + 2S_2O_3^{2-} \longrightarrow 2I^- + S_4O_6^{2-}$

Solution: The oxidation number of I changes from 0 to -1, so $I_2$ gains electrons and is reduced. Therefore, $I_2$ is the oxidizing agent. The oxidation number of S changes from +2 to +2½. Thus, S loses electrons and is oxidized. Thiosulfate ion, $S_2O_3^{2-}$, is the reducing agent.

b. $2Sn^{2+} + IO_3^- + 6H^+ + 14Cl^- \longrightarrow 2SnCl_6^{2-} + 3H_2O$

Solution: Tin changes from oxidation state +2 to +4. It is oxidized and, thus, is the reductant. Iodine's oxidation number changes from +5 to +1. Therefore, $IO_3^-$ is the oxidant, and iodine is reduced.

c. $Hg_2Cl_2 + 2OH^- \longrightarrow Hg + HgO + H_2O$

Solution: This is a disproportionation reaction. Mercury (I) is both an oxidizing and a reducing agent. Half of the mercury atoms are reduced to metallic mercury, an oxidation number change of +1 to 0. The other half are oxidized to mercury (II), a change in oxidation number from +1 to +2.

You should identity the oxidizing and reducing agents in homework problems 20, 21, and 22.

## SECTION 6-6: BALANCING OXIDATION-REDUCTION EQUATIONS

Four cardinal principles should guide you when you balance redox equations:

- For every oxidation there must be a simultaneous reduction, and vice versa;
- electrons lost must be balanced by electrons gained; electrons can't be left floating around;
- in basic solutions, balance H and O with $H_2O$ and $OH^-$, as required; add $H^+$ and $H_2O$ in acidic solutions;
- there is nothing wrong with fractional coefficients.

There are two reliable methods for balancing redox equations, the oxidation-number technique and the half-reaction system. Trial and error is not a good method and is a waste of time in most cases. You should learn both methods, but you will find that some equations are more easily balanced by one than the other.

Some people find equations involving basic media trickier to balance than those using acid. Keep in mind that $H_2O$ and $OH^-$ can be added to whatever side of the equation requires them, left or right. You may want to work a few extra problems having reactions in basic solution.

Example 5

Balance the following equation. The reaction occurs in acidic aqueous solution.

$$HS_2O_3^- \rightarrow S + HSO_4^-$$

Solution: Notice that this is a disproportionation reaction: some S atoms are oxidized and the others are reduced. Oxidation numbers of S are written above each formula:

$$\overset{+2}{HS_2O_3^-} \rightarrow \overset{0}{S} + \overset{+6}{HSO_4^-}$$

Method 1: Oxidation numbers

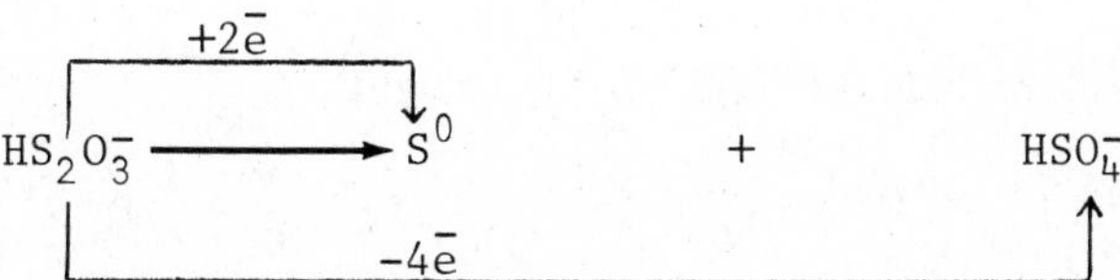


To balance the oxidation-number change, twice as many $S^0$ atoms as $HSO_4^-$ ions must be produced.

$$3/2\ HS_2O_3^- \rightarrow 2S^0 + HSO_4^-$$

Now balance H and O. There are more H and O atoms on the left than on the right. Add $H_2O$ to the right side to provide O atoms.

$$3/2\ HS_2O_3^- \rightarrow 2S^0 + HSO_4^- + 1/2\ H_2O$$

Add $H^+$ on the left to balance H.

$$1/2\ H^+ + 3/2\ HS_2O_3^- \rightarrow 2S^0 + HSO_4^- + 1/2\ H_2O$$

Check:

| left side | | right side |
|---|---|---|
| 3 | S | 3 |
| 9/2 | O | 4½ |
| 2 | H | 2 |
| -1 | charge | -1 |

The equation is balanced.

Method 2: Half reactions

Oxidation: $HS_2O_3^- \rightarrow HSO_4^- + 4\bar{e}$/S atom

Balance S: $HS_2O_3^- \rightarrow 2HSO_4^- + 8\bar{e}$

Balance O by adding $H_2O$ on the left:

$5H_2O + HS_2O_3^- \rightarrow 2HSO_4^- + 8\bar{e}$

Balance H by adding $H^+$ on the right:

$5H_2O + HS_2O_3^- \rightarrow 2HSO_4^- + 8\bar{e} + 9H^+$

Check:

| left side | | right side |
|---|---|---|
| 2 | S | 2 |
| 8 | O | 8 |
| 11 | H | 11 |
| -1 | charge | -1 |

The half-reaction is balanced.

Reduction: $HS_2O_3^- + 2\bar{e}$/S atom $\rightarrow S^0$

Balance S: $HS_2O_3^- + 4\bar{e} \rightarrow 2S^0$

Balance O by adding $H_2O$ on the right:

$HS_2O_3^- + 4\bar{e} \rightarrow 2S^0 + 3H_2O$

Balance H by adding $H^+$ on the left:

$5H^+ + HS_2O_3^- + 4\bar{e} \rightarrow 2S^0 + 3H_2O$

Check:

| left side | | right side |
|---|---|---|
| 2 | S | 2 |
| 3 | O | 3 |
| 6 | H | 6 |
| 0 | charge | 0 |

The half-reaction is balanced.

Add the oxidation and reduction half-reactions together, balancing electrons:

$$5H_2O + HS_2O_3^- \rightarrow 2HSO_4^- + 8\bar{e} + 9H^+$$

$$2(4\bar{e} + 5H^+ + HS_2O_3^- \rightarrow 2S^0 + 3H_2O)$$

---

$$5H_2O + 10H^+ + 3HS_2O_3^- \rightarrow 2HSO_4^- + 4S^0 + 9H^+ + 6H_2O$$

$$H^+ + 3HS_2O_3^- \rightarrow 2HSO_4^- + 4S^0 + H_2O$$

Check to see that the equation is balanced. It should be, unless an error was made in the last step, since both half-reactions were balanced.

Example 6

Balance the following equation. The reaction takes place in basic solution.

$$Ag_2S + CN^- + O_2 \rightarrow S + Ag(CN)_2^-$$

Oxidation numbers are written above the atomic symbols:

$$\overset{+1}{Ag_2}\overset{-2}{S} + \overset{+2}{C}\overset{-3}{N^-} + \overset{0}{O_2} \rightarrow \overset{0}{S} + \overset{+1}{Ag}(\overset{+2}{C}\overset{-3}{N})_2^-$$

Solution: One concludes that S is losing electrons while Ag, C, and N remain unchanged. Thus, O must gain electrons, and some oxygen-containing species having O in the -2 state must be added to the right side of the equation. If $H_2O$ is added on the right, then $H^+$ would have to be added on the left to balance H atoms. Since the reaction medium is basic, this makes no sense. Therefore, add $OH^-$ on the right and $H_2O$ on the left.

-2ē (S → $S^0$)

$$H_2O + Ag_2S + CN^- + O_2 \rightarrow S^0 + Ag(CN)_2^- + OH^-$$

+2ē/O atom (O → $OH^-$)

Balance oxidation-number change:

$$H_2O + Ag_2S + CN^- + \tfrac{1}{2}O_2 \rightarrow S^0 + Ag(CN)_2^- + OH^-$$

Balance O by adding $OH^-$ on the right, and balance Ag and $CN^-$:

$$H_2O + Ag_2S + 4CN^- + \tfrac{1}{2}O_2 \rightarrow S^0 + 2Ag(CN)_2^- + 2OH^-$$

Check:

| left side | | right side |
|---|---|---|
| 2 | Ag | 2 |
| 4 | $CN^-$ | 4 |
| 1 | S | 1 |
| 2 | O | 2 |
| 2 | H | 2 |
| -4 | charge | -4 |

The equation is balanced.

Method 2: Half-reactions

$$\text{Oxidation:}\quad Ag_2S + CN^- \rightarrow S^0 + Ag(CN)_2^- + 2\bar{e}$$

Balance Ag and $CN^-$:

$$Ag_2S + 4CN^- \rightarrow S + 2Ag(CN)_2^- + 2\bar{e}$$

Check:

| left side | | right side |
|---|---|---|
| 1 | S | 1 |
| 2 | Ag | 2 |
| 4 | CN | 4 |
| -4 | charge | -4 |

The equation is balanced.

$$\text{Reduction:}\quad O_2 + 2\bar{e}/\text{O atom} \rightarrow OH^- \text{ or } H_2O$$

If $H_2O$ is added on the right, $H^+$ must be added on the left. This is not sensible, since the reaction medium is basic. Therefore add $OH^-$ on the right, and provide H atoms on the left by adding $H_2O$.

$$H_2O + O_2 + 2\bar{e}/\text{O atom} \rightarrow OH^-$$

Since the oxidation half-reaction involves a $2\text{-}\bar{e}$ change, simplify matters by making the reduction process a $2\text{-}\bar{e}$ one as well.

$$H_2O + \tfrac{1}{2}O_2 + 2\bar{e} \rightarrow OH^-$$

Balance H and O by adding $OH^-$ on the right:

$$H_2O + \tfrac{1}{2}O_2 + 2\bar{e} \rightarrow 2OH^-$$

Check:

| left side | | right side |
|---|---|---|
| 2 | O | 2 |
| 2 | H | 2 |
| 2 | charge | 2 |

The half-reaction is balanced. Add half-reactions.

$$Ag_2S + 4CN^- \rightarrow S + 2Ag(CN)_2^- + 2\bar{e}$$

$$H_2O + \tfrac{1}{2}O_2 + 2\bar{e} \rightarrow 2OH^-$$

---

$$H_2O + Ag_2S + \tfrac{1}{2}O_2 + 4CN^- + 2\bar{e} \rightarrow S + 2Ag(CN)_2^- + 2OH^- + 2\bar{e}$$

$$H_2O + Ag_2S + \tfrac{1}{2}O_2 + 4CN^- \rightarrow S + 2Ag(CN)_2^- + 2OH^-$$

Unless an addition error has been made, the equation should be balanced. You should check this.

## SECTION 6-7: REDOX TITRATIONS

The use of oxidizing and reducing agents as quantitative analytical reagents is the topic of this section. The normality unit of concentration can be employed in these kinds of analyses, defined in terms of moles of electrons transferred between reductant and oxidant. Refer to Chapter 2 for a review of the normality of solutions of acids and bases. Normality is equivalents per liter of solution,

$$N = \text{eq}/V \text{ sol'n, L}$$

An equivalent in a redox reaction is that quantity of material which loses or gains a mole of electrons, or will produce one mole of oxidation-number change. Normality in redox reactions can be calculated only if both reactants and products are known.

### Example 7

How many equivalents per mole are there for iodate ion, $IO_3^-$, when it reacts to produce iodine?

Solution: The oxidation number of I in $IO_3^-$ is +5, while in $I_2$ it is 0. Five electrons must be added to each iodine atom, so there are 5 equivalents per mole of $IO_3^-$ for this process.

### Example 8

What is the equivalent weight of $KIO_3$ in the process in which $IO_3^-$ is converted to $I^-$?

Solution: The definition of equivalent weight is just the one you learned in Chapter 2:

$$\text{equivalent weight} = \frac{\text{molecular weight}}{\text{equivalents/mol}}$$

In this reaction, $IO_3^-$ changes oxidation state from +5 to -1, a 6-electron reduction. Thus there are 6 equivalents/mol and

$$\text{eq. wt.} = (1/6)\ \text{MW}$$

$$\text{eq. wt.} = (1\ \text{mol}/6\ \text{eq})(214.00\ \text{g/mol}) = 35.667\ \text{g/eq}$$

### Example 9

What is the normality of a solution containing 2.1400 g $KIO_3$ per liter in which $IO_3^-$ will be converted to paraperiodic acid, $H_5IO_6$?

Solution: To find normality one needs the number of equivalents in the sample, hence the equivalent weight, equivalents per mole, and molecular weight.

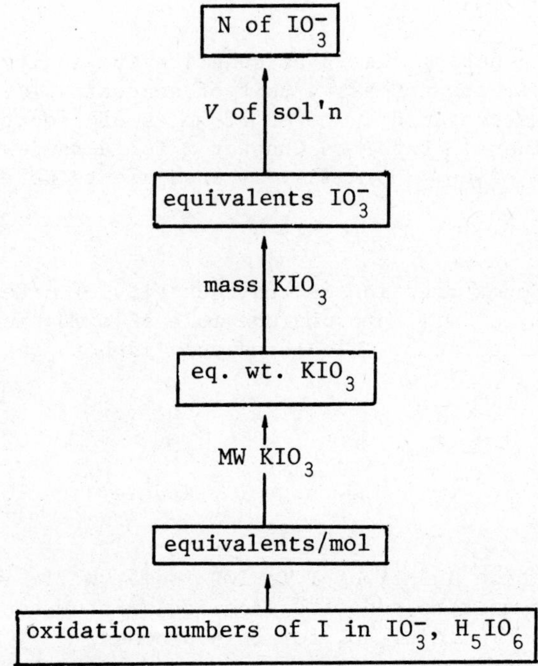


Iodine changes from +5 in $IO_3^-$ to +7 in $H_5IO_6$, a 2-$\bar{e}$ oxidation. There are 2 equivalents/mol.

$$\text{eq. wt. } KIO_3 = (1 \text{ mol}/2 \text{ eq})(214.00 \text{ g/mol}) = 107.00 \text{ g/eq}$$

$$\text{eq } KIO_3 = 2.1400 \text{ g}/(107.00 \text{ g/eq}) = 0.02000 \text{ eq}$$

$$\text{N } KIO_3 = 0.02000 \text{ eq}/1.00 \text{ L} = 0.0200 \text{ N}$$

Example 10

How many mL of the $KIO_3$ solution in the previous example can be oxidized to paraperiodic acid by 2.40 g ozone? The reaction is

$$O_3 + H^+ + IO_3^- + 2H_2O \rightarrow H_5IO_6 + O_2 .$$

Solution: In redox reactions, just as in acid-base titrations, the equivalence point is reached when equal numbers of equivalents of oxidizing agent and reducing agent have reacted:

equivalents oxidant = equivalents reductant

The equivalents of ozone, the oxidizing agent, are calculated from the oxidation-number change of oxygen and the molecular weight, just as we have done in previous examples.

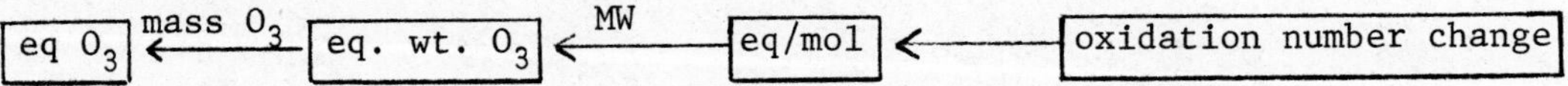


Only one O atom in $O_3$ changes oxidation number, from 0 to -2 in $H_5IO_6$. Thus, there are 2 eq/mol $O_3$.

$$\text{eq. wt. } O_3 = (1 \text{ mol}/2 \text{ eq})(48.0 \text{ g/mol}) = 24.0 \text{ g/eq}$$

$$\text{eq } O_3 = 2.40 \text{ g}/(24.0 \text{ g/eq}) = 0.100 \text{ eq}$$

$$\text{eq } KIO_3 = \text{eq } O_3 = 0.100 \text{ eq}$$

$$\begin{aligned}\text{volume } KIO_3 \text{ solution} &= 0.100 \text{ eq}/0.0200 \text{ N}\\ &= 0.100 \text{ eq}/(0.200 \text{ eq/L})\\ &= 5.00 \text{ L}\end{aligned}$$

## Terms to Know

acid anhydride
actinide
alkali metal
alkaline earth metal
amphoteric
basic anhydride
binary compounds
binary oxide
boiling point
bridging atom
combining capacity
density
disproportionates
group
halogen
lanthanide
melting point
metal
metalloid
oxidation
oxidation number
oxidation state
oxidizing agent
period
periodic law
periodic table
rare earth
redox equivalent
redox equivalent weight
redox reaction
reducing agent
reduction
semimetal
spectator ion
tetrahedral
transition metal

## Test Yourself

1. Predict the following properties of astatine, At, the heaviest halogen:

   a. boiling point
   b. formula of sodium salt
   c. formulas of oxyacids

Consult the Handbook of Chemistry and Physics, found at the reference desk in the library, for pertinent information about the other halogens. Recall that acids are discussed in Chapter 5 of the text.

2. Locate the following collections of elements in the periodic table, and list the individual elements:

   a. alkaline earth metals
   b. second transition series
   c. metalloids
   d. actinides

3. Arrange these elements in order of increasing metallic character: As, P, Bi, N, Sb.

4. Complete and balance these equations:

   a. $SO_2 + H_2O \rightarrow$

   b. $Cs_2O + H_2O \rightarrow$

   c. $P_4O_6 + H_2O \rightarrow$

   d. $BaO + H_2O \rightarrow$

5. Gallium is immediately below aluminum in Group IIIA. Many of its chemical properties are similar to those of aluminum, such as the amphoteric behavior of gallium oxide. Write balanced equations which illustrate how gallium oxide dissolves in acidic and basic solutions.

6. Assign oxidation numbers to all elements in these compounds: $Na_2S_2O_3$, $CH_3CN$, $Na_3AlF_6$, $BiO(NO_3)$, $OPCl_3$, $Ag_3AsO_4$, $S_2F_{10}$, $SO_2Cl_2$, $Na_2SnO_2$.

7. Balance the following equations, and identify the oxidizing and reducing agents, as well as the elements oxidized and reduced, in each case.

   a. $SO_4^{2-} + Br^- \rightarrow SO_2 + Br_2$ (acidic solution)

   b. $Sn \rightarrow SnO_3^{2-} + H_2$ (basic solution)

   c. $SO_4^{2-} + H_2S \rightarrow SO_2 + S$ (acidic solution)

   d. $Zn + NO_3^- \rightarrow NH_3 + [Zn(OH)_4]^{2-}$ (basic solution)

   e. $NO_3^- \rightarrow O_2 + NO_2$ (acidic solution)

   f. $MnO_4^- + Se^{2-} \rightarrow MnO_2 + Se$ (basic solution)

8. Calculate the normality of a 0.025 M $MnO_4^-$ solution used according to the reaction in problem 7f.

9. Copper metal can be prepared by reduction of a copper(II)-ammonia complex with dithionite ion in basic solution:

$$[Cu(NH_3)_4]^{2+} + S_2O_4^{2-} \rightarrow SO_3^{2-} + Cu + NH_3$$

   a. Balance the equation.
   b. Calculate the equivalent weight of $Na_2S_2O_4$, as used in this process.
   c. How many grams of $Na_2S_2O_4$, sodium dithionite, are required to prepare 1.00 g of copper?

# 7 Quantum Theory and Atomic Structure

## CHAPTER OVERVIEW AND OBJECTIVES

The evolution of ideas about the structure of atoms is traced from the turn of the century up to the present. Aside from the discovery of the nucleus, most of the questions treated in this chapter concern the electrons. Light is an especially useful research tool for investigating electrons in atoms and molecules because it has both wave-like and particle-like aspects, as do electrons.

When you finish this chapter you should be able to:

1. Explain how Rutherford's experiment demonstrated the existence of the nucleus, and why the Rutherford atomic model had to be modified;

2. Do the following pertaining to light:

   - Know and be able to use equations relating wavelength, frequency, speed, and energy;
   - Explain the photoelectric effect and its significance and be able to calculate how much of the energy of the impinging photon is transferred to the photoelectron as kinetic energy;
   - Use the Rydberg equation to predict wave numbers of the photons emitted by hydrogen atoms;
   - Explain what is meant by the wave-like and particle-like aspects of light and cite experimental evidence for each aspect;

3. Do the following with Bohr's model of the atom:

   - Describe Bohr's atomic model in terms of his postulates;
   - Show how the model explains the observed atomic emission spectrum of hydrogen and one-electron ions;
   - Calculate the radii of Bohr orbits and the energy of an electron in an orbit;
   - Calculate ionization energies, both ground and excited state, of hydrogen and one-electron ions;
   - Describe the shortcomings of the Bohr model;

4. Do the following relating to the quantum-mechanical theory of atomic structure:

   - Explain what is meant by the wave-like and particle-like aspects of electrons, protons, and other matter and be able to write and use de Broglie's equation relating momentum and wavelength;
   - Apply Heisenberg's uncertainty principle to experimental measurements;
   - Describe qualitatively how the motion of an electron in an atom is treated

as a wave;

- o Explain what an orbital is;
- o Name the quantum numbers, give physical interpretations of them, and deduce their values for an electron in any orbital in an atom.

## SECTION 7-1: RUTHERFORD AND THE NUCLEAR ATOM

In the opening years of this century the accepted visualization of the structure of the atom was J. J. Thomson's plum-pudding model. The entire volume of the atom was thought to be occupied by its mass, most of which was positively charged. A very small percentage of the atomic mass resided in the electrons, known to be extremely small and light, each with -1 charge. The electrons were the raisins in this atomic pudding, uniformly distributed throughout.

If Thomson's model were correct, then a small, massy, rapidly moving charged object, such as an $\alpha$ particle, should penetrate a thin sheet of atoms and pass right on through, with hardly any alteration in its path. The fact that an $\alpha$ particle occasionally bounced backward off the metal foils in Rutherford's laboratory indicated that it had hit something that was also small, massy, and positively charged. Rutherford and his associates proposed a new atomic model in which most of the mass resides in the nucleus, with the electrons moving around it in nearly empty space.

Example 1

If one wanted to make a physical model of an atom, how big would it have to be so that the nucleus could be seen?

Solution: Let's say that a 1-mm diameter nucleus is large enough. Rutherford, Geiger, and Marsden calculated the radius of the gold nucleus to be less than $10^{-12}$ cm. The radius of the atom was known to be about $10^5$ times this size, or $(10^{-12}\text{ cm})(10^5) = 10^{-8}$ cm. The radius of our atomic model must then be $(10^5)(0.5\text{ mm}) = 5 \times 10^4$ mm or 50 meters. The diameter of the model would be 100 meters or about 90 yards.

Rutherford's atomic model was by no means the last word on the subject. There was the nagging question of what kept the negative electrons and the positive nucleus apart, or, why didn't the electron spiral down into the nucleus?

## SECTION 7-2: THE QUANTIZATION OF ENERGY

The theme of this section is light and its use as a research tool for inquiring into atomic structure. You will need to learn the following terms and relationships having to do with light:

- o electromagnetic radiation: a general term for all kinds of light, whether visible or not, from gamma rays to radio waves
- o wavelength, $\lambda$: the distance between corresponding parts of a wave
- o frequency, $\nu$: the number of waves passing an observer per unit time
- o $v$: velocity of a wave; $v = \nu\lambda$, in general
- o $c$: velocity of all electromagnetic waves (light), $3.0 \times 10^8$ m/s; $\nu\lambda = c$, a constant, only for electromagnetic radiation
- o wave number, $\bar{\nu}$: reciprocal of $\lambda$, $\bar{\nu} = 1/\lambda$
- o quantum: an individual packet of something; apples, eggs, and electrons are quantized, they can only be counted out by whole numbers
- o photon: a quantum of light

- Planck's relationship for light energy: $E = h\nu$, where $E$ is the energy of one photon and $h$ is Planck's constant, $6.6262 \times 10^{-34}$ joule·second, the constant of proportionality between $E$ and $\nu$
- photoelectric effect: light of appropriate energy falling on a metal causes electrons to be released; provides evidence for quantization and particle aspect of light
- spectrum: a collection of light waves of various $\lambda$ or a collection of photons of various $\nu$;

  a. continuous spectrum: all values of $\lambda$ ( or $\nu$) are present
  b. line spectrum: only a few values of $\lambda$ (or $\nu$) are present
  c. emission spectrum: collection of photons (or waves) given off by a material
  d. absorption spectrum: collection of photons (or waves) taken up by a material

- Rydberg equation: empirical equation describing the emission spectrum of hydrogen;

  $\bar{\nu} = R_H(1/n_1^2 - 1/n_2^2)$

  where $R_H$ = 109,678 $cm^{-1}$

  $n_1$ and $n_2$ = integers relating to various series of spectral lines

Example 2

The energy of a particular photon of visible light is $3.1 \times 10^{-19}$ $J$.

a. What is the frequency of this photon?

Given: $E = 3.1 \times 10^{-19}$ $J$ for 1 photon

Find: $\nu$

Solution: Relationships involving $\nu$ of photons that you have learned thus far are $\nu = c/\lambda$ and $E = h\nu$. Since $\lambda$ is not known, but $E$ is,

$$\nu = E/h = 3.1 \times 10^{-19}\ J/6.6262 \times 10^{-34}\ J{\cdot}s = 4.7 \times 10^{15}\ s^{-1}$$

b. What is the wavelength of this photon?

Given: $E$ and $\nu$ of a photon

Find: $\lambda$

Solution: $\nu = c/\lambda$

$$\lambda = c/\nu = (3.00 \times 10^{10}\ \text{cm/s})/4.7 \times 10^{15}\ s^{-1} = 6.4 \times 10^{-5}\ \text{cm}$$

Note that the units of $c$ determine the units of $\lambda$. Use either m/s and m or cm/s and cm. Angstroms (Å) are often used to measure length on the atomic scale. 1Å = $10^{-8}$ cm = $10^{-10}$ m. Here, $\lambda = 6.4 \times 10^{-5}$ cm/($10^{-8}$ cm/Å) = ($6.4 \times 10^{-5}$ cm)(1Å/$10^{-8}$ cm) = $6.4 \times 10^3$ Å. This is a wavelength of red-orange light (see Figure 7-6).

c. What is the wave number of this photon?

Given: $E$, $\nu$, and $\lambda$ of a photon

Find: $\bar{\nu}$

Solution: You have learned two equations for $\bar{\nu}$ so far: $\bar{\nu} = 1/\lambda$ and $\bar{\nu} = R_H(1/n_1^2 - 1/n_2^2)$. The Rydberg equation is not appropriate for this problem, since we aren't considering the hydrogen atom spectrum.

$$\bar{\nu} = 1/\lambda = 1/6.4 \times 10^{-5}\ \text{cm} = 1.6 \times 10^4\ \text{cm}^{-1}$$

d. What would be the total energy of five of these photons?

Solution: Total energy is just the sum of the energies of the individual photons:

$$E_{\text{total}} = (5\ \text{photons})(3.1 \times 10^{-19}\ J/\text{photon}) = 1.6 \times 10^{-18}\ J$$

Example 3

What is the velocity of photoelectrons ejected from the surface of gold by light of $\lambda = 2.25 \times 10^{-5}$ cm? The work function of gold, or the energy needed just to release an electron, is $7.72 \times 10^{-19}$ $J$.

Given: light, $\lambda = 2.25 \times 10^{-5}$ cm, striking Au;
energy to release one $\bar{e} = 7.72 \times 10^{-19}$ $J$

Find: $v$ of photoelectron

Solution: The impinging light does two things: part of its energy goes to prying the electron loose (the work function), and the rest is transferred to the electron as kinetic energy. We can write

$$E_{\text{light}} = \text{work function} + \text{kinetic energy of } \bar{e}$$

$$h\nu = \text{work function} + (\tfrac{1}{2})mv^2$$

Solving for kinetic energy of the photoelectron:

$$\tfrac{1}{2}mv^2 = (6.6262 \times 10^{-34}\ J{\cdot}S)(3.00 \times 10^{10}\ \text{cm/s})/(2.25 \times 10^{-5}\ \text{cm}) - 7.72 \times 10^{-19}\ J$$

$$\tfrac{1}{2}mv^2 = 8.83 \times 10^{-19}\ J - 7.22 \times 10^{-19}\ J = 1.11 \times 10^{-19}\ J$$

Each photoelectron has acquired $1.11 \times 10^{-19}$ $J$ of kinetic energy from the light. Solving for velocity:

$$v^2 = 2(1.11 \times 10^{-19}\ J)/(9.1095 \times 10^{-31}\ \text{kg}) = 0.244 \times 10^{12}\ \text{m}^2/\text{s}^2$$

$$v = (24.4 \times 10^{10}\ \text{m}^2/\text{s}^2)^{\frac{1}{2}} = 4.94 \times 10^5\ \text{m/s}$$

Note that the mass of the electron must be given in kilograms when energy is in joules, and that units for velocity come out to be meters/second. Convert this velocity to km/hr or mph to get a better feel for just how fast the photoelectron is moving.

Einstein's interpretation of the photoelectric effect was an important piece of evidence for the particle aspect of the nature of light. Light does not exist sometimes as a wave and sometimes as a particle. Light is what it is, but it has properties of both waves and particles. Sometimes we observe the wave-like aspect of light, and at other times, the particle-like aspect. Electrons also have both particle-like and wave-like aspects.

The Rydberg equation is an empirical relationship that describes the line spectrum of hydrogen. This equation was not derived from an atomic model; it was developed from experimental data, i.e., some of the wavelengths in hydrogen's emission spectrum:

$$\bar{\nu} = R_H(1/n_1^2 - 1/n_2^2)$$

where $R_H$ = 109,678 cm$^{-1}$ (not the gas constant, $R$)
$n_1$ = an integer, 1, 2, 3 ... (not moles of gas, $n$)
$n_2$ = another integer, larger than $n$

Several series of spectral lines are observed. In a particular series, the value of $n_1$ is constant, and the value of $n_2$ varies. The Balmer series, $n_1$ = 2, was the first to be discovered. Balmer formulated an equation to describe that series which was later generalized by Rydberg.

Example 4

Compare the line spacing between the first two lines and lines 11 and 12 of the Brackett series.

Given: Brackett series of lines in the H spectrum

Find: Spacing, $\Delta\bar{\nu}$ or $\Delta\lambda$, between lines 1 and 2, 11 and 12

Solution: The value of $n_1$ for the Brackett series is needed. It is given in the text: $n_1$ = 4. Therefore the smallest value $n_2$ can have is 5. The $n_2$ values for the lines to be calculated are these:

| line: | 1 | 2 | 11 | 12 |
|---|---|---|---|---|
| $n_2$: | 5 | 6 | 15 | 16 |

$$\bar{\nu}_1 = R_H(1/4^2 - 1/5^2)$$

$$\bar{\nu}_2 = R_H(1/4^2 - 1/6^2)$$

$$\bar{\nu}_2 - \bar{\nu}_1 = R_H(1/4^2 - 1/6^2 - 1/4^2 + 1/5^2) = R_H(1/5^2 - 1/6^2)$$

$$\bar{\nu}_2 - \bar{\nu}_1 = R_H(1/25 - 1/36) = 109,678\ \text{cm}^{-1}(0.040 - 0.028)$$

$$\bar{\nu}_2 - \bar{\nu}_1 = 1316\ \text{cm}^{-1}$$

Alternately, we could have calculated the values of $\bar{\nu}_1$ and $\bar{\nu}_2$ and then subtracted, but this would have entailed more work. Don't be tempted to start furiously calculating without first examining the equations to see if simplification is possible.

Let's try to predict whether the spacing between lines 11 and 12 will be greater or less than that between lines 1 and 2.

$\bar{\nu}_{11} = R_H(1/4^2 - 1/15^2)$

$\bar{\nu}_{12} = R_H(1/4^2 - 1/16^2)$

$\bar{\nu}_{12} - \bar{\nu}_{11} = R_H(1/4^2 - 1/16^2 - 1/4^2 + 1/15^2) = R_H(1/15^2 - 1/16^2)$

The difference between $1/15^2$ and $1/16^2$ will be smaller than the difference between $1/5^2$ and $1/6^2$, so lines 11 and 12 will be closer together than lines 1 and 2.

$\bar{\nu}_{12} - \bar{\nu}_{11} = R_H(4.44 \times 10^{-3} - 3.91 \times 10^{-3}) = 109{,}678(0.53 \times 10^{-3})\ cm^{-1}$

$\bar{\nu}_{12} - \bar{\nu}_{11} = 58\ cm^{-1}$

As predicted, lines 1 and 2 are much farther apart than lines 11 and 12, 1316/58 = 23 times farther, in fact.

## SECTION 7-3: BOHR'S THEORY OF THE HYDROGEN ATOM

Bohr's model of the hydrogen atom was the first one to work perfectly, at least for one-electron systems. While studying this section, think about the process Bohr used in developing his theory. He took a new direction and was not afraid to abandon existing theory for a hypothesis that could potentially explain more observations. The two postulates of Bohr's theory acknowledge the experimental observation of hydrogen's emission spectrum:

1. The energy of an electron orbiting a nucleus is quantized, thus its angular momentum, mvr, is quantized:

   $mvr = nh/2\pi$

2. An orbiting electron only emits energy, as a photon, when it changes from a higher to a lower orbit.

Example 5

Consider an electron in the fourth Bohr orbit of hydrogen.

a. What is the energy of this electron?

Solution: The energy of an electron in the Bohr atom is quantized:

$E = -k/n^2$
where $k$ = 1312 $kJ$/mol = 13.595 eV/atom
$n$ = 1, 2, 3, ...

An electron in the fourth orbit has quantum number $n = 4$, thus

$E = -(13.595\ \text{eV/atom})/4^2 = -0.8497\ \text{eV}$

Alternately, the energy of a mole can be calculated from the other value of $k$. Divide the result by Avogadro's number to obtain the energy of one electron in joules. Or, one can use the conversion factor 1 electron volt = $1.6022 \times 10^{-19}\ J$.

b. What is the radius of the 4th orbit?

Solution: The radius is also determined by the quantum number $n$:

$$r = n^2 a_0$$

where $a_0 = 0.529\text{Å} = 5.29 \times 10^{-4}$ m, the radius of the ground state (first) orbit

Thus, $r = 4^2(0.529\text{Å}) = 8.46\text{Å}$

Notice how rapidly the size of orbits increases.

c. How much energy is required to ionize this atom?

Solution: The electron is already in an excited state, so the ionization energy I.E., the energy necessary to remove the electron from the atom, will be less than that for ionization of a ground-state electron. Ionization is equivalent to taking the electron to the $n = \infty$ energy level.

$$\Delta E = \text{I.E.} = E_\infty - E_4 = -k/\infty^2 - (-k/4^2)$$

$$\Delta E = 0 + k/4^2$$

The negative of this number was calculated in part a; I.E. = +0.8497 eV/atom.

d. If electrons were to fall from $n = 4$ back to the ground state, how many spectral lines could possibly be observed?

Solution: An electron in an excited state higher than $n = 2$ can fall to the ground state in one large jump, or in a series of smaller ones. The possibilities for these $n = 4$ electrons are 4→1, 4→3, 3→1, 3→2, 2→1, 4→2. A diagram shows this more clearly.

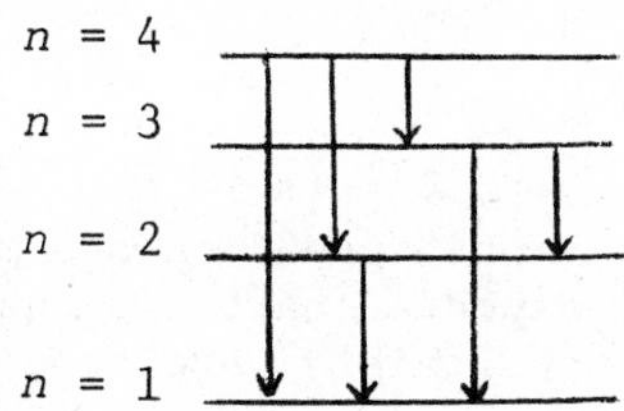


Thus, six lines could potentially be seen.

While the Bohr theory beautifully explained the spectrum of atomic hydrogen and one-electron ions, it failed for the rest of the periodic table, and had to be abandoned in favor of a more general theory.

## SECTION 7-4: PARTICLES OF LIGHT AND WAVES OF MATTER

Phenomena such as the photoelectric effect and blackbody radiation highlight the particle-like aspect of light. Under other physical conditions, the wave-like aspect of light is more obvious. de Broglie hypothesized that perhaps electrons, and other things that one usually thinks of as particles, might have wave-like properties. His hypothesis was later demonstrated to be correct by the observation that crystals diffract beams of electrons as well as beams of X rays.

An alternate derivation of de Broglie's equation starts from two expressions for energy.

$$E = h\nu = mc^2$$

$$hc/\lambda = mc^2$$

$$h/\lambda = mc$$

The left side of this equation emphasizes the wave-like aspect of light. The right side, which is an expression for momentum, emphasizes the particle-like aspect. By analogy, de Broglie wrote a similar expression for electrons and other matter,

$$mv = h/\lambda$$

The wave-like characteristics of electrons, neutrons and other things we usually consider to be particles only become apparent under certain conditions. de Broglie's concept of matter-waves led directly to the modern model of the atom, in which the wave-like aspect of electrons predominates.

Example 6

Neutron diffraction by crystals is a technique used to locate the positions of hydrogen atoms in molecules. What must be the velocity of a beam of neutrons so that the wavelength is 1.50Å?

Given: beam of neutrons, $\lambda = 1.50$Å

Find: $v$ of the neutrons

Solution: The relationship for matter-waves is $mv = h/\lambda$. Looking up the mass of neutron we find it to be $1.675 \times 10^{-27}$ kg. Thus

$$v = 6.6262 \times 10^{-34}\ J/(1.50\text{Å})(10^{-10}\ \text{m/Å})(1.675 \times 10^{-27}\ \text{kg})$$

$$v = 2.64 \times 10^3\ \text{m/s}$$

## SECTION 7-5: THE UNCERTAINTY PRINCIPLE

The principle of being unable to know exactly both position and momentum of a particle is built into the concept of the dual aspects, particle and wave, of the natures of matter and light. However, the uncertainty permitted by Heisenberg's principle,

$$[\Delta x][\Delta(mv_x)] \geq h/4\pi \text{ or } 5.273 \times 10^{-35}\ J\cdot s$$

is so very small that the precision allowed in macroscopic measurements is, in fact, quite good.

The limitations on precision in measurement become a problem only when the systems being studied are extremely small. For example, if we want to locate an electron in an atom, we must receive a signal from it. If the electron sends the signal directly, it must change position; in Bohr's terms, it must move from one orbit to another. On the other hand, if we try to locate the electron by letting it reflect a photon whose wavelength is small enough to be useful, then the collision between photon and electron will knock the electron off course.

Another version of the uncertainty principle was given by Einstein:

$$\Delta E \Delta t \geq h/4\pi$$

where $E$ and $t$ have their usual meanings. This statement is useful when trying to measure the energy of an excited electronic state of an atom. If the lifetime of the state, the amount of time the electron spends in it, is very small, then the uncertainty in the energy of the state becomes significant. The longer an electron remains in the state, the easier it is to measure its energy.

## SECTION 7-6: WAVE EQUATIONS

de Broglie's concept of matter-waves inspired Schrödinger to develop an equation describing the wave behavior of particles. Bohr's atomic model viewed electrons strictly as particles. The atomic model which emerged from Schrödinger's theory of wave mechanics emphasizes the wave-like property of electrons.

Because we are dealing with electrons in atoms, three boundary conditions, or restrictions, are applied to the equation. The boundary conditions allow only certain solutions to the equation to be acceptable. The equation is written in terms of the wave function, $\psi$, which corresponds to the amplitude of vibration of a string, such as a piano string. $|\psi|^2$ gives the probability of finding the electron in a certain region of space in an atom. The restrictions on $|\psi|^2$ are that it must be

- continuous: if the electron exists, then it must be somewhere in the universe, but it can't be in two places at the same time;
- single-valued: at one point in space at a given time there can only be one value of the probability of finding the electron;
- finite: the electron does not disappear and reappear, but is permanent, so the probability of finding it somewhere in the universe remains constant.

These boundary conditions on $|\psi|^2$ restrict, or quantize, the values that the energy of the electron may have.

Be sure to study 7-16(a) and (b), which depict the analogous situation of a vibrating string.

## SECTION 7-7: THE HYDROGEN ATOM

An acceptable solution to the Schrödinger equation, a wave function, $\psi$, mathematically describes the motion of an electron of a certain energy in an atom. These solutions are characterized by three quantum numbers, $n$, $l$, and $m$. Recall that the Bohr model featured one quantum number, $n$. Whereas the electron moved in circular tracks, or orbits, in the Bohr model, in the wave-mechanical model, electrons move in certain regions of space with particular shapes around the nucleus. These regions of space in the atom are called orbitals, and are described by the quantum numbers.

Physical interpretations and allowed values of the quantum numbers are these:

- principal quantum number, $n$: specifies orbital energy; values can be 1, 2, 3, 4, 5 ...
- azimuthal quantum number, $l$: specifies orbital shape; values can be 0, 1, 2, 3 ... $n$-1
- magnetic quantum number, $m$: specifies spatial orientation of orbital; values can be 0, ±1, ±2, ... ± $l$

There is also a fourth quantum number, $s$, which specifies the spin on an electron, and has values $+\frac{1}{2}$ and $-\frac{1}{2}$.

The values of $l$ have been assigned letters which are the commonly used designations for orbital shape:

| *l*: | 0 | 1 | 2 | 3 | 4 |
|---|---|---|---|---|---|
| | *s* | *p* | *d* | *f* | *g* |

Refer to Figures 7-20 through 7-26 in the text illustrations of many of the orbitals. (A popular student-memory aid of years gone by correlates the shapes of the orbitals with their letter designations, as *s* = sphere, *p* = peanut, *d* = double peanut, and *f* = all fouled up. Actually, the *f* orbitals look rather like flowers.)

The values of the magnetic quantum number specify how many orbitals of each shape there can be for a given value of *n*. These are the following:

| orbital shape | values of m | orbitals/set |
|---|---|---|
| *s* | 0 | 1 |
| *p* | -1,0,1 | 3 |
| *d* | -2,-1,0,1,2 | 5 |
| *f* | -3,-2,-1,0,1,2,3 | 7 |

Example 7

List the number and types of orbitals which have principal quantum numbers 1-3.

Solution: The rules for quantum number values allow the following orbitals only:

| | | |
|---|---|---|
| $n = 1$ | 1*s* | 1 orbital total |
| $n = 2$ | 2*s*, 2*p* | 1 + 3 = 4 orbitals total |
| $n = 3$ | 3*s*, 3*p*, 3*d* | 1 + 3 + 5 = 9 orbitals total |

The direction, or spatial orientation, of a *p*, *d*, or *f* orbital is designated by a letter subscript, e.g., $p_y$ or $d_{xz}$. Since *s* orbitals are spherically symmetrical about the nucleus, they need no such designation. An electron in an atom is completely described by the values of its four quantum numbers, *n*, *l*, *m*, and *s*. The next chapter describes how the quantum-mechanical model of the atom can be extended to multi-electron atoms, something that is not possible with the Bohr model.

Terms to Know

absorption spectrum
angular momentum
atomic orbital
atomic spectrum
atomic unit
azimuthal quantum number
Balmer series
blackbody radiation
Bohr radius
Bohr's theory of the hydrogen atom
boundary conditions
canal rays
cathode rays
continuous spectrum
contour diagram (of an orbital)
electromagnetic waves
electron spin
emission spectrum

excited state
frequency
ground state
ionization energy
line spectrum
Lyman series
magnetic quantum number
node
orbital
orbital-orientation quantum number
orbital-shape quantum number
Paschen series
Pfund series
photoelectric effect
photon
Planck's constant
principal quantum number
probability density
quantized
quantum
quantum number
radioactivity
Rydberg constant
Rydberg equation
Schrödinger equation
spin quantum number
standing wave
ultraviolet catastrophe
uncertainty principle
visible spectrum
wave function
wave number
wavelength
wave-particle duality
X rays

## Test Yourself

1. Briefly describe the experimental work of Geiger, Marsden, and Rutherford that led to the discovery of the nucleus of the atom. Clearly state how the presence of the nucleus was inferred from their experimental results.

2. Microwave radiation, which is used in microwave ovens, has wavelengths between 1 and 0.01 cm.

   a. For a microwave of $\lambda = 0.50$ cm, calculate $E$, $\nu$, and $\bar{\nu}$
   b. Will the energy, frequency, and wave number of a 0.10 cm microwave be greater than or less than that of a 0.50 cm wave?

3. Selenium (Se) is used in photocells, light meters, and Xerox machines. What wavelength of light striking the surface of selenium will eject a photoelectron of velocity $5.25 \times 10^5$ m/s? The work function of selenium is 4.62 eV/electron.

4. What is the energy of one mole of the photons described in question 3?

5. What wavelength of radiation will raise the electron in an excited hydrogen atom from the fourth to the seventh Bohr orbit?

6. The Pfund series of lines in the hydrogen emission spectrum is characterized by $n_f = 5$. Calculate the longest wavelength possible for a spectral line in this series.

7. The ionization energy of hydrogen in its ground (unexcited) state is 1312 kJ/mol. What is the ionization energy of an excited $Li^{2+}$ ion of quantum number $n = 3$?

8. What experimental evidence exists for the particle-like aspect of the nature of light?

9. What is Superman's wavelength when he is traveling faster than a speeding bullet, or about 560 mph? Assume Superman's mass to be 195 lbs.

10. If the uncertainty in Superman's speed in question 9 is 10 mph, what is the uncertainty in his location? What would be the uncertainty in the position of a neutron having the same speed and its associated uncertainty? Would it be difficult to observe either Superman or the neutron?

11. Explain what an orbital is.

12. How many nodes does a 5*d* orbital have? Sketch a $5d_{xz}$ orbital, indicating the positions of all the nodes.

13. Which of the following sets of quantum numbers cannot exist?

    a. $n = 2,\ l = 1,\ m = -1$
    b. $n = 2,\ l = 2,\ m = 2$
    c. $n = 5,\ l = 4,\ m = 4$
    d. $n = 5,\ l = 3,\ m = -4$
    e. $n = 3,\ l = 2,\ m = 0$

14. To which atomic orbitals do the acceptable sets of quantum numbers in question 13 belong?

# 8 Electronic Structure and a Description of the Elements

## CHAPTER OVERVIEW AND OBJECTIVES

The electronic configurations, or the arrangement of electrons in energy levels, of multielectron atoms can be predicted in a straightforward manner in most cases. Electronic configurations correlate with the arrangement of elements in the periodic table and help explain why the table is effective in predicting so many chemical properties. We will be concerned primarily with ground-state, or lowest-energy, configurations. These can be used to predict:

- ionization energies (ionization potentials);
- electron affinities;
- relative sizes of atoms and ions;
- oxidation states and types of ions that form;
- type of bonding between different elements.

Sections 8-4 - 8-8 describe some of the chemistry of elements throughout the periodic table and the connection between chemical properties and electron configuration.

When you finish this chapter you should be able to:

1. Write the ground-state orbital electronic configuration of any atom or simple ion, using the periodic table.

    - Understand and use the aufbau process;
    - Order electronic energy levels in multielectron atoms using the periodic table;
    - Recognize excited electronic states and disallowed electronic configurations;
    - Rationalize apparent anomalies in electronic configurations.

2. Correlate the periodic variation in electronic configuration with properties of the elements.

    - Define the terms ionization energy (potential), electron affinity, and electronegativity;
    - Predict trends in ionization potential, electron affinity, electronegativity, and size of atoms and simple ions throughout the periodic table;
    - Predict the type of bonding, ionic, covalent, or polar covalent, expected between two elements based on their position in the periodic table and their electronegativities.

3. Use oxidation or reduction potentials to predict the relative likelihood of two oxidation (or two reduction) processes happening.

4. Rationalize observed chemical behavior of the elements on the basis of electronic configuration.

## SECTION 8-1: BUILDUP OF MANY-ELECTRON ATOMS

Orbitals, or energy levels, of multielectron atoms are called hydrogen-like because they are very similar to those of the hydrogen atom. One must now consider not only attractive forces between electrons and the nucleus, but also repulsive forces among electrons. Thus orbital energy in multielectron atoms depends not only on the principal quantum number, *n*, but also on the azimuthal quantum number, *l*. Recall the types of orbitals:

- o *s* orbitals, 1 per set, set accommodates 2$\bar{e}$;
- o *p* orbitals, 3 per set, set accommodates 6$\bar{e}$;
- o *d* orbitals, 5 per set, set accommodates 10$\bar{e}$;
- o *f* orbitals, 7 per set, set accommodates 14$\bar{e}$;

Pauli's aufbau process for determining ground-state electronic configurations rests on three principles:

1. Pauli exclusion principle -- no two electrons in the same atom can have the same four quantum numbers.

2. Orbitals are filled in order of increasing energy.

3. Hund's rule -- for a degenerate, or equal energy, set of orbitals, electrons fill in each energy level singly first with spins parallel, and pair up only after all members of the set contain one electron.

The order of energies of orbitals is easy to remember by constructing the diagram shown. First write down in block form all the types of orbitals, designated by their *n* and *l* quantum numbers:

| | | | |
|---|---|---|---|
| 1*s* | | | |
| 2*s* | 2*p* | | |
| 3*s* | 3*p* | 3*d* | |
| 4*s* | 4*p* | 4*d* | 4*f* |
| 5*s* | 5*p* | 5*d* | 5*f* |
| 6*s* | 6*p* | 6*d* | |
| 7*s* | | | |

Next, connect the levels with arrows along the diagonal, as shown.

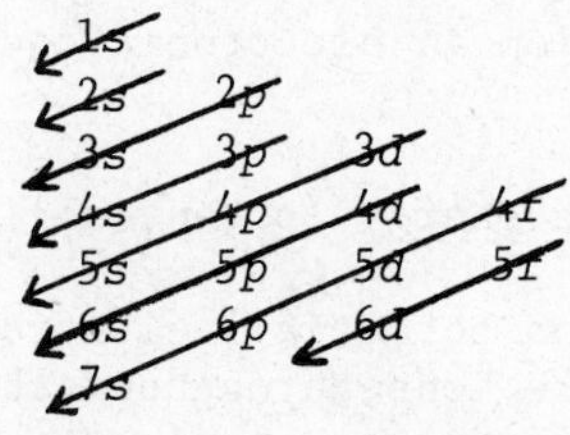


Read the diagram, starting from the top, by following the arrows from the head of one to the end of the one below. Thus, the order is 1*s*, 2*s*, 2*p*, 3*s*, 3*p*, 4*s*, 3*d*, 4*p*, 5*s*, 4*d*, etc. This diagram only takes a minute to write out and is foolproof.

Example 1

Write the complete orbital electronic configuration for vanadium (V), element number 23.

Solution: The periodic table, in combination with the relative orbital energy diagram just constructed, is enormously helpful in predicting ground-state electronic configurations. The sketch shows which energy levels are the highest-occupied ones in various sections of the periodic table.

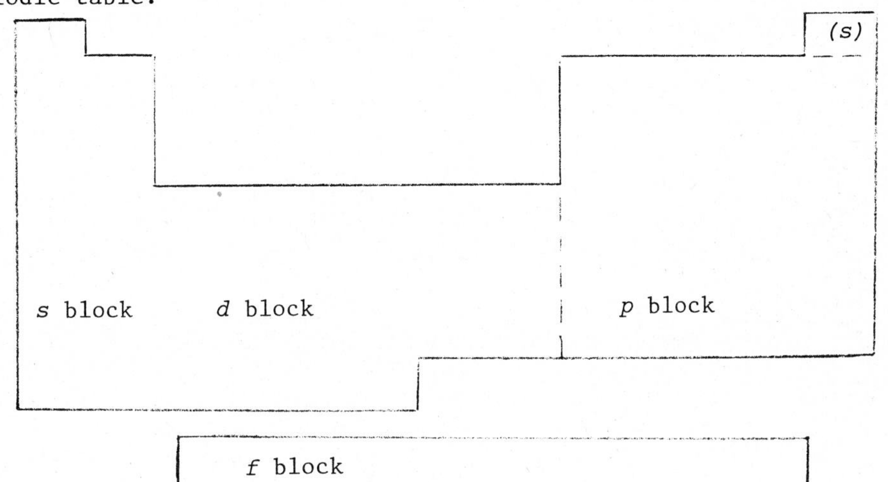


Vanadium is a *d*-block element in the fourth period, first transition series. The 3*d* orbitals are the highest energy levels occupied by electrons. The complete electronic configuration is $1s^2\ 2s^2\ 2p^2\ 3s^2\ 3p^6\ 4s^2\ 3d^3$. It makes no difference whether one writes $3p^6\ 3d^3\ 4s^2$ or $3p^6\ 4s^2\ 3d^3$. Notice also that the designation $3d^3$ means that three of the five 3*d* orbitals are singly occupied. We have no way of knowing which three *d* orbitals -- $d_{xy}$, $d_{yz}$, $d_{xz}$, $d_{x^2-y^2}$, or $d_{z^2}$ -- are occupied; any three could be. Thus, it is just as correct to expand the $3d^3$ designation to $3d_{xy}\ d_{xz}\ d_{z^2}$ or any other combination that gives the same result. This is because all the 3*d* orbitals are degenerate, that is, they each have the same energy. This is true for any set of degenerate orbitals, *p*, *d*, or *f*.

There is a shorthand method for writing electronic configurations in which completely filled energy levels corresponding to the configuration of the noble gas immediately preceding the element in question are abbreviated by enclosing the symbol for the gas in brackets. Argon is the noble gas that comes just before vanadium, so the shorthand configuration is [Ar] $4s^2 3d^3$. The electrons corresponding to those of the noble gas are referred to as core electrons. The outer electrons are called valence electrons and are the ones that participate in chemical reactions.

Example 2

The newest elements to be discovered are synthesized in accelerators, in which the nucleus of one element is bombarded with that of another. The last elements to be produced by these reactions form part of the 4th transition series.

a. What is the highest energy level that is occupied by electrons in the ground states of elements 104-109?

Solution: Using the periodic table and the relative orbital energy diagram, one predicts that the $6d$ orbitals are the highest-occupied energy levels in these elements.

b. As more elements are discovered, what is the next set of energy levels to be occupied after $6d$?

Solution: Again, consulting the periodic table, we can predict that the $6d$ orbitals will be completely filled at element 112. Using the periodic table or the relative orbital energy diagram, one can predict that the $7p$ orbitals would be the next highest in energy.

Example 3

The observed valence electronic configurations for molybdenum (Mo) and silver (Ag) are $5s^14d^5$ and $5s^14d^{10}$, respectively. Rationalize these observations.

Solution: First, a few words must be said about how the rules for predicting electronic configurations came to be. The electrons in atoms know nothing at all about the aufbau process and its associated principles. The method for formulating electronic configurations was developed to explain experimental observations. This method works fairly well, accurately predicting the configurations of most elements. When anomalies have been observed, the theory has been modified to account for the observations. Thus, the fact that the valence configuration of Mo is $5s^14d^5$ rather than $5s^24d^4$ is evidence for particular stability of a half-filled set of degenerate energy levels.

Two energy terms representing interactions among electrons must be taken into account to rationalize the observed ground-state configurations of Cr, Mo, Cu, and Ag. One of these is pairing energy, the repulsive energy that arises from pairing two electrons in the same orbital, which places them in close proximity.

Electron pairing tends to increase the total energy of an atom. There is also the exchange energy term, which arises from spin correlation of electrons in separate orbitals. That is, the spins tend to all be parallel, which lowers the overall energy of the atom. In the observed configurations of Mo and Cr, $s^1d^5$, electron pairing is minimized and exchange energy is maximized; there are six unpaired electrons with parallel spins. The alternate configuration, $s^2d^4$, has two electrons paired and only four unpaired electrons with parallel spins, and thus is higher in energy and corresponds to an excited electronic state.

Now let's look at Ag and Cu. The possible configurations are $s^2d^9$ and $s^1d^{10}$. Both of these have one unpaired electron, so the exchange energy is the same for each. One might expect the pairing energy to be identical for the two states as well, until the size and shape of $d$ and $s$ orbitals are considered. Repulsion due to electron pairing is less in a $d$ orbital, which is quite spread out, relative to $s$ and $p$ orbitals. Thus, the $s^1d^{10}$ configuration is the lower-energy one.

Periodic trends in properties of atoms such as ionization energy (ionization potential), electron affinity, types of ions formed, and size are a direct consequence of electronic configuration. Moreover, a careful examination of configurations account for apparent anomalies in these trends.

Ionization energy, also called ionization potential, is defined as the energy required to remove an electron from an atom or positive ion in the gas phase to form a cation in the gas phase. This definition is important to learn in its entirety. Don't forget that a gas-phase process is specified. The first ionization potential refers to the process

$$\text{I.E.} + X(g) \rightarrow X^{+}(g) + \bar{e}$$

the second to the process

$$\text{I.E.} + X^{+}(g) \rightarrow X^{2+}(g) + \bar{e}$$

and so on.

In general, ionization potential increases from left to right across a period, as nuclear charge increases. It becomes easier to remove an electron going down a group, as the valence electrons get farther away from the nucleus, and thus ionization potential decreases. There are some values of ionization energy which, at first glance, seem to be exceptions to this rule.

Example 4

Why is the first ionization potential of selenium (Se) less than that of arsenic (As)?

Solution: Selenium, element 34, follows arsenic in the periodic table. The general trend of increasing ionization energy left to right across a period predicts that arsenic, not selenium, should be more difficult to ionize. Let's look at the valence electronic configurations of the other atoms and ions in question.

| | | | |
|---|---|---|---|
| As | $4s^2p^3$ | Se | $4s^2p^4$ |
| $As^+$ | $4s^2p^2$ | $Se^+$ | $4s^2p^3$ |

The solution to this problem can be determined by comparing valence configurations of Se and $Se^+$. Ionization of Se is helped by the loss of pairing energy in a $4p$ orbital. Remember that pairing electrons in an orbital costs energy; it increases the total energy of an atom. On the other hand, there is no energy savings resulting from the ionization of arsenic. Selenium's ionization potential is lower, then, because the savings in pairing energy outweighs the effect of the higher nuclear charge of Se compared to As.

Electron affinity is defined as the energy accompanying the formation of a negative ion (anion) from a neutral atom, in the gas phase:

$$X(g) + \bar{e} \rightarrow X^{-}(g)$$

This definition should also be learned, but be mindful that the process of ion formation is a gas-phase one. Unlike ionization energies, which are always positive, electron affinities can be of either sign. Moreover, measurement of ionization potential is usually a straightforward experimental process, while electron affinities must often be evaluated indirectly.

Electron affinities generally increase, i.e., become more positive, moving from the alkali metals to the halogens. Deviations from this trend can be accounted for by energy differences between *s* and *p* orbitals and by electron pairing. So few electron affinity values are known that no clear trends emerge from groups in the periodic table.

The types of ions that elements tend to form can be predicted by examining their electronic configurations. The general trend is toward achievement of a noble-gas-type configuration in the ion. However, ions of charge greater than ±3 are generally not observed. $Ce^{4+}$, one of the lanthanides, is an exception to this rule.

Example 5

Which ion of sulfur would be expected to be more likely to form, $S^-$ or $S^{2-}$? Why?

Solution: $S^{2-}$ is observed, while $S^-$ is not. Moreover, formation of divalent anions is characteristic of Group VIA. To account for this observation, we first write out the appropriate valence configurations.

| | |
|---|---|
| S | $3s^2p^4$ |
| $S^-$ | $3s^2p^5$ |
| $S^{2-}$ | $3s^2p^6$ |

Sulfide ion, $S^{2-}$, is isoelectronic with the noble gas argon. Noble-gas electronic configurations are observed to be extremely stable. The noble gases are "noble" because of their very low chemical reactivity.

Bear in mind that ions do not form in a vacuum. Ionization of S to $S^{2-}$ is accompanied by concurrent formation of a cation of some other element, such as hydrogen or a metal. While the energies of ions are higher than those of their corresponding neutral atoms, the coulombic attraction between cations and anions more than compensates for the energy required for ion formation.

Example 6

Why do the divalent cations of the second transition series metals form by loss of the 5*s* electrons, rather than 4*d* electrons?

Solution: Even though a small portion of the 5*s* orbital penetrates to the nucleus and thus feels the full effect of nuclear charge, the majority of the electron density in this orbital is farther away from the nucleus than are the 4*d* orbitals. The 5*s* electrons are more shielded from the nuclear charge than are the 4*d*, and thus are the most loosely held.

## SECTIONS 8-2 AND 8-3: TYPES OF BONDING; ELECTRONEGATIVITY

Bonds between atoms can be divided into two broad classifications: covalent and ionic. Covalent bonds result from atoms sharing valence electrons of similar energies. Ionic bonds are formed by coulombic attraction between cations and anions. Electron transfer from one atom to another occurs when the valence orbital energies are markedly different, as reflected in ionization energies and electron affinities. Bond energy is that required to separate two bonded atoms.

Bond distances, or lengths, are distances between the nuclei of bonded atoms. Atomic radii are determined from measurements of covalent-bond distances in elements. Ionic radii are obtained from bond lengths of ionic compounds.

Because electrons in orbitals of the same principle quantum number do not shield each other effectively, atom radii increase smoothly from left to right across a period, as effective nuclear charge increases. Atomic radii increase going down a group. There is periodic variation in ionic radii as well: cations are smaller than, and anions larger than, the corresponding neutral atoms. With cations, the decrease in size results from decreased electron repulsion and increased positive-charge density on the ion, which draw the remaining electrons in toward the nucleus. Anions are larger than their parent atoms due to increased electron repulsion. Isoelectronic moieties, those with the same number of electrons, decrease in size as nuclear charge increases. Be sure to study Figure 8-5 in the text carefully, placing it in the context of the periodic table.

Electronegativity, $\chi$, is useful for predicting whether bonds will be ionic, covalent, or intermediate in character. It is defined as the attraction of an atom for the electrons in a covalent bond that it makes with another atom. The rule of thumb to be followed in predicting bond type is that ionic bonds form if the electronegativity difference between atoms is 2.0 or greater, and covalent bonds form if the difference is 0.4 or less. Atoms having differences between 0.4 and 2.0 form polar covalent bonds; electrons are shared between the atoms, but unequally. The degree of ionic character of these bonds increases with increasing electronegativity difference. Fluorine is the most electronegative of all elements. Electronegativity decreases as one moves through the periodic table away from fluorine, being lowest for cesium (Cs), which is diagonally opposite fluorine.

Example 7

Predict whether the bonds in the compounds below will be ionic, covalent, or polar covalent. Assign charges to the atoms, as appropriate.

a. $Cs_2S$ c. $PH_3$

b. $SrBr_2$ d. $PCl_3$

Solution: First, estimate the types of bonds formed from the locations of the atoms in the periodic table. The metals Cs and Sr are on the opposite side of the table from S and Br, so their compounds will probably be ionic. P, Cl, and H are all nonmetals and thus are expected to bond covalently, but with some degree of polarity. Next, fine-tune these predictions by using electronegativity values, found in Table 8-1 in the text.

| atom | Cs | Sr | H | P | S | C |
|---|---|---|---|---|---|---|
| $\chi$ | 0.79 | 0.95 | 2.20 | 2.19 | 2.58 | 3.16 |

a. $Cs_2S$ $\Delta\chi = 2.58 - 0.79 = 1.79$ The bonds will be covalent, but with a high degree of ionic character, since $\Delta\chi$ is not quite 2.0. Sulfur, being the more electronegative, carries a partial negative charge, $\delta^-$, while that of cesium is $\delta^+$.

b. $SrBr_2$ $\Delta\chi = 2.96 - 0.95 = 2.01$ This compound is ionic, $Sr^{2+}$, $Br^-$.

c. $PH_3$ $\Delta\chi = 2.20 - 2.19 = 0.01$ The bonds are almost 100% covalent. Extremely small partial charges could be assigned as $\delta^+$ for H and $\delta^-$ for P, but this is really splitting hairs.

d. $PCl_3$ $\Delta\chi = 3.16 - 2.19 = 0.97$ These bonds are polar covalent with intermediate ionic character. Partial charges are $\delta^-$ on Cl and $\delta^+$ on P.

There is a spectrum of bond types in compounds, ranging from 100% ionic to 100% covalent, with many intermediate possibilities. A perusal of Table 8-1 will show that relatively few combinations of atoms lead to strictly ionic bonds; there are many more of the polar-covalent type.

Be sure to study Example 9 in the text and work problems 16-18 to become familiar with the methods of calculating electronegativity values.

## SECTION 8-4: CHEMICAL PROPERTIES REVISITED: OXIDATION AND REDUCTION POTENTIALS

The remainder of this chapter might also be titled "Through the Periodic Table with Gun and Camera." It is a survey of chemical behavior of the elements related to their electronic configurations. To prepare for this expedition, one needs to have a basic understanding of oxidation and reduction potentials.

Oxidation potential, $E^0$, indicates the tendency of an oxidation half-reaction, relative to the half-reaction

$$\tfrac{1}{2}H_2(g) \rightarrow H^+(aq) + \bar{e}$$

to take place in aqueous solution. The oxidation of hydrogen is the reference point on the scale of oxidation potentials. This is analogous to $^{12}C$ being the reference point on the atomic-weight scale. $E^0$ for the oxidation of hydrogen has been arbitrarily assigned as 0.000 volts. You should memorize this value of $E^0$. A reference half-reaction is needed because half-reactions do not occur by themselves. An oxidation half-reaction can only take place concurrently with a reduction half-reaction, and therefore absolute values of oxidation potentials cannot be measured.

One can also speak of the tendency for a reduction half-reaction to occur, relative to

$$H^+(aq) + \bar{e} \rightarrow \tfrac{1}{2}H_2, \qquad E^0 = 0.000 \text{ V}$$

which is measured by the corresponding reduction potential. The reduction potential for a given half-reaction is equal in magnitude but opposite in sign to the oxidation potential for the reverse half-reaction.

Another way to think of the reference half-reaction is that, in a reaction such as

$$Zn(s) + 2\,H^+(aq) \rightarrow Zn^{2+}(aq) + H_2(g)$$

all the tendency for the reaction to occur has been assigned to $E^0$ for the half-reaction

$$Zn(s) \rightarrow Zn^{2+}(aq) + 2\bar{e}$$

A positive oxidation potential for a half-reaction, or a negative reduction potential, means that the half-reaction is more likely to take place than the oxidation of hydrogen.

Example 8

How likely are these reactions to happen?

$$Zn(s) \rightarrow Zn^{2+}(aq) + 2\bar{e}\ , \qquad E^0 = +0.7628\ V$$
$$Cu(s) \rightarrow Cu^{2+}(aq) + 2\bar{e}\ , \qquad E^0 = -0.3402\ V$$

Solution: The $E^0$ values given above really indicate the inclination for the reactions

$$Zn(s) + 2H^+(aq) \rightarrow Zn^{2+}(aq) + H_2(g)$$
$$Cu(s) + 2H^+(aq) \rightarrow Cu^{2+}(aq) + H_2(g)$$

to take place. The positive $E^0$ for oxidation of zinc means that this reaction is spontaneous, unless stopped by an applied opposing potential of 0.7628 V or more. On the other hand, oxidation of copper by hydrogen ion is not spontaneous, but would occur if more than 0.3204 V were applied to force it to the right. A negative $E^0$ value just means that the reverse reaction is spontaneous. Thus hydrogen reduces $Cu^{2+}$ to metallic copper. If the oxidation half-reactions involving Zn and Cu were coupled with a different reduction half-reaction, their relative tendencies to occur would be the same: Zn would be more easily oxidized than Cu.

## SECTION 8-5: CHEMICAL PROPERTIES: THE *s*-ORBITAL METALS

In this section, and those that follow, a wealth of information about the chemistry of various elements is presented. You are certainly not expected to memorize all these facts. However, as you study this material, look for

- o features common to a group of elements (a column in the periodic table);
- o trends within a group; and
- o differences among groups.

Keep in mind that chemical and physical properties of the elements correlate nicely with their electronic configurations. In other words, hang the information you read about on the framework provided by the periodic table.

### Groups IA and IIA

Some similarities and differences between these two groups are listed here:

- o strong tendency to occur as ions, so much so that the free metals are not found in nature;
- o metals are excellent reducing agents;
- o relatively weak metallic bonds in the metals, reflected in their physical properties;
- o charge density of alkaline earth metal ions higher than for alkali metal ions, due to higher charge in combination with smaller size, reflected in such things as relative solubilities of compounds, relative basicity of oxides, and covalent-bonding character of beryllium compounds;
- o simple ions of both groups colorless in aqueous solution.

## SECTION 8-6: THE FILLING OF THE *d* ORBITALS: TRANSITION METALS

Seven trends in the transition metals are listed at the end of this section. You should try to relate them to electronic configurations of the elements and their ions. The transition metals are those we usually think of as metals. There are thirty transition metals, not counting the latest elements to be synthesized, numbers 104-109 in the fourth transition series. Don't be intimidated by all the information that is given, but rather try to organize it on the basis of electronic configuration. Have fun!

Example 9

Why are the elements of the third transition series about the same size as those of the second, while the first series of transition metals is considerably smaller?

Solution: The second transition series metals are larger than those of the first series, as one would expect, because electrons have been added in orbitals one principal quantum number farther from the nucleus. However, between the second and third series come the lanthanides, as well as the *s*- and *p*-block elements. The nuclear charge has increased by 32, and 14 of the electrons have been added to the $4f$ orbitals. Electrons in *f* orbitals hardly shield each other at all, so that there is a steady decrease in size from lanthanum (La) to lutetium (Lu) as the effective nuclear charge increases. This offsets the expected size increase for third transition series, with the result that the radii of the two series of elements are nearly identical, as are many of their chemical properties.

Example 10

a. What is the maximum oxidation state for elements of the vanadium group?

Solution: The rule of thumb for determining the maximum oxidation state of a transition element is 2 plus the number of unpaired *d* electrons in the +2 ion. The valence electronic configuration of V is $4s^2 3d^3$.

$$\underset{4s}{\uparrow\downarrow} \quad \uparrow \quad \uparrow \quad \underset{3d}{\uparrow} \quad \_\_ \quad \_\_$$

and that of $V^{2+}$ is $3d^3$. Since there are three unpaired *d* electrons, the highest oxidation number for V and the other members of the group, niobium and tantalum, is +5.

b. Vanadium displays all the integral oxidation states from -1 (rare) to +5 in its compounds. What oxidation states do you expect for niobium (Nb) and tantalum (Ta)?

Solution: Generally, members of the second and third transition series tend to form compounds in the highest oxidation states for their group. Thus, most chemistry of Nb and Ta involves the +5 state, although a few compounds in lower states are known. Oxidation potentials decrease going down a group, as the valence electrons become farther from the nucleus and are thus more loosely held.

Example 11

The melting points of the fluorides of chromium, $CrF_2$, $CrF_3$, $CrF_4$, $CrF_5$ and $CrF_6$, decrease dramatically (over a range of more than 1000°C) from $CrF_2$ to $CrF_6$. Advance an explanation for this trend.

Solution: The oxidation state of Cr in these compounds ranges from +2 to +6. Atoms in very high oxidation states do not exist as simple ions; the charge density would be prohibitively high. Instead, they are stabilized by covalent bonding to fairly electronegative atoms such as F, O, and Cl. One only finds salts and simple ions of metals in their lower oxidation states. Thus, while $CrF_2$ and $CrF_3$ are ionic compounds and so have very high melting points, $CrF_5$ and $CrF_6$ are covalently bonded molecules.

## SECTION 8-7: THE FILLING OF *f* ORBITALS: LANTHANIDES AND ACTINIDES

The members of these groups, lanthanides and actinides, are nearly alike in their chemistry. All have the same electronic configurations in their outermost orbitals, while the differences occur in the *f* orbitals, two principal quantum numbers closer to the nucleus. The lanthanides are found mixed together in nature as the oxides, or earths. These elements are so chemically similar that over ninety years passed between their discovery and separation from each other.

## SECTION 8-8: THE *p*-ORBITAL OR REPRESENTATIVE ELEMENTS

Whereas chemical properties change smoothly within groups of the *s*- and *d*-block elements, only the halogens display this characteristic among the *p*-block elements. In groups IIIA-VIA, there is a definite shift from nonmetallic to metallic behavior down each group. Elements along the metal-nonmetal border, the semimetals, display combinations of characteristics. This border moves lower in the groups as one progresses from left to right across the periodic table.

The halogens, however, are all nonmetals and display strong group resemblances, as do the alkali and alkaline earth metals. While the *s*-block metals are excellent reducing agents, the halogens display the opposite characteristic. They are all superb oxidizing agents. Their oxidizing power, as measured by their reduction potentials, decreases from fluorine to iodine. Fluorine will oxidize virtually anything, often explosively so. In contrast, the elements of Group IVA, the carbon group, are the most chemically dissimilar of any group in the entire periodic table.

You should note the characteristic oxidation states for each group, as well as the trends in preferred oxidation states moving down a group. Try to relate these trends to the changes from nonmetallic to metallic characteristics, such as bonding patterns and acid-base properties.

Terms to Know

atomic radius
aufbau process
bond distance
bond energy
core electrons
covalent bond
effective nuclear charge
electrolyze

electron affinity
electronegativity
half-filled set of orbitals
Hund's rule
ionic bond
ionic radius
ionization energy (or potential)
lanthanide contraction
noble gases
orbital electronic configuration
oxidation potential
paired spins
partial ionic character of a bond
Pauli exclusion principle
polar covalent bond
reduction potential
solvated electron
valence electrons

## Test Yourself

1. Write orbital electronic configurations for

   a. Bi  e. $At^-$
   b. $Au^+$  f. Fr
   c. $P^{3-}$  g. Rn
   d. $Tc^{2+}$  h. Ce

2. Why is the ionization potential of thallium less than that of mercury?

3. The ionization potential of fluorine is unusually high, compared to the other halogens, while its electron affinity is low. Advance an explanation for this anomalous behavior of fluorine.

4. Predict whether the following bonds will be ionic, covalent, or polar covalent. Indicate charges where appropriate.

   a. Cs-I  d. P-H
   b. Sr-O  e. Ag-S
   c. Hg-Cl  f. N-O

5. Stannous oxide, SnO, is amphoteric. Write equations describing the dissolution of tin(II) oxide in acidic and basic solutions.

6. Metallic copper is only attacked by oxidizing acids, such as nitric and sulfuric acids, rather than by nonoxidizing ones. Complete and balance equations describing these processes. All yield copper(II) salts and small gaseous molecules such as $SO_2$, NO, and $NO_2$, plus water.

   a. $Cu(s) + H_2SO_4(aq) \rightarrow SO_2(g) + \ldots$
   b. $Cu(s)$ + concentrated $HNO_3 \rightarrow NO(g) + \ldots$
   c. $Cu(s)$ + dilute $HNO_3 \rightarrow NO_2(g) + \ldots$

7. Based on your knowledge of the relative sizes of metals in the first, second, and third transition series, would you expect elements 104-109 to be significantly larger than elements 72-77, hafnium through iridium?

8. Write an equation which describes the reaction of europium with water. What other group of elements reacts with water in similar fashion?

9. Aqueous solutions of praeseodymium(III) are green.

   a. What color and wavelength light do these solutions absorb?
   b. What is the electronic configuration of $Pr^{3+}$?

# 9 Lewis Structures and the VSEPR Method

## CHAPTER OVERVIEW AND OBJECTIVES

The first comprehensive theory of chemical bonding is described in this chapter, along with several of its applications. This theory can be used to predict acid-base properties of substances, relative strength of oxygen-containing acids, and structures of simple molecules.

When you finish this chapter you should be able to:

1. Write acceptable Lewis, or electron-dot, structures for virtually any molecule, atom, or ion;

2. Recognize molecules or ions for which resonance structures must be written;

3. Recognize Lewis acids and bases and predict how they would react together;

4. Correlate acidity of oxyacids with oxidation number and formal charge on the central atom, and the number of oxygen atoms not bonded to hydrogen;

5. Predict relative strengths of oxyacids from the number of their oxygen atoms that are not bonded to hydrogen;

6. Use valence-shell electron-pair repulsion (VSEPR) theory to predict structures of simple molecules and polyatomic ions, including approximate values of bond angles.

## SECTION 9-1: LEWIS STRUCTURES

Valence-bond (VB) theory, developed by Gilbert N. Lewis, Linus Pauling, and others in the early years of this century, was the first comprehensive theory of chemical bonding to be formulated. Its underlying concept is that pairs of valence electrons are shared between two atoms to form covalent bonds. Electron-dot, or Lewis, structures are part of the notation of valence-bond theory. Although the VB theory is an old one, and is not applicable to all molecules, it is still very useful and convenient. For instance, Lewis structures are an essential element of the valence shell electron-pair repulsion (VSEPR) theory for predicting molecular geometry, and they are used extensively for explaining and predicting reactions of polyatomic molecules.

Lewis structures which adequately represent the ground, or lowest-energy, state of a molecule are those in which

- o the octets of all atoms, except hydrogen, are filled;
- o the number of bonds is maximized; and
- o formal-charge separation is minimized.

The steps listed here summarize the process involved in formulating good Lewis structures, i.e., those that fulfill these three conditions.

1. Decide whether the species is a molecule or an ion.

2. Count up the total number of valence electrons.

3. Decide which element has the largest (positive or negative) oxidation number and attach the other atoms to this one with single bonds. Often this central atom is the least electronegative one in the molecule.

4. Fill the octets of the outer atoms, except hydrogen.

5. Assign any remaining electrons to the central atom.

6. Calculate the formal charge on each atom and compare with the total charge on the species.

7. Minimize formal charges and fill any unfilled octets by the use of multiple bonds. Repeat step 6.

8. Write all acceptable resonance structures.

Example 1

Write the Lewis structure for nitrosyl fluoride, NOF.

Solution: The atoms in this molecule have oxidation numbers of -1 for F, -2 for O, and +3 for N. The N is the central atom. There are 7 + 5 + 6 = 18 valence electrons in the molecule. Since all atoms are in the second period, the octet rule should be obeyed. Connecting the atoms with single bonds gives the structure

$$|\overline{\underline{F}} - \overline{N} - \overline{\underline{O}}| \qquad \text{(A line represents a pair of electrons.)}$$

This structure has the correct number of electrons, 18, but N does not have an octet. Shifting a lone pair of electrons from O to make a double bond to N gives

$$|\overline{\underline{F}} - \overline{N} = \overline{O}|$$

Now all three atoms have complete octets. The next step is to calculate the formal charge as a check. In using this convention, electrons in a Lewis structure that belong to a particular atom are half of those in bonds to that atom and all of its lone pairs. Compare this number of electrons with the number of valence electrons that the atom has in its unbonded state. In the structure of nitrosyl fluoride above, formal charges are as follows:

F: 3 lone pairs, 1 bond → $7\bar{e}$ vs $7\bar{e}$ in free atom; zero formal charge

O: 2 lone pairs, 2 bonds → $6\bar{e}$ vs $6\bar{e}$ in free atom; zero formal charge

N: 1 lone pair, 3 bonds → 5ē vs 5ē in free atom; zero formal charge

This structure fulfills the three criteria for a good Lewis structure: filled octets, maximum bonds, minimum formal charge.

Consider the structure

$|\overline{F} = \overline{N} - \underline{\overline{O}}|$

which could also be drawn to fill the octets of all three atoms. In this one, there are six electrons assigned to F and seven assigned to O, giving them formal charges of +1 and -1, respectively. This is not a good Lewis structure because formal charge separation exists and because F, the most electronegative element in the molecule, has a positive formal charge.

Example 2

Write the Lewis structure for nitrosyl ion, $NO^+$.

Solution: This cation has ten valence electrons: 5 from N and 6 from O, less 1 for the +1 charge. Some possible Lewis structures are these four:

$[|\overline{N} - \overline{O}|]^+$, $[|N = \overline{O}|]^+$, $[|\overline{N} = O|]^+$, $[|N \equiv O|]^+$

1 2 3 4

Checking for complete octets, we find that structure 1 fails because neither octet is filled: both O and N are associated with only six electrons. In structure 2, O has a complete octet but N does not, while the opposite is true in structure 3. In structure 4 the octet rule is satisfied for both atoms.

Formal charge separation must be minimized in a good Lewis structure. In structure 4, N has three bonds and one lone pair or five electrons, compared with five in the free atom, for zero formal charge. Oxygen has five electrons also, compared with six in the free atom, for a +1 formal charge. Recall that the charge on the ion is also +1. In Lewis structures of ions, at least one atom must bear a formal charge. Even though oxygen is more electronegative than nitrogen, it has a formal positive charge because this is the only structure which gives complete octets to both atoms.

Example 3

Write the Lewis structures for phosphoric acid, dihydrogen phosphate ion, and phosphate ion.

Solution: Oxidation numbers of the atoms in phosphoric acid, $H_3PO_4$, are -2 for O, +1 for H, and +5 for P. Thus P is the central atom. Since hydrogen can only make one bond, it must be on the outside of the structure.

```
          O
          |
H - O - P - O - H
          |
          O
          |
          H
```

There are 5 + 3 × 1 + 4 × 6 = 32 valence electrons in this molecule. Filling octets, we have

```
          |O̅|
           |
   H - O̲̅ - P - O̲̅ - H
           |
          |O|
           |
           H
```

All 32 electrons have been used and all atoms have octets, except for hydrogen, which gets only two electrons. Calculation of the formal charge yields this:

P: 4 bonds → 4ē vs 5ē in free atom; +1 formal charge

O bonded to H: 2 bonds, 2 lone pairs →
6ē vs 6ē in free atom; zero formal charge

O bonded only to P: 1 bond, 3 lone pairs →
7ē vs 6ē in free atom; -1 formal charge

Formal charge separation can be eliminated by shifting a lone pair on the unique oxygen atom to make a P ═ O double bond:

```
           O̅|
           ||
   H - O̲̅ - P - O̲̅ - H
           |
          |O|
           |
           H
```

This gives P ten electrons, but these can be accommodated by the 3*d* orbitals of P. This structure is preferable to the previous one.

Dihydrogen phosphate ion, $H_2PO_4^-$, is obtained by the loss of a proton ($H^+$) from phosphoric acid. It has 32 valence electrons. One Lewis structure is

```
  ┌                    ┐-
  |       |O̅           |
  |        ||          |
  | H - O̲̅ - P - O̲̅ - H  |
  |        |           |
  |       |O̲|          |
  └                    ┘
```

in which the -1 charge is localized on one oxygen atom. However, this structure is equivalent to

```
  ┌                    ┐-
  |       |O̅|          |
  |        |           |
  | H - O̲̅ - P - O̲̅ - H  |
  |        ||          |
  |        O̲|          |
  └                    ┘
```

in which the charge is localized on another oxygen atom. These two equivalent Lewis structures are referred to as <u>resonance structures</u>.

Neither one, by itself, adequately represents the electronic structure of $H_2PO_4^-$. The actual structure is a resonance hybrid of these two and is written

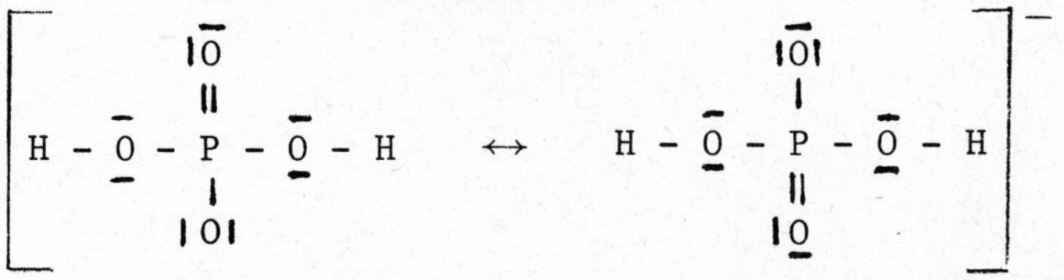

```
                 _                              _          ¯
 ┌              |O                             |O|         ┐
                 ||                              |
       _         _                          _         _
   H - O - P - O - H         ↔          H - O - P - O - H
       ¯     |    ¯                         ¯   ||    ¯
            |O|                                 |O
 └                                               ¯         ┘
```

The double-headed arrow is used only in resonance notation, and should not be confused with equilibrium arrows, ⇌ . The two oxygen atoms bonded only to phosphorus are structurally equivalent with a bond length intermediate between a double and a single bond. The structure of the resonance hybrid can be thought of as a superposition of the resonance structures written above, or it is sometimes written

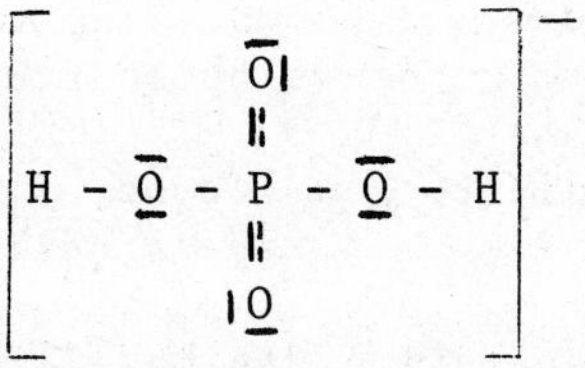

```
  ┌            _          ┐¯
               O|
               |:
       _           _
   H - O - P - O - H
       ¯       |:  ¯
               |O
  └            ¯          ┘
```

Phosphate ion, $PO_4^{3-}$, results when three protons have been removed from a phosphoric acid molecule. Many resonance structures can be written for this ion, which has 32$\bar{e}$.

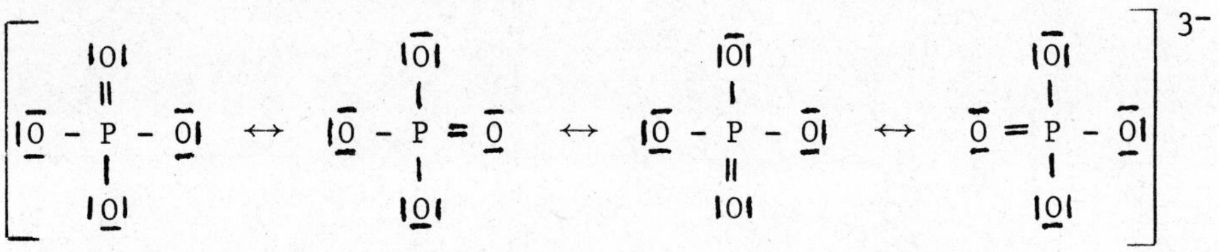

```
┌                   _               _                _         ┐3-
      |O|          |O|             |O|              |O|
       ||           |               |                |
 _       _     _       _       _       _       _         _
|O - P - O|  ↔ |O - P = O   ↔  |O - P - O|  ↔  O = P - O|
 ¯   |   ¯     ¯    |   ¯      ¯   ||   ¯      ¯   |     ¯
    |O|            |O|             |O|              |O|
└    ¯              ¯                                ¯         ┘
```

These four structures place negative formal charge on the more electronegative oxygen atoms. The actual -3 charge on this ion is distributed over all five atoms, but more electron density is expected on the oxygen atoms than on phosphorus, since it is less electronegative.

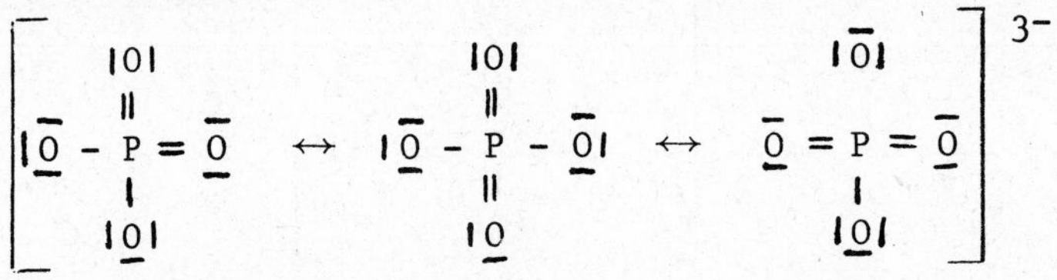

```
┌                                        _       ┐3-
     |O|             |O|                |O|
      ||              ||
 _       _       _         _       _       _
|O - P = O  ↔   |O - P - O|   ↔    O = P = O
 ¯   |   ¯       ¯    ||   ¯        ¯   |   ¯
    |O|              |O                |O|
└    ¯                ¯                 ¯        ┘
```

If you calculate formal charges on the atoms in the structures above, you will see that part of the negative charge is placed on phosphorus, which is considerably less electronegative than oxygen. Thus, these latter structures are not expected to contribute as much to the resonance hybrid structure of $PO_4^{3-}$ as do the former group, which are the best Lewis structures.

Example 4

Calculate the oxidation numbers of all atoms in $PO_4^{3-}$, using the Lewis structure

```
 ┌            ┐3-
 │    |O̅      │
 │     ‖      │
 │|O̲̅ - P - O̲̅|│
 │     |      │
 │    |O̲|     │
 └            ┘
```

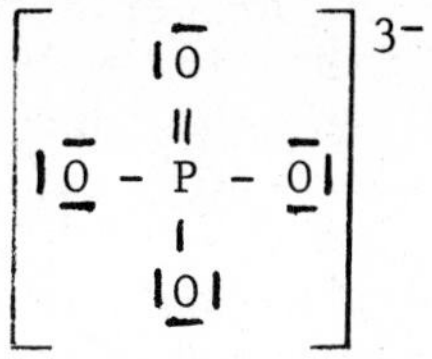

Solution: To calculate oxidation numbers using a Lewis structure, pretend that all the electrons in a covalent bond belong to the more electronegative atom, i.e., that all the bonds are ionic. In fact, they are not; oxidation numbers, remember, are a formalism, and do not represent actual charges on atoms, except for monatomic ions. Physically, a high oxidation state means that an atom is more likely to bond covalently, by electron-pair sharing, rather than form ions.

In the structure above, all the oxygen atoms have eight electrons, two more than free oxygen atoms do. Thus their oxidation state is -2. Five electrons were removed from phosphorus in this accounting method, so its oxidation state is +5. Alternately, one can say that phosphorus has no valence electrons, compared to five in the free atom, and thus its oxidation number is +5.

Example 5

Which of the following moieties are Lewis bases?

$NF_3$, $HS^-$, $CH_4$, $NH_4^+$, $H_3C - O - CH_3$

Solution: Electron pairs lie at the heart of Lewis' definition of acids and bases: acids accept one or more pairs of electrons, while bases donate them. Writing the Lewis structures of molecules and ions is necessary in order to classify them as acids or bases:

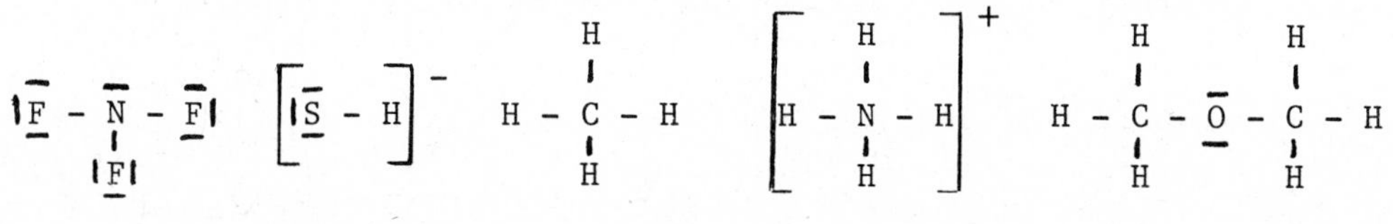

```
                                H         ┌  H  ┐+       H       H
                                |         │  |  │        |       |
|F̲̅ - N̅ - F̲̅|   [|S̲̅ - H]-   H - C - H     │H - N - H│    H - C - O̲̅ - C - H
      |                         |         │  |  │        |       |
     |F̲|                        H         └  H  ┘        H       H
```

Trifluoramine ($NF_3$), hydrosulfide ion ($^-SH$), and dimethyl ether ($CH_3$-O-$CH_3$) are all Lewis bases, because they have one or more lone pairs of electrons which are available for sharing. $CH_3$-O-$CH_3$ and $^-SH$ each contain only one atom that can act as a Lewis base. $NF_3$ appears to contain four such atoms, but in fact only the nitrogen atom is basic. Fluorine is so electronegative that it hangs onto its electrons too firmly to share them easily with another atom, and thus is a poor Lewis base. This is true of $F^-$ as well.

$CH_4$ and $NH_4^+$ are neither acids nor bases. They have no lone pairs of electrons, nor can they accommodate more electron pairs in their valence orbitals. $NH_4^+$ is a Lewis acid-base adduct produced by reaction of the Lewis base:$NH_3$ with the Lewis acid $H^+$.

## SECTION 9-2: ACIDITY OF OXYACIDS

This section briefly surveys the acid-base properties of compounds containing hydroxyl (OH) groups and then examines criteria for predicting acidity of oxyacids. In general, compounds containing M–O–H units will be basic if the M–O bond breaks more easily in water than does the O–H bond, and acidic if the converse is true. As one moves from left to right across the periodic table, basicity decreases.

In the vicinity of the metalloids one finds amphoteric compounds, those which react with both acids and bases. Ampholytes can be hydroxides of metals ($Al(OH)_3$) or semimetals ($As(OH)_3$). Hydroxyl compounds of the nonmetals, on the right-hand side of the periodic table, are generally acidic. This trend of decreasing basicity and increasing acidity moving left to right across a period correlates with the electronegativity of atom M.

Three criteria for predicting acidity of oxyacids are given:

1. Oxidation state: This indicator works well when comparing oxyacids of the same element having the same number of acidic protons, e.g., $HNO_3$ and $HNO_2$. It is not a good predictor for acids of different elements.

2. Formal charge: This is a reasonable method for predicting acidity if a Lewis structure that strictly obeys the octet rule can be written. It cannot be used with acids whose central atom has coordination number greater than four, e.g., $Te(OH)_6$ (telluric acid) and $(HO)_5IO$ (periodic acid).

3. Number of oxygen atoms not bonded to hydrogen: This criterion gives ball-park values for acid strength ($K_a$) and is the most generally applicable of the three.

Example 6

Choose the stronger acid in each pair, and explain the choices.

a. $H_2SeO_4$ and $H_2SeO_3$

Solution: Selenic and selenious acids are analogous to sulfuric and sulfurous acids. The central atoms, S and Se, are in the same group in the periodic table. Both are diprotic (two acidic hydrogen atoms), so acid strength can be predicted from oxidation state of selenium. In $H_2SeO_3$, Se is in the +4 state, while in $H_2SeO_4$ it is in the +6 state. Thus, $H_2SeO_4$ should be the stronger acid. In fact, $K_a$ is about $10^3$, while for $H_2SeO_3$, $K_a$ is $3.5 \times 10^{-3}$ for the first proton.

One can also compare the number of oxygen atoms not bonded to hydrogen. The Lewis structures are

```
                                              _
                                              O|
                                              ||
H - O - Se - O - H                  H - O - Se - O - H
         ||                                   ||
        |O                                   |O
```

Thus, selenic acid should be stronger than selenious acid, since it contains two oxygen atoms bonded only to selenium.

Try the formal charge method for yourself.

b. $H_2SeO_4$ and $HBrO_4$

Solution: The oxidation number method cannot be used in this case, because the central atoms in the two acids are different, as are the number of acidic protons. Comparing oxygen atoms not bonded to hydrogen, we find

```
            O                              O|
            ||                             ||
H - O - Se - O - H         and     H - O - Br == O
            ||                             ||
            O                             |O
```

Perbromic acid should be the stronger of the two, since it contains three such oxygen atoms, while selenic acid has only two. In fact, $K_a$ is $\geq 10^8$ for $HBrO_4$ and $\sim 10^3$ for the first proton of $H_2SeO_4$.

## SECTION 9-3: THE VALENCE-SHELL ELECTRON-PAIR REPULSION (VSEPR) METHOD

Valence-shell electron-pair repulsion (VSEPR) theory is a powerful tool for predicting structures of simple molecules. Its basis is that like charges repel each other. Electron pairs, both bonding and nonbonding, around the central atom of a molecule arrange themselves so as to be as far apart as possible. This leads to the geometries summarized in Table 9-3 and Figures 9-2 and 9-3 in the text.

To apply VSEPR theory, follow this procedure:

1. Draw the best Lewis structure of the molecule or ion.

2. Determine the steric number (SN) by counting the number of groups bonded to the central atom plus any lone pairs of electrons on the central atom.

3. Use the steric number (SN) to determine the arrangement of electron pairs.

4. Find the geometry, i.e., the atom positions, of the molecule.

5. Modify the ideal geometry, if necessary, to account for lone pairs, multiple bonds, or dissimilar groups bonded to the central atom.

Example 7

Predict the geometry of the compounds and ions below, giving approximate values for all bond angles:

a. $BF_4^-$

Solution: The Lewis structure of tetrafluoroborate ion is

```
[      |F|      ]-
[       |       ]
[ |F — B — F|   ]
[       |       ]
[      |F|      ]
```

Boron, the central atom, is bonded to four other atoms and has no lone pairs of electrons. Thus, the steric number (SN) is four and the geometry is tetrahedral. Bond angles are all 109.5°, the ideal tetrahedral angle.

b. $Cl_2CF_2$, freon-12

Solution: The Lewis structure of this refrigerant is:

```
       _
      |F|
       |
 __        __
|Cl| — C — Cl|
 ‾‾   |    ‾‾
      |F|
       ‾
```

Because carbon is bonded to four atoms and has no lone pairs of electrons, SN = 4. However, the bond angles are not all equal because two different kinds of atoms, fluorine and chlorine, are bonded to the central atom. The geometry is a distorted tetrahedron.

c. NOF

Solution: The Lewis structure of nitrosyl fluoride was worked out in Example 1:

```
 _    _   _
|O =  N - F|
          ‾
```

Nitrogen, the central atom, has one lone pair and makes bonds to two different atoms. The steric number is three, but the geometry of the molecule is referred to as bent, not as trigonal planar. The lone pair of electrons is expected to compress the bond angle somewhat, so that it should be less than the ideal trigonal planar angle of 120°. Lone pairs occupy more space close to the central atom than do bonding pairs of electrons.

d. $COCl_2$

Solution: Phosgene, a highly toxic gas, has the Lewis structure

```
 _        __
|O = C — Cl|
     |
    |Cl|
     ‾‾
```

Carbon, the central atom, is bonded to three other atoms and has no lone pairs of electrons, so the steric number is three. The geometry of phosgene is distorted trigonal planar. The Cl-C-Cl bond angle is predicted to be less than the O-C-Cl angles because double bonds require more space than do single bonds. The C-O double bond is "fatter" than the C-Cl single bonds; this compresses the Cl-C-Cl angle below 120°.

e. $ICl_2^-$

Solution: This ion's Lewis structure is:

```
   __   /\   __
[ |Cl -  I - Cl| ]⁻
   ‾‾    ‾   ‾‾
```

Because the central iodine atom is bonded to two chlorine atoms and has three lone pairs of electrons, the steric number is five. The electron pairs are arranged in a trigonal bipyramidal fashion about the iodine atom. Since there is more room at the equitorial positions than at the axial ones, the lone pairs will occupy equitorial sites, resulting in linear geometry.

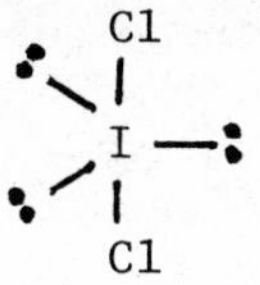

Cl
I
Cl

## Terms to Know

amphiprotic
amphoteric
axial
bond order
coordinate covalent bond
double bond
equitorial
formal charge
Lewis acid
Lewis base
Lewis structure
lone pairs
molecular geometry
octahedral
octet
octet rule
open shell
oxyacid
resonance hybrid
resonance structures
sawhorse
square planar
square pyramidal
steric number
tetrahedral
trigonal bipyramidal
trigonal planar
trigonal pyramidal
triple bond
valence-shell electron-pair repulsion theory

## Test Yourself

1. Write all acceptable Lewis structures for the following moieties:

   a. $COF_2$
   b. $AsCl_4^+$
   c. NOBr
   d. $Al(OH)_4^-$
   e. $HgCl_2$
   f. $S_2O_3^{2-}$ (one S atom is central)
   g. $SbF_5^{2-}$
   h. $CSe_2$
   i. $TeCl_4$
   j. $KrF_2$
   k. $PSF_3$

2. Draw Lewis structures for triiodide ion, $I_3^-$, including at least three resonance forms. For each of these, calculate formal charges on all the iodine atoms.

3. Draw Lewis structures for $XeOF_2$, $XeOF_4$, and $XeO_6^{4-}$. Compare the relative xenon-oxygen bond lengths in these species.

4. Arsenic acid, $H_3AsO_4$, is an analogue of phosphoric acid. Draw Lewis structures for the parent acid and its three anions. Compare the relative arsenic-oxygen bond lengths in all of these species.

5. Classify the following species as Lewis acids, Lewis bases, Lewis acid-base addition compounds, or none of these:

   $HONH_2$, $BF_2Cl$, $OH^-$, $H_3O^+$, $CH_3OH$, $Ni^{2+}$, $BeF_4^{2-}$, $CHBr_3$,

   $F_3BNC(CH_3)_3$, CO, $Ag(CN)_2^-$, $I^-$, $Al(OH)_3$, $H_2O$, $NH_4^+$, $CO_2$, $H^+$

6. Identify the Lewis acids and bases in these equations:

   a. $Sb_2S_3(s) + 3S^{2-} \rightarrow 2SbS_3^{3-}$

   b. $2BeCl_2 \rightarrow$ Cl – Be(–Cl–)(–Cl–)Be – Cl (two Cl atoms bridging the two Be atoms)

7. Classify the following hydroxyl compounds as acids, bases, or ampholytes:

   $Ge(OH)_4$, $Ca(OH)_2$, $O_2BrOH$, $Ga(OH)_3$, KOH

8. Choose the stronger acid in each pair below and explain the reasons for your choices:

   a. $HBrO_4$, $HBrO_3$

   b. HBrO, $HNO_2$

   c. $HNO_2$, $HIO_2$

   d. $H_2SO_4$ (first proton), $HNO_3$

9. Predict the structures of these moieties:

   a. HCN

   b. $AsF_6^-$

   c. $ICl_3$

   d. $BeF_2$

   e. $SOCl_2$

   f. $ClHC = CCl_2$ (trichloroethylene, a cleaning fluid)

   g. $BF_2Cl$

   h. $BrF_5$

   i. $PBr_4^+$

   j. $XeOF_2$

   k. $CH_3NH_2$

# 10 Inorganic Reactions

## CHAPTER OVERVIEW AND OBJECTIVES

Reactions of inorganic materials can be classified as to the degree of participation by valence electrons and the relative amount of energy transferred. These categories and their principal features are:

- oxidation-reduction: transfer of electrons between atoms, large energy losses or gains;
- acid-base: sharing of electron pairs between atoms, moderate amounts of energy evolved or absorbed;
- metathesis: essentially no electron shifts, very little energy released or acquired.

When you finish this chapter you should be able to:

1. Identify a given reaction as oxidation-reduction, acid-base, or metathesis.

2. Write a few examples of each type of reaction.

3. Predict the products of acid-base reactions, using the Arrhenius, Brønsted-Lowry, or Lewis definitions as necessary.

4. Predict the products of metathesis reactions, using the rules for aqueous solubility of ionic compounds.

## SECTION 10-1: OXIDATION-REDUCTION REACTIONS

These reactions are characterized by an exchange of electrons between oxidant and reductant, resulting in corresponding changes in oxidation state. Spontaneous redox processes are usually accompanied by the release of large amounts of energy, some of which can be harnessed to do useful work, or at least to provide heat. There are three broad categories of redox reactions:

- addition: two or more elements, molecules, or ions combine;
- elimination: a molecule or ion breaks up into smaller fragments;
- displacement: exchange of atoms or ions plus electrons, or electrons only, occurs.

Example 1

Classify these reactions as redox addition, elimination, displacement, or other types.

a. $4Al + 3Sn^{4+} \longrightarrow 4Al^{3+} + 3Sn$

b. $Hg_2^{2+} + S^{2-} \longrightarrow Hg + HgS$

c. $AgCl + 2NH_3 \longrightarrow Ag(NH_3)_2^+ + Cl^-$

d. $H_2C = CH_2 + Cl_2 \longrightarrow H_2ClC - CClH_2$

Solution: a. Displacement or exchange: Aluminum is oxidized from the zero to the +3 state, while tin is reduced from the +4 state to zero. Except for the water molecules hydrating $Al^{3+}$ and $Sn^{4+}$, only electrons are exchanged.

b. Elimination: Mercury (I) disproportionates to mercury (0) and mercury (II). The oxidation state of sulfur remains -2. Alternately, one can say that mercury (0) is eliminated from $Hg_2^{2+}$, leaving $Hg^{2+}$, which precipitates as HgS. The driving force for this reaction is provided by the formation of HgS, which is extremely insoluble.

c. This is not an oxidation-reduction process at all, but a Lewis acid-base displacement reaction. $Ag^+$ is the acid; $Cl^-$ and $NH_3$ are the bases being exchanged.

d. Addition: Chlorine is reduced from zero to -1, while carbon is oxidized from -2 to zero.

## SECTION 10-2: ACID-BASE REACTIONS

If you have not yet studied Chapter 5, pay close attention to the definitions of terms used in this section. Those who have already finished Chapter 5 will find that this section reinforces and expands upon some ideas presented earlier. Three definitions of acids and bases are given; in historical order, they are those of Arrhenius, Brønsted and Lowry, and G. N. Lewis. The Lewis definition, that a base is an electron-pair donor and an acid is an electron-pair acceptor, is the most general. Brønsted-Lowry acids and bases are all protonic, and most also fit the Lewis definition.

Acid-base reactions can be divided into two categories: addition and elimination. These reactions are characterized by electron-pair sharing, rather than electron transfer. Addition reactions are those between

- an acid and a base;
- an acidic or a basic anhydride and water; and
- an acidic anhydride and a basic anhydride.

Elimination reactions result in the loss of small molecules, such as $CO_2$, from acids, bases, or salts. There is no change in oxidation state in acid-base reactions, and the amounts of energy involved are generally less than in redox reactions.

Example 2

Complete and balance the following equations:

a. $CH_3NH_3^+Cl^-(s) + H_2O(l) \longrightarrow$ (methylammonium chloride)

b. $(NH_4)_2CO_3(s) \xrightarrow{\Delta}$

c. $P_4O_{10}(s) + H_2O(l) \longrightarrow$

d. $BaO(s) + SO_3(g) \longrightarrow$

Solution: a. $CH_3NH_3^+Cl^-(s) + H_2O(l) \rightleftharpoons CH_3NH_2(aq) + H_3O^+(aq) + Cl^-(aq)$

Methylammonium chloride is a salt of the weak base methylamine and hydrochloric acid. Methylammonium ion is thus an acid and hydrolyzes in aqueous solution.

b. $(NH_4)_2CO_3(s) \xrightarrow{\Delta} CO_2(g) + 2NH_3(g) + H_2O(g)$

Ammonium carbonate is a salt of ammonia and carbonic acid and is used commercially as baking powder. Note that it yields four molecules of gaseous products per salt unit when decomposed, contrasted with one or two for other leavening agents.

c. $P_4O_{10}(s) + 6H_2O(l) \longrightarrow 4H_3PO_4(l)$

Phosphorus(V) oxide is the acid anhydride of phosphoric acid. It is used in chemical laboratories as a drying agent.

d. $BaO(s) + SO_3(g) \longrightarrow BaSO_4(s)$

Barium oxide is the anhydride of the base barium hydroxide, and sulfur trioxide is the anhydride of sulfuric acid. Anhydrides are Lewis acids and bases and react together to produce salts.

## SECTION 10-3: IONIC EXCHANGE OR METATHESIS

Metathesis reactions are driven by differences in solubility of ionic compounds. The reactions discussed in this section occur in an aqueous medium, but the underlying principles are applicable to nonaqueous polar solvents as well. The solubility of a particular compound depends on the balance between its crystal-lattice energy and the hydration (or solvation) energy of its ions. Compared to redox and acid-base reactions, very little energy transfer results from metathesis reactions.

The following solubility rules are useful additions to those given in the text:

- Rule 7 addition: Include chromates, borates, and arsenates in the list;
- Rule 7a: The sulfides of all metals except barium, calcium, magnesium, the alkali metals, and ammonium ion are insoluble in water;
- Rule 8: All silver salts are insoluble in water, except fluoride, nitrate, and acetate salts. Silver sulfate is slightly soluble.

Example 3

What compounds might be expected to precipitate from a mixture of aqueous solutions containing $Ag^+$, $Ni^{2+}$, $Rb^+$, $PO_4^{3-}$, $NO_3^-$, $F^-$, $Br^-$, and $CO_3^{2-}$ ions?

Solution: The solubility rules predict the following precipitates:

- $Ag_2CO_3$ rule 7
- $NiCO_3$ rule 7
- $NiF_2$
- $Ag_3PO_4$ rule 7
- $Ni_3(PO_4)_2$ rule 7
- $AgBr$ rule 3

No compounds of $Rb^+$ will precipitate, as it is an alkali metal (rule 1). Similarly, $NiBr_2$ does not precipitate (rule 3) and AgF is one of the few soluble fluorides and silver salts. Nitrate salts are all soluble (rule 1).

## Terms to Know

acid anhydride
acid-base reaction
addition reaction
base anhydride
displacement reaction
elimination reaction
Lewis acid, base
metathesis reaction
oxidation-reduction reaction

## Test Yourself

1. Balance the following equations, and classify the reactions as oxidation-reduction, acid-base, or metathesis:

   a. $SO_2 + Cl_2 \longrightarrow SO_2Cl_2$

   b. $AgF(aq) + Ni(NO_3)_2(aq) \longrightarrow NiF_2(s) + AgNO_3(aq)$

   c. $CO_2 + Ba(OH)_2 \longrightarrow BaCO_3 + H_2O$

   d. $Cl_2O_7 + H_2O \longrightarrow HClO_4$

   e. $NaNO_3 \longrightarrow NaNO_2 + O_2$

   f. $H_2SO_4(aq) + CaF_2(aq) \longrightarrow HF(aq) + CaSO_4(s)$

2. Which compounds are soluble in water?

   $CuSO_4$, $Ag_3AsO_4$, $Rb_2CO_3$, $NH_4I$, AgF, $Ni(C_2H_3O_2)_2$, $Al(OH)_3$, $PbBr_2$, $Pb(ClO_3)_2$

3. Classify the following oxidation-reduction reactions as addition, elimination, or displacement:

   a. $Sn + 2NaOH \longrightarrow Na_2SnO_2 + H_2$

   b. $Na_2SO_3 + H_2SO_4 \longrightarrow SO_2 + Na_2SO_4 + H_2O$

   c. $PCl_3 + \frac{1}{2}O_2 \longrightarrow OPCl_3$

d. $Br_2 + H_2O \longrightarrow HBr + HOBr$

e. $(NH_4)_2Cr_2O_7 \longrightarrow N_2 + Cr_2O_3 + H_2O$

4. Complete and balance these equations:

a. $N_2O_3 + H_2O \longrightarrow$

b. $NaHSO_3 + H_2O \longrightarrow$

c. $HF + BF_3 \longrightarrow$

d. $HCl + BaCO_3 \longrightarrow$

e. $C_2H_3O^- + H_3PO_4 \longrightarrow$

5. From the list of aqueous solutions which follows, choose a) three pairs which, when mixed, would form a precipitate, and b) three pairs which would remain homogeneous when mixed. Write the formulas of the precipitates in part a.

$MnSO_4$, $AgNO_3$, $NH_4Cl$, $Pb(C_2H_3O_2)_2$, $NiCl_2$, $K_2CO_3$, $NH_4Cr_2O_7$, $Ca(HCO_3)_2$

6. Complete and balance these equations:

a. $Na_2CO_3(aq) + NiSO_4(aq) + AgC_2H_3O_2(aq) \longrightarrow$

b. $Zn(s) + H_2SO_4(aq) \longrightarrow$

c. $F_2(g) + KI(aq) \longrightarrow$

d. $Al(OH)_3(s) + OH^-(aq) \longrightarrow$

e. $Al(s) + Cu^{2+}(aq) \longrightarrow$

# 11 Diatomic Molecules

## CHAPTER OVERVIEW AND OBJECTIVES

Chapter 9 discussed some aspects of the valence-bond (VB) theory of bonding. Lewis structures lie at the heart of the valence-bond approach. In Chapter 11, molecular-orbital (MO) theory, a newer treatment of chemical bonding, is applied to simple molecules. Molecular-orbital theory answers some questions that the valence-bond treatment cannot, such as what the bonding is in $O_2$.

When you finish this chapter you should be able to:

1. Construct an MO diagram for any homonuclear or heteronuclear diatomic molecule or ion made up of elements in the first three periods;

2. Use the MO diagrams in objective 1 to predict orbital electronic configurations, magnetic properties, relative bond energies, and relative bond lengths of diatomic molecules and ions;

3. Calculate the percent ionic character of a bond from the bond length and dipole moment.

## SECTION 11-1: MOLECULAR ORBITALS

Just as electrons in atoms can be described as occupying atomic orbitals (AO's), electrons in molecules can be thought of as occupying molecular orbitals (MO's). The wave functions of existing valence atomic orbitals are mathematically combined to produce a new set of wave functions for an entire molecule. This process, called linear combination of atomic orbitals (LCAO), yields a set of bonding MO's, which are lower in energy than the original AO's, and a set of antibonding MO's, higher in energy than the constituent AO's. The number of MO's formed equals the number of AO's which are combined.

The molecular "glue" that bonds atoms together is the attraction of the nucleus of one atom for the electrons of another. Thus the shapes of bonding orbitals are such that electron density is concentrated between the nuclei. On the other hand, electrons in antibonding orbitals are located outside the internuclear region, as illustrated in Figure 11-4. Bonding occurs only if more electrons occupy bonding MO's than antibonding ones, so that the total energy of the molecule is lower than the total energy of the atoms when separated.

The general procedure for describing bonding in molecular-orbital terms involves three steps:

1. Combine appropriate valence atomic orbitals to make an equal number of molecular orbitals.

2. Order the molecular orbitals according to increasing relative energy.

3. Feed the valence electrons into the molecular orbitals, following the aufbau principle that is used for atoms.

Be sure to study Figures 11-4 and 11-5 thoroughly. You should be able to construct the molecular-orbital diagram for $H_2$ and related species -- e.g., $He_2^+$ -- from memory. Use the diagram to find the orbital electronic configuration, bond order, relative bond length and relative bond energy of $H_2$, $H_2^+$, $H_2^-$, $He_2$, and $He_2^+$. Check your results with the information in Table 11-1 and Example 1.

## SECTION 11-2: DIATOMIC MOLECULES WITH ONE TYPE OF ATOM

Figure 11-7 is an excellent illustration of both the bonding and antibonding orbitals formed from linear combinations of *s* and *p* orbitals. You can rationalize the shapes of the bonding orbitals by representing a set of *p* atomic orbitals with the thumb and first two fingers of one hand held at right angles to each other. Use both hands to represent two atoms coming together to form a molecule, and you will see that only one *p* orbital from each atom can overlap end to end. The other two must overlap sideways, because of the geometry of a set of *p* orbitals. Because the sign of the wave function is different in the two lobes of a *p* orbital, there is no overlap between two *p* orbitals at 90° to one another. Overlap only occurs between orbitals or lobes of orbitals having the same sign.

End-to-end overlap of two *p* orbitals produces a sigma bonding molecular orbital. Electron density is concentrated between the nuclei, and the orbital is cylindrically symmetrical along the internuclear axis. On the other hand, sideways overlap of *p* orbitals results in formation of a pi ($\pi$) bonding orbital, which has a node along the internuclear axis. The sign of the wave function for a pi molecular orbital changes at the internuclear axis, so these orbitals do not have cylindrical symmetry.

### Example 1

Construct a molecular-orbital diagram for nitrogen molecule.

a. Use it to write valence electronic configurations for $N_2$, $N_2^+$, and $N_2^-$.

Solution: Molecular orbitals for second-period diatomic molecules are formed by the linear combination of the 2*s* and 2*p* atomic orbitals of the two atoms. Refer to Figure 11-8 in the text. Notice that the $\pi$ bonding orbitals are degenerate, that is, they have the same energy, as do the $\pi$* antibonding orbitals.

The valence electronic configurations are as follows:

$N_2$, 10 valence electrons: $(\sigma_s)^2(\sigma_s*)^2(\pi)^4(\sigma_p)^2$

$N_2^+$, 9 valence electrons: $(\sigma_s)^2(\sigma_s*)^2(\pi)^4(\sigma_p)^1$

$N_2^-$, 11 valence electrons: $(\sigma_s)^2(\sigma_s*)^2(\pi)^4(\sigma_p)^2(\pi*)^1$

b. Compare bond orders, bond lengths, bond energies, and magnetic properties of $N_2$, $N_2^+$, and $N_2^-$.

Solution: Bond order is the number of bonds in a molecule or ion, or the net number of occupied bonding orbitals. It can be calculated using the formula

B.O. = ½(bonding electrons - antibonding electrons)

$N_2$: B.O. = ½(8 - 2) = ½(6) = 3

$N_2^+$: B.O. = ½(7 - 2) = ½(5) = 2½

$N_2^-$: B.O. = ½(8 - 3) = ½(5) = 2½

Thus, $N_2$ has the highest bond order, 3, corresponding to a triple bond. Both $N_2^+$ and $N_2^-$ have 2½ bonds. Notice that bond order can decrease by either adding electrons to antibonding orbitals, or by removing them from bonding ones. Bond length is inversely related to bond order, while bond energy varies directly with it. Thus, triple bonds, as in $N_2$, are shorter and stronger than those of lower bond order, such as $N_2^+$ or $N_2^-$. $N_2$ has no unpaired electrons and is thus diamagnetic. The ions $N_2^+$ and $N_2^-$ are both paramagnetic, having one unpaired electron each.

Example 2

In its ground state, $O_2$ has two unpaired electrons with parallel spins, one in each of the degenerate π* orbitals. Electronic configurations of two excited states of $O_2$ are as follows:

| | | |
|---|---|---|
| a. | ↑ σ* | ― σ* |
| | ↑ ― * | ↑ ↓ π* |

All lower-energy orbitals are filled and are not included in these diagrams. Which of these excited states is higher in energy, and which is paramagnetic?

Solution: Recall the discussion of exchange and pairing energies in Chapter 8 of this study guide. The relative energies of states a and b depend on the relative energies of the π* and σ* orbitals. If the energy difference between these orbitals is small relative to the energy required for two electrons in degenerate orbitals to have opposite spins, state a is of lower energy. However, if the separation between the π* and σ* levels is large relative to this energy requirement, then state b will be the lower-energy one, which, in fact, it is. State b is slightly higher than the ground state due to loss of exchange energy.

## SECTION 11-3: DIATOMIC MOLECULES WITH DIFFERENT ATOMS

For atomic orbitals to overlap so that bonding can occur, two requirements must be met:

- They must be close in energy; and
- They must have the appropriate geometry because only wave functions of the same sign can interact to give overlap.

Ionization potential measures the energy of the highest occupied orbital, while electronegativity is a useful predictor of relative energies of orbitals of the same type in different atoms. In general, the more electronegative an atom is, the lower in energy will be its orbitals.

Bonds between atoms of different electronegativity are polar because the bonding electrons are shared unequally. The bonding molecular orbitals have more of the character of the atomic orbitals of the more electronegative atom and are closer in energy to them than to the atomic orbitals of the less electronegative atom. Conversely, the antibonding orbitals more closely resemble the atomic orbitals of the less electronegative atom and are closer in energy to them than to those of the other atom. The logical extreme of this tendency is the ionic bond, in which the bonding molecular orbitals are identical to the contributing atomic orbitals of the more electronegative element, while the antibonding orbitals are identical to the contributing atomic orbitals of the less electronegative one.

Example 3

Write the valence electronic configuration for cyanide ion.

a. Calculate its bond order.
b. Comment on its magnetic properties.
c. Predict the direction of the electric dipole of $CN^-$, if one exists.

Solution: Refer to Figure 11-13 in the text. Since nitrogen is more electronegative than carbon, its orbitals are lower in energy. The bonding orbitals in $CN^-$ more closely resemble the atomic orbitals of N than than of C, while the reverse is true for the antibonding orbitals. $CN^-$ has 4 + 5 + 1 or 10 valence electrons.

$$\text{Electronic configuration:} \quad (\sigma_s)^2(\sigma_s^*)^2(\pi)^4(\sigma_p)^2$$

a. B.O. = $\frac{1}{2}(2 + 4 + 2 - 2) = \frac{1}{2}(6) = 3$
b. $CN^-$ is triply bonded, as is $N_2$, and is diamagnetic, since all its electrons are paired.
c. Since N and C have different electronegativities, $CN^-$ is polar. The negative end of the dipole is near the more electronegative N atom.

Example 4

The dipole moment of carbon monoxide is 0.112 D, and its bond distance is 1.1283 Å. What is the percent ionic character of the C-O bond?

Solution: The ionic character of a bond can be determined by comparing the true dipole moment with that which the bond would have if there were complete electron transfer between the two atoms. Dipole moment is defined as

$$\mu \equiv qr$$

where $\mu$ = dipole moment
$r$ = bond distance
$q$ = charge on each atom

Percent ionic character equals $\mu_{observed}/\mu_{calculated}$, where $\mu_{calculated}$ assumes complete charge separation, or 4.80 debye/angstrom.

$$\% \text{ ionic character} = \frac{0.112 \text{ D}}{(4.80 \text{ D/Å})(1.1283 \text{ Å})} = 0.0207 = 2.07\%$$

Surprisingly, the bond in carbon monoxide is almost completely covalent, even though the electronegativity difference between C and O is 0.89. The distribution of electron density between carbon and oxygen is so nearly equal that, when CO acts as a Lewis base, it coordinates to metal atoms through carbon rather than oxygen. The best Lewis structure that can be drawn for CO is

$$|C \equiv O|$$

in which oxygen has a +1 formal charge and carbon has a -1 formal charge. Again, this is not what one would expect from electronegativity values, but it reflects the Lewis-base behavior of this molecule as well as its bond energy, 1070.3 kJ $mol^{-1}$. Compare this with the energy of the triple bond in the isoelectronic $N_2$ molecule, 941.7 kJ $mol^{-1}$.

## Terms to Know

antibonding orbital
bond length
bonding orbital
debye
degenerate
diamagnetic
electric dipole moment
heteronuclear molecule
homonuclear molecule
molecular-orbital theory
molecular orbitals
net bonding action
nodal plane
overlap
paramagnetic
percent ionic character
pi orbital
sigma orbital

## Test Yourself

1. Explain why the bond in $C_2$ is longer than that in $O_2$.

2. Why is the bond in $O_2$ weaker than that in $C_2$?

3. Compare SN and PN on the following points:

   a. bond order
   b. relative bond length
   c. magnetic properties
   d. relative bond energy

   Be sure to include explanations for similarities or differences in these species.

4. Arrange the following species in order of decreasing bond length: CO, $CO^+$, CS, $CO^-$.

5. Which of the following are paramagnetic: CO, $CO^-$, $Ge_2$, SCl, $Se_2$?

6. Explain the differences in bond energies and bond lengths of SnO and SnS. Which bond has the greater ionic character? Why?

7. Calculate the percent ionic character for LiF and LiH. The dipole moments and bond lengths are 6.33 D, 1.5639 Å for LiF; 5.88 D, 1.5953 Å for LiH. Are these values consistent with the electronegativity differences between Li and H and F?

8. Dipole moments, bond lengths, and bond energies for the lithium halides are given below. Calculate the percent ionic character for these compounds, and correlate the data and your results with the periodic table.

| compound | $\mu$(D) | bond length (Å) | bond energy (kJ $mol^{-1}$) |
|---|---|---|---|
| LiF | 6.33 | 1.5639 | 568.2 |
| LiCl | 7.13 | 2.018 | 473.8 |
| LiBr | 7.27 | 2.1704 | 423 |
| LiI | 7.43 | 2.3919 | 339 |

9. Which molecule should be more ionic, SrO or SrS? Which should have the smaller dipole moment?

# 12 Polyatomic Molecules

## CHAPTER OVERVIEW AND OBJECTIVES

Molecular-orbital theory is extended to many-atom molecules and ions in this chapter. In many cases the MO treatment can be simplified by the use of localized orbitals extending over only two or three atoms, rather than over the entire molecule. For other species this approximation fails, and the pi bonding in the molecule must be described using delocalized orbitals. Dipole moments of polyatomic molecules, as deduced from molecular geometry, are treated in Section 12-6. The chapter ends with an introduction to molecular spectroscopy.

When you finish this chapter, you should be able to:

1. Construct localized molecular orbitals for molecules using the hybridization formalism when necessary;

2. Recognize when delocalized molecular orbitals are required for an accurate bonding description;

3. Predict whether molecules will be polar or nonpolar, based on their geometry;

4. List the ways in which a molecule can absorb energy, and correlate these with appropriate regions in the electromagnetic spectrum;

5. List kinds of information about a molecule which can be obtained from the spectroscopic techniques described in objective 4.

## SECTION 12-1: LOCALIZED MOLECULAR ORBITALS FOR $BeH_2$, $BH_3$, AND $CH_4$

One of the most important points to keep in mind when studying this chapter is that the molecular-orbital schemes described for various polyatomic molecules were originally formulated as theoretical explanations for the observed structures of the molecules. The structures were known from experimental evidence before the theory was devised.

Molecular orbitals result from overlap of suitable atomic orbitals. Suitable AO's are those of similar energy and compatible geometry. If the geometry of the valence atomic orbitals of an atom is not consistent with the observed geometry of the molecule containing that atom, then the AO's must first be hybridized before overlap can take place. Hybridization is invoked when demanded by molecular structure. To form hybrid atomic orbitals, atomic orbitals on a single atom are mixed, i.e., mathematically combined. It is rather like mixing paints of different colors to obtain a desired shade. These hybrid AO's overlap with AO's from other atoms to form localized sigma molecular orbitals for the molecule. Characteristics of hybrid orbitals formed by mixing *s* and *p* orbitals are summarized here.

| type of hybrid AO | constituent AO's | no. of hybrid AO's/set | fraction *s*-character | fraction *p*-character | geometry |
|---|---|---|---|---|---|
| $sp$ | $s+p$ | 2 | 1/2 | 1/2 | linear |
| $sp^2$ | $s+p+p$ | 3 | 1/3 | 2/3 | trigonal planar |
| $sp^3$ | $s+p+p+p$ | 4 | 1/4 | 3/4 | tetrahedral |

Example 1

The beryllium compound $Be(C_4H_9)_2$ is linear at room temperature. What type of hybrid orbitals are used by Be to bond to the $C_4H_9$ groups?

Solution: The valence electronic configuration of Be is $2s^2$. The linear geometry of this compound requires formation of two *sp* hybrid atomic orbitals on Be. Each of these *sp* hybrid AO's can overlap with appropriate orbitals from the $C_4H_9$ groups to form localized sigma MO's for the molecule.

Example 2

Indicate what type of hybrid orbitals would be used by the central atoms in the species that follow and predict their geometry.

a. $BF_3$
b. $CCl_4$
c. $BH_4^-$
d. $CH_3OH$

Solution: The boron atom in $BF_3$ is bonded to three other atoms. Boron's valence electronic configuration is $2s^22p^1$. Three equivalent bonds can be made if the *s* and two of the *p* orbitals on boron hybridize, forming a set of $sp^2$ atomic orbitals. VSEPR theory predicts trigonal-planar geometry for $BF_3$, which is consistent with $sp^2$ hybridization.

The central atoms in the remaining species are each bonded to four groups. Because there are no lone pairs of electrons on any of the central atoms, tetrahedral geometry for these species is predicted by VSEPR theory. This shape demands that a set of $sp^3$ hybrid orbitals be used by the central carbon and boron atoms.

Note that $BH_4^-$ is isoelectronic with $CH_4$, which is discussed in detail in the textbook. Also note that while $BH_4^-$ and $CCl_4$ are regular tetrahedra with 109.5° bond angles, methyl alcohol, $CH_3OH$, is a distorted tetrahedron, since different groups are bonded to the central atom. VSEPR theory remains the most powerful predictor of simple molecular structure.

## SECTION 12-2: HYDROGEN BRIDGE BONDS

Bridging hydrogen atoms are observed in a number of compounds of boron which are electron-deficient. Examples in addition to diborane, $B_2H_6$, are $B_4H_{10}$, $B_5H_{11}$, and $B_5H_9$. Hydrogen bridge bonds might seem unusual because the sigma-bonding molecular orbital is delocalized over three atoms, but contains only two electrons. In fact, many molecules are best described by delocalized MO's, although most of them are not electron-deficient.

In compounds such as $B_2H_6$ and $B_4H_{10}$, the B atoms are four-coordinate. Bridging MO's can be constructed from two $sp^3$ hybrid AO's, one from each B, and the 1*s* orbital of H. The remaining $sp^3$ hybrid AO's on the boron atoms overlap with 1*s* orbitals of the other hydrogen atoms to make ordinary localized MO's.

## SECTION 12-3: LOCALIZED MOLECULAR-ORBITAL THEORY FOR MOLECULES WITH LONE ELECTRON PAIRS

Localized molecular orbitals are constructed for molecules having lone pairs of electrons on the central atom in much the same way that they are for other molecules. Atomic orbitals are hybridized when required by molecular structure. VSEPR theory works well for predicting geometry, except in cases of heavy central atoms, as noted in Chapter 9. When formation of hybridized orbitals is necessary, bonds are formed by overlap of the hybrid orbitals with appropriate atomic orbitals on the other atoms involved in bonding, as usual. The lone electron pairs are assigned to the remaining hybrid orbitals.

### Example 3

For the molecules phosphine ($PH_3$), arsine ($AsH_3$), and stibine ($SbH_3$):

a. Represent their electronic structures with localized molecular-orbital structures.
b. Predict their shapes, including relative bond angles.
c. Predict relative bond lengths.

Solution: a. The valence electronic configuration of all three central atoms, P, As, and Sb, is $s^2p^3$. One model of bonding for these hydrides uses the *p* orbitals for bond formation, through overlap with 1*s* hydrogen orbitals. The lone electron pair remains in the *s* orbital. On the other hand, the hybridization model calls for formation of a set of four $sp^3$ orbitals on the central atom. Three of these are used for bonding, by overlap with hydrogen 1*s* orbitals, while the lone pair resides in the fourth $sp^3$ orbital.

b. Both of the bonding models discussed above predict pyramidal geometry. Hybridization calls for approximately tetrahedral bond angles, while bond formation using unhybridized *p* orbitals on the central atom predicts 90° bond angles, since *p* orbitals are orthogonal to each other. VSEPR theory predicts geometry consistent with the hybridization model.

However, we have seen that exceptions to VSEPR theory occur frequently in molecules with heavy central atoms. Thus, we might expect stibine and arsine to have bond angles close to 90°, while perhaps phosphine's bond angles might be larger. In fact, the observed bond angles are 93.7° for $PH_3$ and 91.8° for $AsH_3$. For comparison, the bond angle in the lightest member of this series of compounds, $NH_3$, is 107.3°. The trend is for decreasing bond angles moving down the group from nitrogen to antimony. Thus $sp^3$ hybridization works well for ammonia, but not for the other hydrides. Electron-pair repulsion apparently becomes less important for larger central atoms, since the valence electrons are farther away from each other.

c. As one moves down a group in the periodic table, atomic size increases. Thus, increasing bond length from $NH_3$ to $SbH_3$ is predicted and observed.

## SECTION 12-4: SINGLE AND MULTIPLE BONDS IN CARBON COMPOUNDS

Localized molecular orbitals work fairly well for describing most singly bonded compounds. They are also appropriate for describing sigma bonds in multiply-bonded species and, in some instances, pi bonds. Thus, a carbon-carbon double bond is depicted as consisting of one sigma bond, formed by overlap of an $sp^2$ hybrid orbital from each C atom, and one pi bond, formed by sideways overlap of a *p* orbital from each of the C atoms. Triple bonds are made up of one sigma and two pi bonds. Only the sigma bonds are formed from hybridized atomic orbitals.

### Example 4

Describe the bonding in the following compounds in localized MO terms:

a. $CH_3-CH_2-NH_2$

Solution: Ethylamine, an organic base, is said to be saturated, because the carbon atoms are bonded to four other atoms; all their valence orbitals are used for sigma bonds. Bond angles in this compound are all approximately tetrahedral, so carbon and nitrogen use hybrid orbitals. Nitrogen uses three of its $sp^3$ orbitals for bonding to C and H atoms, while the fourth contains the lone pair of electrons. The carbon-carbon and carbon-nitrogen bonds result from overlap of two $sp^3$ orbitals, one on each atom. Bonds to hydrogen are made by overlap of $sp^3$ orbitals with hydrogen 1*s* orbitals.

b. $CH_3-N=C(CH_3)(CH_2-CH_3)$

Solution: This compound, which features a carbon-nitrogen double bond, is called a Schiff base. The carbon atom in the N=C unit is bonded to two other atoms; the local geometry about this carbon is expected to be approximately trigonal planar, which is observed. Thus, carbon uses $sp^2$ hybrid orbitals for sigma-bond formation. The nitrogen atom is also $sp^2$ hybridized; two $sp^2$ orbitals are used for bonding, while a lone electron pair resides in the third one. The double bond consists of one sigma bond, formed by overlap of an $sp^2$ orbital on nitrogen with another on carbon, and one $\pi$ bond, formed by sideways overlap of two *p* orbitals, one each on carbon and nitrogen. This situation is analogous to the bonding in ethylene, which is discussed in the text. The remaining carbon atoms are each bonded to three other atoms, using $sp^3$ hybrid orbitals.

c. $CH_3-C\equiv N$

Solution: The linear molecule acetonitrile contains a carbon-nitrogen triple bond, a feature of all nitriles. The carbon atom in the C≡N unit uses *sp* hybrid orbitals for sigma bonding to nitrogen and the methyl ($CH_3$) carbon atom. Linear geometry, and thus *sp* hybridization, is generally observed for carbon atoms bonded to only two other atoms.

There is no way of knowing whether the nitrogen atom uses *sp* hybrid orbitals, because it is bonded only to one atom. There is no bond angle about nitrogen to measure. The triple bond consists of one sigma bond and two pi bonds. Sigma orbitals can be built from an *sp* orbital on carbon and a *p* orbital on nitrogen. This would leave two *p* orbitals each on carbon and nitrogen, which could overlap sideways, making two perpendicular sets of pi orbitals. The lone pair of electrons would remain in the 2*s* orbital on nitrogen. Alternately, one can think of nitrogen using one *sp* hybrid orbital for sigma bonding and the other one for the lone pair. The *p* orbitals would overlap with those on carbon as before. However, hybridization need be involved only when required by molecular structure.

## SECTION 12-5: BENZENE AND DELOCALIZED ORBITALS

Benzene is an example of a molecule which demands the use of delocalized molecular orbitals, at least for the pi system of orbitals. Localized MO's are adequate to describe the sigma bonds in benzene, but fail to account for the fact that all the carbon-carbon bonds are the same length and thus have the same electron-density distribution.

As a rule of thumb, any molecule or ion for which resonance Lewis structure can be written should be described by delocalized molecular orbitals. Some familiar examples are $SO_3$, $PO_4^{3-}$, and $HNO_3$.

Example 5

Represent the electronic structure of acetate ion, $CH_3CO_2^-$, with Lewis structures and in molecular orbital terms.

Solution: Two resonance structures can be written:

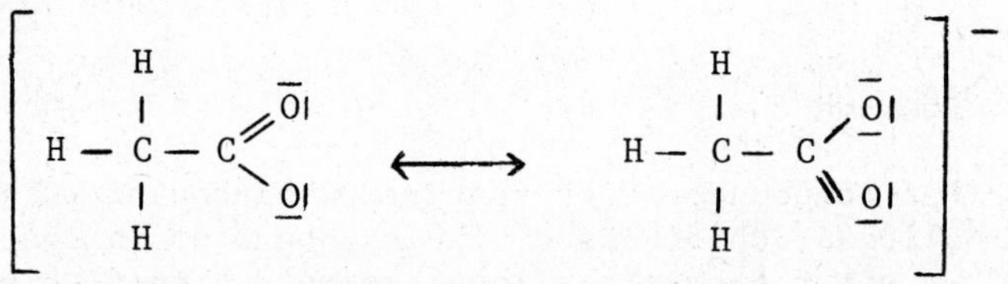

$$\left[ H-\underset{H}{\overset{H}{C}}-C\begin{smallmatrix} \diagup\!\!\!\!\diagup \overline{O}| \\ \diagdown \underline{\overline{O}}| \end{smallmatrix} \longleftrightarrow H-\underset{H}{\overset{H}{C}}-C\begin{smallmatrix} \diagup \underline{\overline{O}}| \\ \diagdown\!\!\!\!\diagdown \overline{O}| \end{smallmatrix} \right]^-$$

A molecular-orbital description uses hybrid orbitals on the carbon atoms and delocalized pi orbitals for the carbon-oxygen multiple bonds. The methyl ($CH_3$) carbon is $sp^3$ hybridized, being bonded to four other atoms. The carbon atom in the carboxylate ($-CO_2^-$) group uses $sp^2$ hybrid orbitals for sigma bonds. Three *p* orbitals, one from each of the atoms in the carboxylate group, overlap to form pi molecular orbitals which are delocalized over all three atoms. One can draw the structure as:

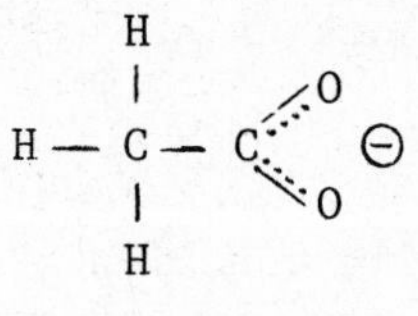

$$H-\underset{H}{\overset{H}{C}}-C\begin{smallmatrix} \therefore O \\ \therefore O \end{smallmatrix}\ \ominus$$

The average bond order for the two carbon-oxygen bonds is 1½.

## SECTION 12-6: POLAR AND NONPOLAR POLYATOMIC MOLECULES

Polyatomic molecules can be polar or nonpolar, depending on their structure. Some molecules have highly polar bonds, due to large differences in electronegativity between bonded atoms, and yet have no net dipole moment. The geometric arrangement of the polar bonds is such that the bond-dipoles cancel each other. If bond moments and contributions from lone electron pairs do not cancel, then the molecule will be polar.

### Example 6

Select the more polar species in each pair:

a. $NH_3$, $NH_4^+$

b. $PF_5$, $PF_6^-$

c. $PF_3$, $PCl_3$

Solution: a. Ammonia is a pyramidal molecule. The electronegativity difference between N and H is 0.84 on the Pauling scale, so the N-H bonds are polar. The lone pair of electrons on nitrogen combines with the bond moments to give the molecule a net dipole moment of 1.47 D. On the other hand, ammonium ion is a regular tetrahedron. Because the four N-H bond moments cancel, this ion is nonpolar.

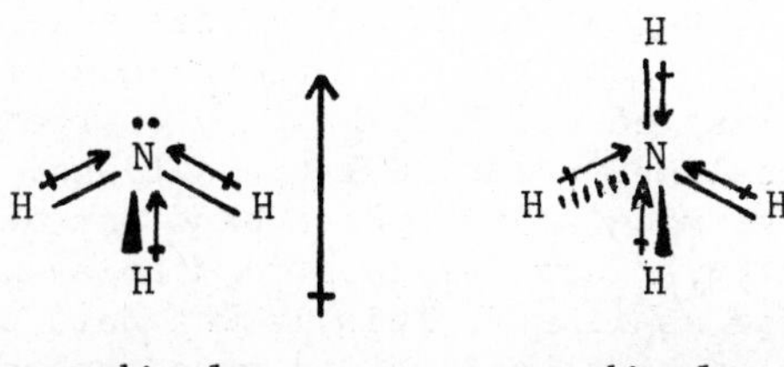


b. Both phosphorus pentafluoride and hexafluorophosphate ion are nonpolar. The individual P-F bond moments cancel in each case, although the geometries of the species are different. $PF_5$ is trigonal bipyramidal. The axial bond moments cancel each other, and the three equitorial bond moments do as well. $PF_6^-$ is octahedral; all the fluorine atoms are equivalent. The bond moments 180° apart cancel pairwise.

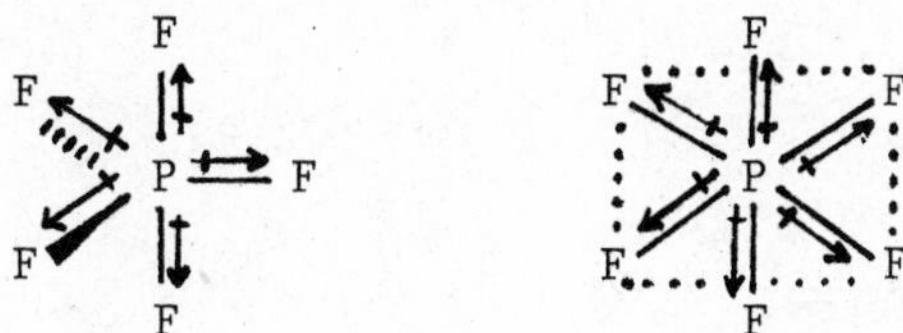


c. Both $PF_3$ and $PCl_3$ have pyramidal geometry, and both are polar. The electronegativity difference between P and F is 1.79, while between P and Cl it is only 0.97. Thus, the P-Cl bond moments are smaller than the P-F moments. In $PF_3$, electron density in the molecule is shifted toward the highly electronegative fluorine atoms. In $PCl_3$, the electron density is more evenly distributed. The measured dipole moments support this analysis: $PF_3$, 1.03 D; $PCl_3$, 0.78 D.

## SECTION 12-7: MOLECULAR SPECTROSCOPY

You are already familiar with atomic emission spectra from the discussion in Chapter 7. Molecules also display electronic spectra, when irradiated with light of the appropriate frequency. In addition, molecules can vibrate and rotate. The energy levels for these modes of motion are quantized, just as electronic energy levels are. Only certain energy levels exist; therefore, particular frequencies of electromagnetic radiation are observed.

The spacing between energy levels is largest for electronic levels and smallest for rotational ones. Thus, electronic transitions require the most energetic incident radiation, and rotational transitions, the least. Microwave radiation, $\lambda = 1 - 30$ cm, is sufficient to study molecular rotations, which give excellent information about bond lengths and bond angles. Vibrational transitions require infrared radiation, $\lambda = 2.5 - 15$ μm, while high-energy visible and ultraviolet light, $\lambda = 10 - 700$ nm, is necessary to promote electronic transitions. Measurements of vibrational spectra can be used to analyze the composition of molecules: which atoms, or groups of atoms, are present; which atoms are bonded together; which types of bonds, single or multiple, are used.

Infrared spectroscopy is an extremely powerful analytical tool. Electronic spectra are analyzed to give information about electronic energy levels in molecules. For compounds which obey Beer's law (see text), electronic spectroscopy can be used for quantitative analysis.

The appearance of spectra changes dramatically as a function of frequency of the electromagnetic radiation used to excite the molecules. Recall that electronic spectra of atoms consist only of lines. In contrast, the electronic transitions in the spectra of molecules appear as broad bands. This is because vibrational and rotational modes are excited at the same time as are the electronic transitions, because the incident radiation must necessarily be very energetic. Gas-phase atoms, of course, can have no vibrational and rotational transitions. Infrared spectra appear as a series of bands of varying width. Each band may be composed of several vibrations and rotations. Finally, microwave spectra display very high resolution; the rotational transitions appear as lines. This is why data obtained from microwave spectroscopy can give such accurate values for bond angles and lengths.

### Terms to Know

Beer's law
bridge bonds
delocalized orbitals
electronic transition
infrared spectroscopy
hybrid orbitals
localized orbitals
microwave spectroscopy
molar extinction coefficient
polyatomic molecule
Raman spectroscopy
resonance stabilization energy
rotational transition
saturated organic molecule
unsaturated organic molecule
vibrational transition

## Test Yourself

1. Predict the structure of $BF_4^-$. What is the hybridization of boron's valence orbitals?

2. Formulate a localized molecular-orbital structure for $CSe_2$. (Hint: Both Se and O are members of Group VIA.)

3. Indicate the hybridization of the carbon atoms in the compound

$$Cl_2C = C\begin{matrix} \diagup H \\ \diagdown CH_2C(CH_3)_3 \end{matrix}$$

4. Describe the electronic structure of $PO_4^{3-}$ using a

   a. Lewis structure
   b. molecular-orbital structure

5. What hybrid orbitals are used by carbon and nitrogen in the compound

$$H_3C\underset{\displaystyle OH}{\underset{|}{C}}HCH_2C\begin{matrix} \diagup\!\!\!\diagup O \\ \diagdown NH_2 \end{matrix}$$

6. For the species $SO_2$, $SO_3$, $SO_3^{2-}$, $SO_4^{2-}$:

   a. predict shapes of the compounds
   b. indicate which neutral molecules are polar, if any
   c. formulate localized molecular-orbital representations of their electronic structures

7. How many $\pi$ bonds are there in the molecule

$$N \equiv C - CH_2\diagdown C(Cl) = C(H)\diagdown C(H) = C(H)\diagup CH_2C\begin{matrix} \diagup\!\!\!\diagup O \\ \diagdown NH_2 \end{matrix}$$

8. Which of the following molecules are polar?

   $CCl_2Br_2$, $ClF_3$, $BF_3$, $PF_3$, $C_6H_6$, $XeF_4$, $AsF_5$

9. In what region of the electromagnetic spectrum are electronic energy transitions observed?

10. Why do microwave spectra consist of lines, while infrared spectra are made up of broader bands?

11. Would you expect the stretching frequency for a nitrile group, $C \equiv N$, to be higher or lower than the stretching frequency for an imine group, $C = N$? Why?

12. In what region of the electromagnetic spectrum are rotational energy transitions observed?

# 13 Bonding in Solids and Liquids

## CHAPTER OVERVIEW AND OBJECTIVES

The various attractive forces, both strong and weak, which bind solids and liquids together are examined in this chapter. These range from the extremely weak van der Waals forces up to covalent and ionic bonds. The chapter closes with a discussion of silicate minerals.

When you finish this chapter you should be able to:

1. Classify solids according to the intermolecular forces that bind them together and give examples of each type of classification;

2. Correlate these intermolecular forces with observed physical properties such as melting point and boiling point;

3. Describe the two existing theories of metallic bonding;

4. Explain how variations in the structure of silicate minerals influence their characteristics.

Be sure to study Table 13-3 carefully. It summarizes many of the important points in this chapter.

## SECTION 13-1: ELEMENTAL SOLIDS

Solid elements can be divided into three groups, according to the type of attractive force which links the atoms or molecules together. Physical properties such as hardness, melting point, and boiling point reflect the strength of these intermolecular forces.

Molecular solids consist of atoms or molecules that are bound to each other by very weak forces. Examples are the noble gases, the halogens, sulfur, and white phosphorus. These solids are relatively soft and melt at low temperatures.

On the other hand, a nonmetallic network solid behaves as one huge molecule; the atoms are covalently bonded together. Carbon, black phosphorus, silicon, and germanium are network solids. Their high melting points and hardness indicate that these crystals are bound by very strong attractive forces.

Metals form the third category of solids. They tend to be electron deficient and form crystals in which each atom is surrounded by eight to twelve nearest neighbors; this structure maximizes electron sharing. Almost all metals crystallize in one of three geometrical arrangements: hexagonal close-packed (hcp), cubic close-packed (ccp), or body-centered cubic (bcc). Note these structures in Figure 13-7.

Example 1

Both diamond and white phosphorus are described as having tetrahedral structures, yet diamond is one of the hardest substances known and melts above 3550°C, while white phosphorus can be cut with a knife and melts at 44.1°C. Reconcile these observations.

Solution: White phosphorus consists of tetrahedral $P_4$ molecules. Each phosphorus atom is covalently bonded to three others; there is a hole, not an atom, in the center of the $P_4$ tetrahedron. The molecules are loosely bound to each other, accounting for the low melting point and softness.

In contrast, the carbon atoms in diamond are each covalently bonded to four others; there is tetrahedral geometry about each carbon atom. The entire crystal is one molecule. In order to melt or cut diamond, covalent bonds between the carbon atoms must be broken.

## SECTION 13-2: IONIC SOLIDS

Ionic solids melt at extremely high temperatures because they are bound together by coulombic forces between the cations and anions. The structures of many ionic crystals are related to the metallic crystal structures mentioned in Section 13-1. One type of ion, anion or cation, makes up the crystal lattice, such as cubic close-packed, while the ion of opposite charge resides in the holes in the lattice. Study the structures in Figures 13-9 and 13-10. Note that cesium chloride does not have a body-centered cubic structure. The $Cl^-$ ions build a simple cubic lattice, while a $Cs^+$ ion occupies the eight-coordinate hole in the center of each cube.

## SECTION 13-3: MOLECULAR SOLIDS AND LIQUIDS

Various weak attractive intermolecular forces which bind molecular solids, pure liquids, and solutions are discussed in this section.

Van der Waals forces operate to hold molecular solids such as $I_2$ and $P_4$ together. There are two types: a short-range electron-electron repulsive force and a longer-range attractive one that results from synchronization of electron motion in adjacent molecules.

The energy due to repulsion of electrons in different molecules is given by

$$E_{\text{repulsive}} = be^{-ar}$$

where $a$ and $b$ are constants and $r$ is the distance between molecules. Since

$$E \propto \frac{1}{e^r}$$

repulsion is only important at short intermolecular distances. Van der Waals attraction results from transient fluctuations in electron density in a molecule, which induces a temporary dipole in an adjacent molecule. These instantaneous dipoles align with each other, giving rise to weak attractive forces. The expression for this London energy of attraction is

$$E_{London} = -\frac{d}{r^6}$$

where $d$ is a constant, $r$ is the intermolecular distance, and the negative sign indicates attraction. The London energy is more important than the repulsive energy at intermediate distances between molecules.

The total potential energy due to van der Waals interactions is

$$P.E. = be^{-ar} - d/r^6$$

Figure 13-13 is a plot of this potential energy as a function of $r$ for helium.

The magnitude of van der Waals forces is a function of molecular weight and atomic size. The more valence electrons there are in a molecule, the more synchronization of electron motion can occur, thus the greater the intermolecular attraction. Large atoms hold their valence electrons more loosely than do small ones. They are more polarizable; that is, their valence electron clouds are more easily deformed than those of small atoms, which feel the nuclear charge to a greater extent.

Example 2

Temperatures for phase transitions for carbon dioxide, carbon disulfide, and carbon diselenide at one atmosphere are as follows:

| Compound | Melting point (°C) | Boiling point (°C) |
|---|---|---|
| $CO_2$ | --- | -78.5 sublimes |
| $CS_2$ | -110.8 | 46.3 |
| $CSe_2$ | -45.5 | 125 |

Explain the differences in melting and boiling temperatures for this homologous series of compounds.

Solution: Van der Waals forces increase from $CO_2$ to $CS_2$ to $CSe_2$; this is reflected in the data given in the table. More energy is required to separate molecules that are more strongly bound. Polarizability increases from oxygen to sulfur to selenium, as the valence electrons become further removed from the nucleus and are thus held more loosely.

Polar molecules are usually attracted to each other more strongly than are nonpolar ones, due to dipole-dipole interactions. Dipole-dipole attractive energy is given by

$$E_{dipole\text{-}dipole} \propto \frac{\mu_1\mu_2}{r^3}$$

where $\mu_1$ and $\mu_2$ are the dipole moments of the molecules and $r$ is the intermolecular distance. London forces also operate in polar molecules. Liquids such as chloroform ($CHCl_3$), acetonitrile ($CH_3$-CN), and acetone ($(CH_3)_2C{=}O$) are polar.

Hydrogen bonding is a particularly strong dipole-dipole interaction, and a very important one as well. Hydrogen bonds form when hydrogen is covalently bonded to highly electronegative atoms such as F, O, and N. Bonds between hydrogen and these atoms are so polar that hydrogen is able to interact strongly with unshared pairs of electrons on other N, O, and F atoms.

While hydrogen bonds are approximately one order of magnitude weaker than typical covalent bonds, physical properties of materials are conspicuously influenced by their presence. Figure 13-19 is a dramatic illustration of the effect of hydrogen bonding on melting and boiling points. Many properties of water are primarily determined by this phenomenon.

Example 3

Account for the unusually high heat capacity, heat of vaporization, and heat of fusion of water. Explain how these properties of water influence climate.

Solution: Ice has a very open structure because each water molecule makes four hydrogen bonds, two from the hydrogen atoms and two involving the unshared electron pairs on the oxygen atom. Only a small fraction of these hydrogen bonds rupture when ice melts, so liquid water is very highly structured. The heat of fusion is large because hydrogen bonds are stronger than ordinary dipole-dipole interactions; more energy is required to overcome them. As liquid water is heated, more hydrogen bonds are ruptured; this is reflected in water's unusually high heat capacity. Vaporization requires that all the hydrogen bonds be broken, which again requires more than the usual amount of energy.

Large bodies of water change temperature very slowly, for the reasons just discussed. Great quantities of heat are absorbed during warm periods, and slowly released during cold ones. This process moderates temperature fluctuations of the bordering land, causing the climate to be milder than it would be otherwise. The effect is most pronounced in areas bordering the oceans, but even lakes the size of the Great Lakes influence climate to some extent.

Example 4

Which of the following substances are soluble in water: $K_2SO_4$, HI, $CCl_4$, $C_2H_5$-O-$C_2H_5$ (diethyl ether), $CH_3OH$?

Solution: Polar liquids such as water dissolve other polar substances through dipole-dipole attractions. Ionic compounds interact even more strongly with polar solvents; each ion is solvated by a group of solvent molecules whose dipoles are positioned so as to partially neutralize the charge on the ion. Hydrogen bonding between solute and solvent also enhances solubility.

$K_2SO_4$ is a salt that is readily soluble in water because of ion-dipole attractions. HI is a polar molecule; thus, it is soluble in water. $CCl_4$ is nonpolar and virtually insoluble in water. A tiny amount dissolves as a result of van der Waals attractions. Diethyl ether is somewhat polar and slightly soluble in water. Methanol, $CH_3OH$, is not only polar but also forms hydrogen bonds, so it is freely soluble in water.

## SECTION 13-4: METALS

There are two models for describing the electronic structure of metals. An acceptable model must account for the observed properties of metals, such as their high electrical and thermal conductivity, malleability, ductility, density, and melting point.

The sea-of-electrons theory is the simpler of the two models. This theory allows the valence electrons to circulate freely through a lattice composed of positively charged atom cores, i.e., nuclei plus electrons in closed shells. It accounts nicely for conductivity, malleability, and ductility, but is not as good at explaining why metals are so dense and have such high melting points.

Band theory is an extension of the molecular-orbital treatment to metals in which the entire piece of metal is treated as a giant molecule. The valence AO's are combined as usual, producing highly delocalized bonding and antibonding MO's. Because there are so many atoms, the MO's are closely spaced and form groups of similar energy called bands. The lower energy levels are filled, while the upper ones remain empty. Metals conduct electricity because a potential applied across a metal excites electrons to higher energy levels in a partially filled band. Electrical resistance results from collisions of electrons with positive atom cores. These collisions increase in number with increasing temperature, so conductivity decreases.

Example 5

Construct an energy level diagram showing the bands built using the valence orbitals in aluminum.

Solution: The valence electronic configuration of Al is $3s^2p^1$. There are $1\frac{1}{2}$ filled orbitals out of 4 valence orbitals per Al atom, so Al is expected to be a good electrical conductor, which it is.

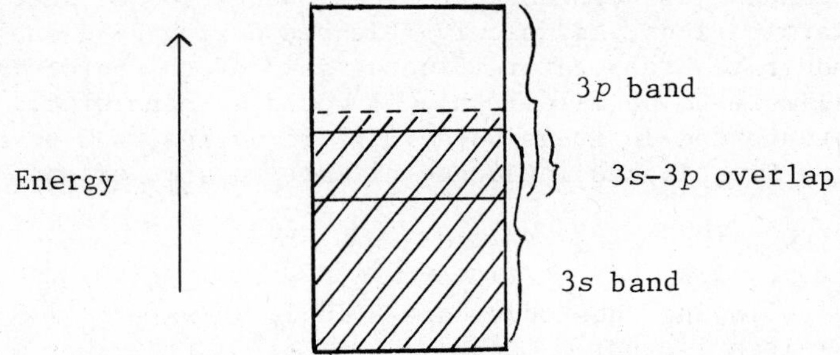


## SECTION 13-5: NONMETALLIC NETWORK SOLIDS

Solids such as diamond are insulators; they do not conduct electrical current. A localized bonding picture accounts for this property, as well as for hardness and melting point. All valence electrons in these materials are used for localized bonding, so none are left free to circulate.

Band theory can also be applied to insulators. The relatively low coordination number in an insulator causes the molecular orbitals to fall into two bands of different energies separated by a band gap. For conduction to occur, electrons in the lower-energy filled band must have sufficient energy to cross this gap into the higher-energy unfilled band. Only high temperatures or strong electrical fields can accomplish this.

The band gap of a semiconductor such as Si or Ge is much smaller than that of an insulator such as diamond. Moderate temperature increases cause semiconductors to begin to conduct electricity. This is just opposite to the dependence of conductivity on temperature exhibited by metals. The band gap in a semiconductor can be narrowed by doping the material with small amounts of elements such as boron or phosphorus. One of these elements provides a few empty valence orbitals, or holes, while the other donates extra valence electrons. Both increase conductivity at room temperature.

## SECTION 13-6: THE FRAMEWORK OF THE PLANET: SILICATE MINERALS

Carbon is able to form compounds containing long chains of carbon atoms, a phenomenon called catenation. Silicon, the next member of Group IVA, forms only short chains, but silicon bonded to oxygen is found in an enormous number of compounds. Silica has the empirical formula $SiO_2$, as does quartz. The silicate minerals contain tetrahedral $SiO_4^{4-}$ ions, which can be linked together in a variety of ways. All the silicates are covalent network solids. They can be treated as giant molecules, consistent with their properties. This section provides a discussion of the many silicate minerals.

### Terms to Know

band gap
band theory
conductor
dipole-dipole interaction
hydrogen bond
insulator
ion-dipole interaction
ionic solids
London energy
molecular solids
nonmetallic network solids
sea-of-electrons theory
semiconductor
silicate mineral
van der Waals forces
van der Waals repulsion energy

### Test Yourself

1. The metals nickel and zinc crystallize in different geometrical arrangements, yet atoms of both have 12 near neighbors. Reconcile these observations.

2. Compare solid $K_2SO_4$ and solid $SO_3$ on the basis of

   a. forces binding the solid together
   b. melting point
   c. hardness

3. Which of the following elements are good electrical conductors?

   Ra, Rn, Ag, Ca, S, I, Pt, C (diamond)

4. Phosphorus and bismuth have the same valence electronic configuration, yet phosphorus is soft and is an insulator, while bismuth is hard and is an electrical conductor. Explain why this is so.

5. What intramolecular forces and intermolecular forces hold solid sulfur together? Recall that sulfur forms $S_8$ molecules. What is the shape of a single $S_8$ molecule?

6. Compare the sea-of-electrons model with the band model of bonding in metals.

7. Using band theory, draw energy-level diagrams for a typical conductor, an insulator, and a semiconductor.

8. Arsenic is sometimes used to dope semiconductors to enhance conductivity. Explain how a trace of arsenic can accomplish this.

9. Both $CH_3CH_2OCH_3$ and $CH_3\underset{\displaystyle OH}{\underset{|}{C}}HCH_3$ have the same molecular weight and the formula $C_3H_8O$, yet the first compound boils at 10.8°C, while the second boils at 82.4°C. Rationalize this observation.

10. Both talc and mica are silicate minerals having sheet structures. Talc is very soft and slippery, while mica is hard and can be cleaved into flakes. How do these physical properties refelct the electronic structures of the minerals?

11. Compare the structure and physical properties of glass with those of quartz.

12. Compare aluminum with silicon on the basis of bonding, conductivity, melting point, and hardness. Data for these elements can be found in the <u>CRC Handbook of Chemistry and Physics</u> in your school library.

# 14 Energy and Enthalpy in Chemical Systems

CHAPTER OVERVIEW AND OBJECTIVES

This chapter and the next provide an introduction to chemical thermodynamics. While the laws of thermodynamics can predict whether a process is spontaneous, that is, whether it can occur without an external energy supply, they say nothing at all about time. Thermodynamics answers yes or no to the question, "Will it react?" Kinetics, the subject of Chapter 20, is the study of reaction rate.

When studying this chapter, pay particular attention to definitions of terms and to the use of language generally. The words used in thermodynamics are powerful in that they imply much more about matter and its behavior than may be apparent at first. Discussing this material with someone else, such as a fellow student or your instructor, is a useful way to study it.

When you finish this chapter you should be able to:

1. Describe the first law of thermodynamics, both in words and mathematically;

2. Calculate PV work for various processes;

3. Apply the first law to chemical and physical processes, and be able to calculate $\Delta E$, $\Delta H$, $q$, and $w$;

4. Use Hess' law, including the bond energy approach, to calculate reaction enthalpies.

SECTION 14-1: WORK, HEAT, AND CALORIC

The history of the formulation of the first law of thermodynamics is the topic of this section. It is also a comment on how opportunities can be missed by a closed mind. The first law is simply a statement that energy is conserved, and that work and heat are both terms of energy which can be interconverted. It is a summary of observations of energy conversion and conservation deriving from our ordinary experiences. Think about situations that you encounter which illustrate the first law.

SECTION 14-2: THE FIRST LAW OF THERMODYNAMICS

The mathematical statement of the first law focuses on the part of the universe we wish to study, called the system. The energy change for a system as a result of some process is the difference between heat added to the system, $q$, and work done by the system, $w$. Or

$$\Delta E = q - w$$

where $q$ is heat in, $w$ is work out.

Work can be of many kinds: expansion (or PV), electrical, magnetic, or gravitational work. Expansion work can be calculated from

$$w = P_{ext}\Delta V$$

where $P_{ext}$ = the external pressure on the system.

The internal energy, $E$, of a system is related to temperature. If the system is heated, its temperature will rise unless it can do an equivalent amount of work on the surroundings. Conversely, a system doing work without added heat will cool. The internal energy of an ideal gas depends only on temperature.

The use of correct terminology is extremely important when discussing thermodynamics. Be sure that you can define the terms at the end of this chapter. An especially important one is state function. A state function is a property of a system whose value depends only on the current condition of the system. Thus, internal energy, $E$, is a state function, but heat and work are not. Values of $q$ and $w$ depend on the path a system travels from one state to another. Think of the work you might do in carrying a box of books from the first to the fourth floor of a building. Your energy depends only on your position, first or fourth floor, while the work you do definitely depends on the path you take: for instance, walking up the stairs or riding an elevator.

Example 1

A gas is heated by the addition of 1500 J and expands, doing 1200 J of PV work. What can be said about $\Delta E$ and $T$ for this gas?

Solution: Since values of $q$ and $w$ are given, $\Delta E$ can be calculated:

$$\Delta E = q - w = 1500 \text{ J} - 1200 \text{ J} = 300 \text{ J}$$

Since energy has increased ($\Delta E$ is positive), the temperature of the gas rises. If the gas is ideal, the rise in temperature can be calculated from $E = 3/2\ RT$.

## SECTION 14-3: ENERGY, ENTHALPY, AND HEAT CAPACITY

Almost all chemical changes either produce heat or absorb it. Heat associated with reactions is of interest to chemists for many reasons: practical, as in the design of engines, and theoretical, as in the measurement of bond strengths. But heat, since it is not a state function but depends on path, can't be associated with a chemical process unless a specific path, or set of conditions, is defined for it. One such specific path is constant volume, for which heat, $q_V$, becomes equal to the internal energy change for the system: $\Delta E = q_V$. Another specific path, and a more useful one for chemists, is constant pressure. Most chemical reactions, including all those in biological systems, occur at constant pressure. Thus, it would be convenient if there were a state function that was related to heat measured under constant pressure conditions.

Thermodynamicists, a clever lot, have defined such a state function, enthalpy, $H$:

$$H \equiv E + PV$$

A change in enthalpy, $\Delta H$, is

$$\Delta H = \Delta E + \Delta(PV) = H_2 - H_1$$

For an ideal gas doing PV work,

$$\Delta E = q - w = q - P\Delta V$$

and $\Delta H = q - P\Delta V + \Delta(PV)$

At constant pressure, $\Delta(PV) = P\Delta V$ and

$$\Delta H = q_p - P\Delta V + P\Delta V = q_p$$

The notation $q_p$ specifies a constant pressure path for $q$, which allows a change in a state function, $\Delta H$, to be calculated from a path-dependent quantity. Note that constant pressure means that there is no net change in pressure during a reaction, $P_1 = P_2$. There may be, however, pressure fluctuations during reaction, but $P_{final}$ must equal $P_{initial}$.

Heat capacity is the amount of heat that must be added to a specified amount of a material to raise its temperature by one kelvin. Heat capacity can be defined under either constant volume or constant pressure conditions. The relative expressions are

$C_V = q_V/\Delta T = \Delta E/\Delta T$ at constant volume

$C_p = q_p/\Delta T = \Delta H/\Delta T$ at constant pressure

Example 2

Which process requires more energy, to heat a gas at constant volume or to heat it at constant pressure?

Solution: Enthalpy and energy are related by $\Delta H = \Delta E + \Delta(PV)$. For an ideal gas, $\Delta(PV) = \Delta(RT) = R\Delta T$ per mole. Thus, $\Delta H = \Delta E + R\Delta T$. Substituting $C_p$ and $C_V$:

$$C_p\Delta T = C_V\Delta T + R\Delta T$$

$$C_p = C_V + R \text{ for one mole of ideal gas}$$

Thus, more energy is required to heat a gas at constant pressure than at constant volume. The reason is that some energy is used to expand the gas, while the rest raises its temperature.

## SECTION 14-4: THE FIRST LAW AND CHEMICAL REACTIONS

This section reviews material first discussed in Chapter 2, section 2-6. You should reread that section of this Study Guide to refresh your memory.

Hess' law of heat summation, introduced in Chapter 2, follows directly from the first law of thermodynamics. Since enthalpy is a state function, the path a system takes from one state to another has no effect on the overall enthalpy change, $\Delta H$. A process which requires one step or fifty has the same $\Delta H$ value, provided that the initial and final states for the two paths are identical. Or, energy is conserved.

Example 3

Demonstrate the validity of calculating enthalpies of reaction from tabulated heats of formation, using the reaction

$$NH_3(g) + HCl(g) \longrightarrow NH_4Cl(s)$$

Solution: The shortcut method for calculating reaction enthalpies is to take the difference between the sums of the heats of formation of products and reactants:

$$\Delta H^0_{reaction} = \Sigma\Delta H^0_f(\text{products}) - \Sigma\Delta H^0_f(\text{reactants})$$

Applying this method to the reaction between HCl and $NH_3$ yields

$$\Delta H^0 = \Delta H^0_f(NH_4Cl(s)) - \Delta H^0_f(NH_3(g)) - \Delta H^0_f(HCl(g))$$

$$\Delta H^0 = [-315.4 - (-46.19) - (-92.312)] \text{ kJ}$$

$$\Delta H^0 = (-315.4 + 138.50) \text{ kJ} = -176.9 \text{ kJ}$$

To prove that this method is a valid one, we must write out the equations for the heats of formation and combine them to give the equation of interest.

(1) $\frac{1}{2}N_2(g) + \frac{1}{2}Cl_2(g) + 2H_2(g) \longrightarrow NH_4Cl(s)$

(2) $\frac{1}{2}N_2(g) + 3/2H_2(g) \longrightarrow NH_3(g)$

(3) $\frac{1}{2}H_2(g) + \frac{1}{2}Cl_2(g) \longrightarrow HCl(g)$

Reverse equations (2) and (3), then add to equation (1):

(1) $\frac{1}{2}N_2(g) + \frac{1}{2}Cl_2(g) + 2H_2(g) \longrightarrow NH_4Cl(s)$

\- (2) $NH_3(g) \longrightarrow 3/2H_2(g) + \frac{1}{2}N_2(g)$

\- (3) $HCl(g) \longrightarrow \frac{1}{2}Cl_2(g) + \frac{1}{2}H_2(g)$

---

(4) $\frac{1}{2}N_2(g) + \frac{1}{2}Cl_2(g) + 2H_2(g) + NH_3(g) + HCl(g) \longrightarrow$
$NH_4Cl(s) + 3/2H_2(g) + \frac{1}{2}N_2(g) + \frac{1}{2}Cl_2(g) + \frac{1}{2}H_2(g)$

Canceling like terms gives

(4) $NH_3(g) + HCl(g) \longrightarrow NH_4Cl(s)$

Thus, (4) = (1) - (2) - (3) and

$$\Delta H^0(4) = \Delta H^0(1) - \Delta H^0(2) - \Delta H^0(3)$$

which agrees with the calculation above.

## SECTION 14-5: BOND ENERGIES

While thermodynamics is strictly concerned only with bulk properties of materials and requires no knowledge of molecular structure, the values of thermodynamic properties can often be interpreted on a molecular level. That is one of the reasons why thermodynamics is a useful tool for chemists. Bond enthalpies, commonly called bond energies, are an example of values that chemists find useful.

The enthalpy required to convert a gaseous molecule into neutral atoms by breaking all its bonds can be measured experimentally. For example, silane, $SiH_4$, can be atomized as follows:

$$SiH_4(g) \longrightarrow 4H(g) + Si(g)$$

and $\Delta H$ for the process can be accurately measured. But the strength of a particular Si-H bond in silane is not just one-quarter of $\Delta H$ for this reaction. The energy required to cleave the first bond, producing H + $SiH_3$, is different from that required to break the next one, and so on.

The tabulated Si-H bond energy is, however, an average energy for Si-H bonds in silane and many other molecules. Predictions of enthalpies of formation for molecules are made using average bond energies from tables. When these calculated $\Delta H$ values are compared with the experimental ones, any large discrepancy between them is a warning flag that the bonding model that was used for the molecule may not correspond to reality. This is strikingly evident for molecules such as benzene and naphthalene and their derivatives. The concept of delocalized pi orbitals in these molecules answers the question of why the true (experimental) enthalpies of formation are so much smaller than those calculated from a localized bonding model.

Example 4

Calculate the heat of formation of cyclohexene,

```
          H
          |
    H    C     H
     \ //  \  /
      C      C—H
      |      |
   H—C      C—H
     / \   / \
    H    C    H
        / \
       H   H
```

using the bond energy approach, and compare it to the measured value, -7.11 kJ mol$^{-1}$.

Solution: The equation for heat of formation is

$$(1) \qquad 6C(gr) + 5H_2(g) \rightarrow C_6H_{10}(g)$$

The bond energy approach requires converting the graphite and hydrogen to gaseous atoms, then combining them to form cyclohexene. Cyclohexene contains one C=C bond, ten C-H bonds, and five C-C bonds.

| | | $\Delta H^\circ_{298}$ |
|---|---|---|
| (2) | $6C(gr) \rightarrow 6C(g)$ | 6(718.4 kJ) = 4310.4 kJ |
| (3) | $5H_2(g) \rightarrow 10H(g)$ | 10(217.9 kJ) = 2179 kJ |
| (4) | $6C(g) + 10H(g) \rightarrow C_6H_{10}(g)$ | [615 + 5(348) + 10(413)] kJ = 6485 kJ |

These equations and enthalpies can be combined using Hess' Law:

$$(1) = (4) - (3) - (2)$$

$$\Delta H°(1) = \Delta H°(4) - \Delta H°(3) - \Delta H°(2)$$

$$\Delta H°(1) = 6485 \text{ kJ} - 2179 \text{ kJ} - 4310 \text{ kJ} = -4 \text{ kJ}$$

Like cyclohexane, cyclohexene is essentially strain-free. Its molecular structure is a puckered, not a flat, ring, so the carbon atoms can make normal tetrahedral and trigonal planar bond angles.

## Terms to Know

bomb calorimeter
bond energy
caloric
closed system
endothermic
enthalpy
exothermic
expansion work
first law of thermodynamics
heat
heat capacity
internal energy
isolated system
open system
path
standard state
state function
system
work

## Test Yourself

1. Power is the rate of change of energy (or work) and has units of watts (W), where 1 W = 1 J/s. A familiar English unit of power is the horsepower (hp), where 1 hp = 746 W. The maximum power output of human muscle is about 0.3 hp/kg. How much power can a 60-kg person who is 45% muscle possibly expend? What is the maximum amount of work she can do in 1 second?

2. An ideal gas expands isothermally from 5.0 L to 20.0 L against a constant external pressure of 1.0 atm. Calculate $w$, $q$ and $\Delta E$ for this process.

3. Calculate the enthalpy change, $\Delta H$, for the process in question 2.

4. The standard heat of formation of silver phosphate, $Ag_3PO_4(s)$, is -713.4 kJ $mol^{-1}$. Write the corresponding chemical equation.

5. Explain why the standard heat of formation of rhombic sulfur is 0.0 kJ $mol^{-1}$, that of monoclinic sulfur is 0.30 kJ $mol^{-1}$, and that of $S(g)$ is 222.8 kJ $mol^{-1}$.

6. Calculate the standard enthalpy change at 25°C for the reaction

$$N_2O_5(s) + H_2O(l) \rightarrow 2H^+(aq) + 2NO_3^-(aq)$$

7. How much heat is required to dehydrate one mole of $BaCl_2 \cdot 2H_2O(s)$ to $BaCl_2(s)$ at 25°C?

8. A 10.0 L sample of an ideal gas at 0.050 atm is isothermally compressed to 0.50 L at 1.0 atm. Calculate $\Delta H$ for this process.

9. The heat capacity of aluminum at constant pressure is 20.7 J $mol^{-1}$ $K^{-1}$. How much heat is required to raise the temperature of a 2.0 kg aluminum spaghetti pot from 25°C to 100°C in order to boil water?

10. Calculate the heat of formation of urea, $H_2N - \overset{\overset{O}{\|}}{C} - NH_2$, using the bond energy approach. Compare it with the observed value, -333.2 kJ $mol^{-1}$.

11. Calculate the standard enthalpy of sublimation of iodine, which is $\Delta H°$ for the process

$$I_2(s) \longrightarrow I_2(g)$$

How much heat is required to sublime 1.0 kg of iodine?

# 15 Entropy, Free Energy, and Chemical Reactions

## CHAPTER OVERVIEW AND OBJECTIVES

This chapter continues to explore the question, "Will it react?" The question is answered, finally, by establishing a criterion for spontaneity called free energy. Free energy is a master function which combines the heat, or enthalpy, changes accompanying reactions with the drive toward maximum disorder, or entropy. The free-energy function enables one to predict whether a system will react spontaneously as written, spontaneously in the reverse direction, or equally in both directions. When left to themselves, systems react to achieve equilibrium, the condition of minimum free energy.

When you finish this chapter you should be able to:

1. Explain the second law of thermodynamics and give several different statements of it;

2. Explain what is meant by entropy and show how the entropy of the system, the surroundings, and the universe are related;

3. Predict relative values of third-law entropies of materials;

4. Explain what is meant by free energy and be able to use it quantitatively to predict spontaneity of reactions;

5. Calculate the equilibrium constant from the standard free energy of reaction and calculate free energy from the reaction quotient.

## SECTION 15-1: SPONTANEITY, REVERSIBILITY, AND EQUILIBRIUM

The principal concepts in this section are summarized in the title. Spontaneous processes are those which occur without any external energy input. Spontaneous reaction occurs until a state of equilibrium is achieved. A system at equilibrium appears to be static, because there is no observable change in its macroscopic properties. However, reaction is still occurring, but in both the forward and reverse directions at equal rates.

At equilibrium a reaction is called reversible; the slightest perturbation causes a net change in the system. On the other hand, spontaneous processes are irreversible; only very large perturbations can halt their inexorable drive toward equilibrium.

## SECTION 15-2: HEAT, ENERGY, AND MOLECULAR MOTION

In Chapter 14, two important ideas emerged. One of these is that heat is an expression of molecular motion, which can be measured by temperature. The second idea is the first law of thermodynamics,

$$\Delta E = E_2 - E_1 = q - w$$

or the change in energy of a system is the difference between the heat added to it from the surroundings and the work it does on the surroundings. We also saw that heat and work can be interconverted. Another way of stating the first law is, "You can't win"; that is, energy is conserved, not created.

In this chapter, we consider the conversion of heat to work in actual processes. The reverse, spontaneous conversion of work to heat, is always possible. Recall Joule measuring temperature differences between the tops and bottoms of waterfalls, or think of any process involving friction. Large-scale motion in such processes is converted to small-scale molecular motion, or heat.

But converting heat into work is not so simple and has never been accomplished with 100% efficiency. To do this would require cooling a body, i.e., extracting heat from it and converting that heat to mechanical work in the same process. Henry A. Bent, in his book The Second Law, describes such a situation:

"Why not operate an oceangoing vessel, for example, off the virtually inexhaustible supply of thermal energy in the oceans? Pump aboard warm water, extract energy from it to operate the ship's mechanical machinery, and when finished eject the cold water, or icebergs, overboard. There being no violation of the First Law, who, except the Coast Guard, could possibly object?"

Of course, no one would object, but unfortunately, no one has ever observed an energy transfer of this sort. One form of the second law of thermodynamics is a statement that heat can never be completely converted to work.

As another example, think about warming your house by using the thermal energy available outdoors. This occurs spontaneously in hot weather. In cold weather, however, one needs a heat pump to transfer heat from outside to inside the house, and the heat pump runs on electricity. Clearly, this is not a spontaneous process.

The second law sums up our collective experience with heat-to-work conversions. It is essentially a statement of frustration: "You can't break even." Or, work is required to transfer heat from a cold object to a hot one.

## SECTION 15-3: ENTROPY AND DISORDER

A consequence of the second law is that a system is changed by the impossibility of converting all added heat energy to work. The energy that is dissipated, or degraded, produces increased molecular motion, i.e., heat, in the system. The state function entropy, $S$, was invented to account for this. It is a measure of the extent of irreversibility of a real process. Since real, or spontaneous, processes move towards equilibrium conditions, the farther away from equilibrium a system is initially, the greater will be the net entropy change for the process. Historically, the idea of entropy grew out of studies of the operation of heat engines and was not initially interpreted on a molecular level.

The entropy change for a system is calculated by imagining a reversible path between the initial and final states of the system. Then

$$\Delta S_{sys} = S_2 - S_1 = q_{rev}/T$$

for the system. In a reversible process, the entropy change in the surroundings which would be necessary to restore the system to its original conditions is $\Delta S_{surr} = q_{rev}/T$, and the difference, or net entropy change of the universe, is zero. Real processes, however, are not reversible, so there is always some net entropy production in the universe because $\Delta S_{sys} \neq \Delta S_{surr}$.

To understand why $\Delta S$ is the ratio of $q/T$, consider two objects at different temperatures, $T_1$ and $T_2$, where $T_2 < T_1$. Let a quantity of heat, $q$, be transferred to the hot object, causing an increase in the motion of its molecules. Now transfer that same amount of heat, $q$, to the cold object. The energy transfer to the hot object is less irreversible, or less spontaneous, than the transfer of the same amount of energy to the cold one. It is easier to give the heat, $q_1$, to the colder object. Thus, temperature must be included with heat in the definition of entropy if $S$ is to be a measure of irreversibility:

$$\Delta S_{hot} = q/T_1$$

$$\Delta S_{cold} = q/T_2$$

$$\text{and } \Delta S_{cold} > \Delta S_{hot}$$

Boltzmann's molecular interpretation of entropy makes this state function more comprehensible. Entropy is just the state of disorder, or randomness. This concept is nicely illustrated in Section 15-3 of the text, in the passage "Life in a Nine-Point Universe." To apply the definition to a real, irreversible process, consider dropping a deck of cards which had been sorted by suit. There are many more ways for the cards to be arranged after having been dropped than before, so their entropy has increased. The cards, now disordered, can be sorted again, but the work required to sort them greatly exceeds the energy expended when they were dropped. The person sorting out the cards cannot do so in a reversible fashion. The increase in the sorter's entropy, due to metabolizing large molecules to many more smaller ones in order to work, is greater than the decrease in the cards' entropy. Thus, $\Delta S$ for the system, the cards, is negative, but $\Delta S$ for the universe is positive. Be careful not to confuse entropy changes in the system with those in the universe.

Example 1

How does the entropy of a gas change when it is liquified? How does the entropy of the universe change?

Solution: As the gas changes to liquid, its entropy, or state of disorder, decreases dramatically. Heat must be withdrawn from the gas by the surroundings. This process can only be spontaneous, of course, if the surroundings are cooler than the gas. Then, because the surroundings are at a lower temperature than the gas, $\Delta S$ for the surroundings is greater than $\Delta S$ for the gas, so the entropy of the universe increases.

## SECTION 15-4: ENTROPY AND CHEMICAL INTUITION

The third law of thermodynamics states that a perfect crystal has zero entropy, or only one arrangement of its atoms, at absolute zero. Absolute, or third-law, entropies are calculated from thermal data such as heat capacities, based on the above premise. Note that a value for the absolute entropy of a material can be obtained experimentally, but only changes in state functions such as enthalpy and internal energy can be measured. The seven rules for predicting relative entropies of materials are self-explanatory. As you can see from the examples given, entropy values are powerful indicators of molecular structure, even though they are obtained from measurements of bulk properties of matter.

Example 2

Predict which substance in each pair has the greater absolute entropy:

a. $Hg(l)$ or $Hg(g)$

b. $H_2S(g)$ or $H_2S(aq)$

c. $SO_2(g)$ or $SO_3(g)$

Solution: a. Mercury vapor is much more disordered than the liquid, and thus has higher entropy, 174.9 vs 77.4 J $mol^{-1}$ $K^{-1}$.

b. Gases become more ordered when dissolved in a liquid, so hydrogen sulfide vapor has more entropy than does an aqueous solution of it. The values are 205.6 J $mol^{-1}$ $K^{-1}$ for the vapor and 122 J $mol^{-1}$ $K^{-1}$ for the solution.

c. $SO_3$ is a more complex molecule than $SO_2$. More atoms can have more modes of vibration, so $SO_3$ should have more entropy than $SO_2$ at the same temperature. Values of $S^\circ_{298}$ are 256.2 J $mol^{-1}$ $K^{-1}$ and 248.5 J $mol^{-1}$ $K^{-1}$, respectively.

## SECTION 15-5: FREE ENERGY AND SPONTANEITY IN CHEMICAL REACTIONS

In the preceding section, we saw that an increase in the entropy of the universe could be taken as a criterion of spontaneity. It would be much more convenient, however, to be able to predict spontaneity in terms of the system only, without concerning ourselves with the rest of the universe. Neither the enthalpy change nor the entropy change of the system can be used individually to predict spontaneity. This dilemma is solved with a new state function, free energy, which combines the drive toward minimum thermal energy with the drive toward maximum disorder.

Free energy, $G$, is the master function of the system which provides the criterion of spontaneity. Reactions occur so as to achieve minimum free energy. The more negative the free-energy change, $\Delta G$, for a process is, the more spontaneous it will be. At equilibrium, free energy is minimized and $\Delta G = 0$.

It can be shown that a negative free-energy change for the system and an increase in entropy of the universe are equivalent criteria for spontaneity. For any process,

$$\Delta S_{universe} = \Delta S_{system} + \Delta S_{surroundings}$$

At equilibrium the process is reversible and

$$\Delta S_{universe} = 0$$

Then

$$\Delta S_{sys} = -\Delta S_{surr}$$

At equilibrium, $T_{sys} = T_{surr}$ and

$$q = q_{rev,sys} = -q_{rev,surr}$$

Then

$$\Delta S_{sys} = -(-q_{rev}/T) = q_{rev}/T$$

If $P$ is also constant,

$$q_{rev} = \Delta H_{sys}$$

and

$$\Delta S_{sys} = \Delta H_{sys}/T$$

or

$$T\Delta S_{sys} = \Delta H_{sys}$$

Because $\Delta G = \Delta H - T\Delta S$ at constant $T$ and $P$,

$$\Delta H = T\Delta S \quad \text{when } \Delta G = 0$$

The free-energy change for a process is also the maximum amount of useful work that can be obtained from a system: $\Delta G = -w_{ext,max}$. If the system only expands or contracts, i.e., does PV work, this is not useful, or external, work. External work is what the system can do in addition to PV work; for example, generating electricity. An analogy to the change in free energy as maximum useful work can be drawn from a shopping expedition. If you have $50 to spend, some of it must be used for transportation and, possibly, some for lunch if the trip is a long one. The money that remains is your useful, or free, money for shopping.

Standard free-energy changes for reactions, $\Delta G°$, can be calculated using tabulated standard free energies of formation. The process is similar to the one used to calculate standard enthalpy changes, $\Delta H°$, and is legitimate because $G$ is a state function. Standard free energies of formation are usually given for 298 K. Since the expression $\Delta G = \Delta H - T\Delta S$ contains temperature explicitly, $\Delta G$ is very sensitive to temperature. $\Delta G°$ at 298 K can be quite different from $\Delta G°$ at another temperature. Be sure you keep in mind what the standard states are for various classes of materials.

Example 3

Calculate the standard free-energy change, $\Delta G°$, at 298 K for the reaction

$$2SO_2(g) + O_2(g) \rightleftharpoons 2SO_3(g)$$

from the data shown. What provides the driving force in this reaction?

| | $SO_2(g)$ | $O_2(g)$ | $SO_3(g)$ |
|---|---|---|---|
| $\Delta H_f°$(kJ mol$^{-1}$) | -269.9 | -- | -395.2 |
| $S°$(J mol$^{-1}$ K$^{-1}$) | 248.5 | 205.03 | 256.2 |

Solution: The standard free-energy change can be obtained from the relationship

$$\Delta G° = \Delta H° - T\Delta S°$$

In this system,

$$\Delta S° = 2S°(SO_3(g)) - S°(O_2(g)) - 2S°(SO_2(g))$$

$$\Delta S° = \{2(256.2) - 205.03 - 2(248.5)\} \text{ J mol}^{-1} \text{ K}^{-1}$$

$$\Delta S° = (512.4 - 205.03 - 497.0) \text{ J mol}^{-1} \text{ K}^{-1}$$

$$\Delta S° = -189.5 \text{ J mol}^{-1} \text{ K}^{-1}$$

$$\Delta H° = 2\Delta H_f°(SO_3(g)) - 2\Delta H_f°(SO_2(g))$$

$$\Delta H° = \{2(-395.2) - 2(-269.9)\} \text{ kJ mol}^{-1}$$

$$\Delta H° = (-790.4 + 539.8) \text{ kJ mol}^{-1} = -250.6 \text{ kJ mol}^{-1}$$

$$\Delta G° = -250.6 \text{ kJ mol}^{-1} - (298 \text{ K})(-189.5 \text{ J mol}^{-1} \text{ K}^{-1}$$

$$\Delta G° = -250{,}600 \text{ J mol}^{-1} + 56{,}471 \text{ J mol}^{-1}$$

$$\Delta G° = -194{,}129 \text{ J mol}^{-1} = -194.1 \text{ kJ mol}^{-1}$$

Because $\Delta G°$ is negative, the reaction is spontaneous. The entropy change is unfavorable, but the process is exothermic. Thus, enthalpy provides the driving force for this reaction.

## SECTION 15-6: FREE ENERGY AND CONCENTRATION

Using the definition of free energy under the most general experimental conditions, one can derive an expression for the free energy of a substance as a function of pressure in a gas-phase system:

$$G = G° + RT \ln (p/p°)$$

where $p° = 1$ atm, the standard state of a gas. If you have not studied calculus, you may start this section at equation 15-17. You won't be missing any chemical principles by doing this.

The ratio of the partial pressure of the gas to its standard state pressure, $p/p°$, is called the activity of the gas. Activity, $a$, can be thought of as effective concentration. The activity of a gas is numerically equal to its partial pressure expressed in atmospheres, but has no units, because it is a pressure ratio. A discussion of the activity concept as applied to solids, liquids, and solutions is found in Chapter 16. The expression for free energy is thus

$$G = G° + RT \ln a$$

The free energy of a gas increases as its activity increases.

The free-energy change for a reaction is

$$\Delta G = \sum G_{\text{products}} - \sum G_{\text{reactants}}$$

or $$\Delta G = \sum \Delta G°_{\text{products}} + \sum RT \ln a_{\text{products}} - \sum \Delta G°_{\text{reactants}} - \sum RT \ln a_{\text{reactants}}$$

$$\Delta G = \Delta G° + RT(\sum \ln a_{\text{products}} - \sum \ln a_{\text{reactants}})$$

But because $\log x - \log y = \log x/y$, and $\log a + \log b = \log a \cdot b$,

$$\Delta G = \Delta G° + RT \ln Q$$

where $Q$ is the reaction quotient. The form of $Q$ is determined by the stoichiometry of the particular reaction under consideration. The equation above enables us to calculate the free-energy change for any reaction under any conditions, as long as the stoichiometry is known. It then becomes possible to predict whether, and in what direction, a system will react under nonstandard conditions.

Example 4

Consider the system

$$2SO_2(g) + O_2(g) \rightleftharpoons 2SO_3(g)$$

Calculate the free-energy change at 298 K for the reaction when $p_{SO_2} = 0.50$ atm, $p_{O_2} = 0.35$ atm, and $p_{SO_3} = 0.75$ atm. Predict in which direction the system will react.

Solution: The free-energy change is calculated from $\Delta G = \Delta G° + RT \ln Q$. The reaction quotient, $Q$, takes its form from the equation:

$$Q = a^2{}_{SO_3}/a^2{}_{SO_2}a_{O_2}$$

$\Delta G°$ was calculated at 298 K in Example 3.

$$\Delta G = -194.1 \text{ kJ} + (8.314 \text{ J mol}^{-1} \text{ K}^{-1})(298 \text{ K}) \ln \frac{(0.75)^2}{(0.50)^2(0.35)}$$

$$\ln x = 2.303 \log x$$

$$\Delta G = -194.1 \text{ kJ} + (8.314 \text{ J mol}^{-1} \text{ K}^{-1})(298 \text{ K})(2.303) \log 6.43$$

$$\Delta G = -194.1 \text{ kJ} + (8.314)(298)(2.303)(0.808) \text{ J}$$

$$\Delta G = -194.1 \times 10^3 \text{ J} + 4611 \text{ J} = -189.5 \text{ kJ}$$

At equilibrium, $\Delta G = 0$ and $Q$ is a constant value, the equilibrium constant, $K_{eq}$.

$$0 = \Delta G° + RT \ln K_{eq}$$

$$\Delta G° = -RT \ln K_{eq} = -RT(2.303) \log K_{eq}$$

The rates of the forward and reverse reactions are the same at equilibrium, and the composition of the system is controlled by $K_{eq}$. Thus, if $\Delta G°$ is known, $K_{eq}$ can be calculated.

Example 5

What is the equilibrium constant at 298 K for the reaction in Example 3?

Solution: Using $\Delta G° = -RT \ln K_{eq}$, we have

$$-194.1 \text{ kJ} = -(8.314 \text{ J mol}^{-1} \text{ K}^{-1})(298)(2.303) \log K_{eq}$$

$$\log K_{eq} = \frac{-(-194.1 \times 10^3)}{(8.314)(298)(2.303)} = 34.02$$

$$K_{eq} = 1.04 \times 10^{34}$$

Note: If the absolute value of $\Delta G°$ is very large, then $K_{eq}$ will be either very large or very small. Since one can always estimate a common log, or the antilog if the common log is given, it is better to use common, rather than natural, logarithms in these calculations. Trying to take the antilog of a very large natural logarithm on a calculator often leads to an error message and frustration rather than an answer. For example:

$$\ln K = -165.35 = 2.303 \log K$$

$$\log K = -165.35/2.303 = -71.798 = 0.202 - 72$$

The order of magnitude of $K$ is $10^{-72}$, i.e., $K$ = (some number) × $10^{-72}$. Taking the antilog of 0.202 gives $K = 1.59 \times 10^{-72}$.

## Terms to Know

activity
Boltzmann's constant
chemical equilibrium
entropy
equilibrium constant
free energy
heat capacity
irreversible reaction
maximum useful work
reversible reaction
second law of thermodynamics
spontaneity
spontaneous process
third-law entropy

## Test Yourself

1. Predict the sign of $\Delta S$ for these processes and explain your choices:

   a. $CO(g) + Cl_2(g) \longrightarrow COCl_2(g)$

   b. $4NH_3(g) + 5O_2(g) \longrightarrow 4NO(g) + 6H_2O(g)$

   c. $4NH_3(g) + 3O_2(g) \longrightarrow 2N_2(g) + 6H_2O(l)$

   d. $I_2(s) + Br_2(l) \longrightarrow 2IBr(g)$

   e. $I_2(g) + Br_2(g) \longrightarrow 2IBr(g)$

2. Choose the substance in each pair having the lower entropy:

   a. $I_2(s)$, $I_2(aq)$

   b. $Kr(g)$, $Rn(g)$

   c. $NH_4Br(s)$, $NH_4Br(aq)$

   d. $Cl_2(g)$, $Cl_2(aq)$

3. Calculate the standard entropy changes at 25°C for the reactions in question 1. For $COCl_2(g)$, $S°$ = 289.2 e.u./mol.

4. When solid ammonium nitrate dissolves in water, the solution becomes very cold. Write the chemical equation describing this process. What provides the driving force for it?

5. Calculate the standard free-energy change and the equilibrium constant for the reaction

$$Al(s) + Fe_2O_3(s) \longrightarrow Al_2O_3(s) + Fe(s)$$

What is $\Delta S°$? What provides the driving force for the reaction?

6. The heat of vaporization of the refrigerant Freon-22, $CHClF_2$, is 18.79 kJ $mol^{-1}$ at its boiling point, -40.75°C. How many grams of Freon-22 must vaporize to freeze one pint (one pound) of water into ice cubes at 0°C? The heat of fusion of ice at 0°C is 6.01 kJ $mol^{-1}$.

7. Sulfuric acid can be synthesized by the oxidation of sulfur with nitric acid:

$$S(s) + 6HNO_3(aq) \longrightarrow H_2SO_4(aq) + 6NO_2(g) + 2H_2O(l)$$

Calculate $\Delta H°$, $\Delta S°$, $\Delta G°$ and $K_{eq}$ at 25°C for this reaction. Take $HNO_3(aq)$ to be $H^+(aq)$ and $NO_3^-(aq)$, and $H_2SO_4(aq)$ as $H^+(aq)$ and $HSO_4^-(aq)$. For $HSO_4^-(aq)$, $\Delta H_f^\circ$ = -885.9 kJ $mol^{-1}$ and $S°$ = 126.8 e.u./mol. Can you suggest a way to improve the reaction yield?

8. Consider the isothermal expansion of one mole of an ideal gas from 1.0 L to 5.0 L at 25°C. Path a is a free expansion, i.e., expansion into a vacuum; path b is expansion against one atmosphere constant external pressure; and path c is a reversible expansion in which 3.99 kJ of work are done. For each path, find $q$, $w$, $\Delta E$, $\Delta H$, $\Delta S$, and $\Delta G$.

9. Phosgene, $COCl_2$, a starting material in the manufacture of polyurethane plastics, is prepared from chlorine and carbon monoxide:

$$CO(g) + Cl_2(g) \rightleftharpoons COCl_2(g)$$

a. Calculate the equilibrium constant at 298 K for this reaction. $\Delta G_f^\circ$ = -210.5 kJ $mol^{-1}$ for $COCl_2$.

b. Calculate the free energy of a mixture of 0.30 atm $COCl_2$, 0.15 atm $Cl_2$, and 0.25 atm CO. In which direction will reaction occur?

10. Is it possible to cool your kitchen on a hot day by opening the refrigerator door? Explain your answer.

# 16 Free Energy and Equilibrium

## CHAPTER OVERVIEW AND OBJECTIVES

In this chapter chemical equilibrium is firmly anchored to its theoretical foundation, thermodynamics. If you have already studied Chapter 4, some of this material will provide a review of equilibrium, but much of it is new. If Chapter 4 is yet to come, use Chapter 4 of this Study Guide as a supplement. It contains additional worked examples of quantitative and qualitative treatment of equilibrium systems.

When you finish this chapter you should be able to:

1. Describe chemical equilibrium from a thermodynamic, as well as a molecular, standpoint;

2. Write the equilibrium-constant expression for any reaction using activities and know how to obtain values for activities;

3. Calculate equilibrium constants from experimental data and from thermodynamic parameters;

4. Use an equilibrium constant to calculate the composition of an equilibrium system;

5. Apply LeChatelier's principle to systems at equilibrium;

6. Interpret the contributions of enthalpy and entropy to free energy, and thus to $K$, on a molecular level.

## SECTION 16-1: THE PROPERTIES OF EQUILIBRIUM

This section describes seven characteristics of an equilibrium system:

1. The forward and reverse reactions occur at equal rates, so that there is no net change in the overall composition of the system;

2. Systems react spontaneously to reach equilibrium;

3. The free-energy change for a process becomes less negative as equilibrium is approached; and the system can do less work;

4. The free-energy change at equilibrium is zero and no work can be done;

5. Equilibrium can be reached from either the product or the reactant side.

6. There is an equilibrium constant, $K_{eq}$, for every process which can be satisfied by various combinations of activities of reactants and products.

7. $K_{eq}$ can be calculated from $\Delta G° = -RT \ln K_{eq}$; $K_{eq}$ changes only with temperature, not with activity.

Example 1

Given the following processes:

(1) $SO_2(g) + \frac{1}{2}O_2(g) \rightleftharpoons SO_3(g)$

(2) $2H_2(g) + O_2(g) \rightleftharpoons 2H_2O(l)$

(3) $H_2O(g) \rightleftharpoons H_2O(l)$

a. Write equilibrium-constant expressions for the equations.

Solution: The expressions for $K_{eq}$ are

(1) $K_{eq} = a_{SO_3}/a_{SO_2}\sqrt{a_{O_2}}$

(2) $K_{eq} = a^2_{H_2O(l)}/a^2_{H_2}a_{O_2}$

(3) $K_{eq} = a_{H_2O(l)}/a_{H_2O(g)}$

The activity of a pure liquid or solid is 1. The activity of a gas is numerically equal to its partial pressure, because it is the ratio of the partial pressure to the standard state pressure of the gas, 1 atm.

The equilibrium-constant expressions above can be rewritten as

(1) $K_{eq} = p_{SO_3}/p_{SO_2}\sqrt{p_{O_2}}$

(2) $K_{eq} = 1/p^2_{H_2}p_{O_2}$

(3) $K_{eq} = 1/p_{H_2O}$

b. These equations can be combined to give

(4) $SO_3(g) + H_2(g) \rightleftharpoons SO_2(g) + H_2O(g)$

Show how this can be done, and show how to calculate $K_{eq}$ for equation (4) from the equilibrium constants for equations (1)-(3).

Solution: The desired equation has one mole each $SO_3$ and $H_2$ on the left, and a mole of $SO_2$ and $H_2O(g)$ on the right. Therefore, equation (1) should be reversed:

-(1) $SO_3(g) \rightleftharpoons SO_2(g) + \frac{1}{2}O_2(g)$

Equation (2) should be halved:

½(2) $H_2(g) + \frac{1}{2}O_2(g) \rightleftharpoons H_2O(l)$

Equation (3) should be reversed:

-(3) $H_2O(l) \rightleftharpoons H_2O(g)$

Adding the equations now gives

$$SO_3(g) + H_2(g) + \tfrac{1}{2}O_2(g) + H_2O(l) \rightleftharpoons SO_2(g) + \tfrac{1}{2}O_2(g) + H_2O(l) + H_2O(g)$$

Canceling like terms:

$$SO_3(g) + H_2(g) \rightleftharpoons SO_2(g) + H_2O(g) \qquad \text{which is (4).}$$

In summary, (4) = -(1) + ½(2) - (3).

To find $K_{eq}$ for (4), first write the expression and compare with those of (1), (2), and (3).

$$K_{eq}(4) = p_{H_2O}p_{SO_2}/p_{SO_3}p_{H_2}$$

$K(1)$ and $K(3)$ must be inverted and the square root of $K(2)$ must be taken. Then all three expressions, after these manipulations, must be multiplied together to calculate $K(4)$.

$$\frac{p_{SO_2}\sqrt{p_{O_2}}}{p_{SO_3}} \times \frac{1}{\sqrt{p^2_{H_2}p_{O_2}}} \times p_{H_2O} = \frac{p_{SO_2}p_{H_2O}}{p_{SO_3}p_{H_2}} = K(4)$$

$$K(4) = \frac{\sqrt{K(2)}}{K(1)K(3)}$$

Problems 1, 3, and 11 in the text reinforce the concept presented in this example.

## SECTION 16-2: REACTIONS INVOLVING GASES

Four types of calculations involving equilibrium gas-phase systems are illustrated in this section:

1. Measurement of $K_{eq}$ from experimental data;
2. Calculation of $K_{eq}$ from thermodynamic data: $\Delta G° = -RT \ln K_{eq}$;
3. Calculation of the activity of one or more components of a system, given $K_{eq}$ and information about the activities of the other components;
4. Calculation of the extent of reaction, $\alpha$.

### Example 2

Formic acid, HCOOH, is a weak acid that partially dissociates into hydrogen ions and formate ions in aqueous solution:

$$HCOOH(aq) \rightleftharpoons H^+(aq) + HCOO^-(aq)$$

a. Calculate the equilibrium constant for this process at 25°C.

Solution: $K$ can be calculated from $\Delta G° = -RT \ln K$ if $\Delta G°$ is known. Using the data in Appendix 2 to calculate $\Delta G°$ gives

$$\Delta G° = \Delta G_f°(H^+) + \Delta G_f°(HCOO^-) - \Delta G_f°(HCOOH(aq))$$

$$\Delta G° = 0.0 - 334.7 \text{ kJ mol}^{-1} - (-356.1 \text{ kJ mol}^{-1})$$

$$\Delta G° = (-334.7 + 356.1) \text{ kJ mol}^{-1} = 21.4 \text{ kJ mol}^{-1}$$

Be sure to use correct units for the gas constant.

$$(21.4 \text{ kJ mol}^{-1})(10^3 \text{ J kJ}^{-1}) = -(8.314 \text{ J mol}^{-1} \text{ K}^{-1})(298)(2.303 \log K)$$

$$\log K = -3.751 = 0.249 - 4$$

$$K = 1.77 \times 10^{-4}$$

b. An aqueous solution is made from 0.500 mol formic acid in 1.00 L solution. What is the concentration of hydrogen ion in this solution at equilibrium?

Solution: The equilibrium-constant expression is

$$K = \frac{a_{H^+}a_{HCOO^-}}{a_{HCOOH}} = 1.77 \times 10^{-4}$$

In dilute solutions, the activity of a solute is numerically equal to its molarity. The symbol for molar concentration of any substance $X$ is $[X]$.

$$K = \frac{[H^+][HCOO^-]}{[HCOOH]} = 1.77 \times 10^{-4}$$

To calculate $[H^+]$ at equilibrium, first set up a chart showing initial conditions, changes necessary to reach equilibrium, and equilibrium conditions. Let $X$ = the concentration of $H^+$ which forms, which is also $[HCOO^-]$, from the reaction stoichiometry.

| | $[HCOOH]$ | $[H^+]$ | $[HCOO^-]$ |
|---|---|---|---|
| initial | 0.500 | 0 | 0 |
| change | $-X$ | $+X$ | $+X$ |
| equilibrium | $0.500 - X$ | $X$ | $X$ |

Now substitute the equilibrium values into the expression for $K$.

$$K = 1.77 \times 10^{-4} = \frac{X^2}{0.500 - X}$$

The expression can be simplified if $X$ can be neglected with respect to 0.500. $X$ can be neglected if $K/[HCOOH]_{initial} \leq 10^{-3}$.

$$1.77 \times 10^{-4}/0.500 = 3.54 \times 10^{-4} \quad \text{which} < 10^{-3}$$

$$1.77 \times 10^{-4} = x^2/0.500$$

$$x^2 = (0.500)(1.77 \times 10^{-4}) = 0.885 \times 10^{-4}$$

$$x = 0.941 \times 10^{-2} = 9.41 \times 10^{-3} = [H^+] = [HCOO^-]$$

c. Calculate the percentage of formic acid molecules which have dissociated, a measure of the extent of reaction.

Solution: The percent dissociation is just the ratio of dissociated formic acid to the original amount of formic acid. Since it is a ratio, it can be calculated from the appropriate concentrations. Formic acid dissociated can be represented by $[HCOO^-]$ (or $[H^+]$, since they are equal). The original formic acid concentration is given in the statement of the problem, 0.500 M. Then

$$\%\text{ dissociation} = (9.41 \times 10^{-3})/0.500$$

$$\%\text{ dissociation} = 1.88 \times 10^{-2} = 1.88\%$$

## SECTION 16-3: LE CHATELIER'S PRINCIPLE

Le Chatelier's principle governs the behavior of equilibrium systems that are subjected to some kind of stress. If an equilibrium system is perturbed in some way, the system will adjust so as to minimize the perturbation. One can perturb a system by

1. Changing the pressure or volume;
2. Adding or removing one or more of the components;
3. Adding or removing a catalyst;
4. Changing the temperature.

Adding or removing a catalyst affects reaction rate, to be sure, but has no effect on equilibrium. This is because a catalyst speeds up both the forward and the reverse reactions. Equilibrium is achieved more rapidly, but the position of equilibrium and the value of $K$ are unaffected.

Changing the pressure, or the volume, of a gas-phase equilibrium system may or may not affect the position of equilibrium. The reaction stoichiometry is the determining factor here. Regardless of the reaction, however, the value of $K$ will not be changed. $K$ changes only with temperature.

Adding or removing a component of the system causes the equilibrium position to shift, as might be expected. Chapter 4 of this Study Guide contains worked examples of this kind of perturbation. It has no effect on the value of $K$.

Changing temperature does change $K$, since it affects the standard free energy of the reaction:

$$\Delta G° = -RT \ln K = \Delta H° - T\Delta S°$$

Temperature appears explicitly in two terms of the expression.

The response of an equilibrium system to a temperature change can be predicted qualitatively if the sign of $\Delta H°$ is known. If the reaction is exothermic, raising the temperature just creates more heat, which impedes the forward reaction and causes a shift to the left. Lowering the temperature would promote the forward reaction over the reverse.

The equation above can be used to calculate $K$ at various temperatures. Keep in mind that $\Delta G°$ is very sensitive to temperature changes; it must be calculated at each new temperature and then used to predict $K$. Remember also that $\Delta H°$ and $\Delta S°$ will change somewhat over very large temperature ranges, but are nearly constant over small ones. Study Table 16-4 in the text, which displays the variation of $K$ and $\Delta G°$ with temperature for the endothermic reaction

$$2SO_3(g) \rightleftharpoons 2SO_2(g) + O_2(g)$$

from room temperature to 1400 K

Example 3

For the equations that follow, predict how the position of equilibrium will be affected by a pressure decrease:

a. $4NH_3(g) + 5O_2(g) \rightleftharpoons 4NO(g) + 6H_2O(g)$

b. $SO_3(g) + H_2(g) \rightleftharpoons SO_2(g) + H_2O(g)$

Solution: Inspecting the equilibrium-constant expressions quickly answers this question.

a. $$K = \frac{p^4_{NO}p^6_{H_2O}}{p^4_{NH_3}p^5_{O_3}}$$

The numerator contains pressure to the tenth power; the denominator, pressure to the ninth power. There is a net pressure increase as reaction proceeds in the forward direction. Decreasing the overall pressure of the system enhances the forward reaction, shifting the position of equilibrium to the right, in favor of products.

b. $$= \frac{p_{SO_2}p_{H_2O}}{p_{SO_3}p_{H_2}}$$

Both numerator and denominator contain pressure to the second power. Since neither the forward nor the reverse reaction produces a net pressure increase, changing the overall pressure of the system will not affect the position of equilibrium.

(Note: These same conclusions can be reached by examining the chemical equations. If the number of moles of gas on the right is greater, a pressure decrease favors the forward reaction. If the number of moles of gas on both sides of the equation are equal, pressure changes will have no effect on the equilibrium, and so forth.)

## SECTION 16-4: THE ANATOMY OF A REACTION

This section provides a detailed analysis of the way in which free energy, and thus $K$, changes with temperature. The expression

$$\Delta G° = \Delta H° - T\Delta S°$$

can be rearranged to

$$\Delta G°/T = \Delta H°/T - \Delta S°$$

A plot of $\Delta G°/T$ vs. $T$, called a Gibbs-Helmholtz plot, gives a curve whose slope is $\Delta H°$. Figure 16-3 confirms that, indeed, $\Delta H°$ is rather insensitive to temperature. Figure 16-4 shows that $\Delta S°$ does not vary much with $T$ either.

Values of $\Delta H°$ and $T\Delta S°$ can be interpreted on a molecular level. Bond-breaking and bond-making processes determine the enthalpy change. For many reactions, the net change in moles of materials primarily determines the entropy change. Endothermic reactions are driven by entropy. They are spontaneous when $T\Delta S°$ exceeds $\Delta H°$, at high temperatures. On the other hand, exothermic reactions having negative entropy changes are driven by enthalpy: $\Delta H°$ exceeds $T\Delta S°$. These reactions, however, are less spontaneous at high temperatures, because the $T\Delta S°$ term becomes large. The best situation, of course, is that in which the reaction is exothermic and has a positive entropy change; both $\Delta H°$ and $T\Delta S°$ contribute to spontaneity.

## Terms to Know

activity
equilibrium constant
equilibrium-constant expression
extent of reaction
free-energy change
Gibbs-Helmholtz plot
Le Chatelier's principle
reaction quotient

## Test Yourself

1. Show how to calculate the equilibrium constant for the reaction

$$SO_2(g) + NO_2(g) \rightleftharpoons SO_3(g) + NO(g)$$

from the equilibrium constants for the reactions

$$2SO_3(g) \rightleftharpoons O_2(g) + 2SO_2(g)$$

$$NO(g) + \tfrac{1}{2}O_2(g) \rightleftharpoons NO_2(g)$$

2. The equilibrium constant for the formation of nitrosyl chloride, $NOCl_2$, from chlorine and nitric oxide,

$$2NO(g) + Cl_2(g) \rightleftharpoons 2NOCl(g)$$

is 52.0 at 500 K. Calculate the partial pressures of NO, $Cl_2$, and NOCl at equilibrium if 1.0 atm of NOCl is placed in an evacuated 10.0 L vessel at 500 K.

3. What will the partial pressures of NO, $Cl_2$, and NOCl be at equilibrium if 0.50 atm each NO and $Cl_2$ are mixed in an evacuated vessel at 500 K?

4. Calculate the percent dissociation of the nitrosyl chloride in question 2.

5. The standard enthalpy change for

$$2NO(g) + Cl_2(g) \rightleftharpoons 2NOCl(g)$$

is -75.57 kJ. What effect will the following changes have on the position of equilibrium and the value of the equilibrium constant?

a. increasing the pressure of the system,

b. raising the temperature,

c. adding a catalyst,

d. removing some chlorine.

6. Calculate the standard free energy change and the equilibrium constant at 25°C for the reaction

$$2NO(g) + Cl_2(g) \rightleftharpoons 2NOCl(g)$$

Thermodynamic parameters for NOCl($g$) are $\Delta H_f^\circ$ = 59.59 kJ mol$^{-1}$, $S^\circ$ = 263 J mol$^{-1}$ K$^{-1}$.

7. What provides the driving force for the reaction in question 6, enthalpy or entropy? Is there a temperature at which this reaction is no longer spontaneous? If so, calculate it.

8. Calculate the equilibrium constants at 25°C for the following reactions:

a. $Zn(s) + CO_2(g) \rightleftharpoons ZnO(s) + CO(g)$

b. $4NH_3(g) + 7O_2(g) \rightleftharpoons 4NO_2(g) + 6H_2O(g)$

c. $2NH_3(g) + CO_2(g) \rightleftharpoons NH_2CONH_2(s) + H_2O(g)$

9. Equation c in question 8 represents the synthesis of urea, an important component of fertilizers. Urea was the first synthetic organic compound.

a. Calculate the equilibrium constant for this reaction at 100°C and compare it to the value at 25°C.

b. Suggest three ways to increase the yield of this reaction.

# 17 Equilibria Involving Liquids and Solids

## CHAPTER OVERVIEW AND OBJECTIVES

Equilibria involving physical, rather than chemical, changes are the topics of this chapter. Phase changes of pure substances are considered first, followed by those of solutions. Practical applications of phenomena described herein are many, varied, and important.

When you finish this chapter you should be able to:

1. Describe phase changes qualitatively and quantitatively using $\Delta H$, $\Delta S$, and $\Delta G$;

2. Calculate the following:

   - boiling point
   - vapor pressure at a given temperature and vice-versa
   - values of $\Delta H°$, $\Delta S°$, $\Delta G°$ for phase changes;

3. Describe the critical state of a substance;

4. Obtain information from phase diagrams and construct a phase diagram given appropriate information about a substance;

5. Describe the four colligative properties and use the mathematical expressions for them.

## SECTION 17-1: MELTING, EVAPORATION, AND SUBLIMATION

Solids melt, or fuse, when enough energy is available to overcome the lattice energy that binds them together. For evaporation to occur, the attractive forces which hold the liquid together must be exceeded by the kinetic energy of molecules escaping into the gas phase. The enthalpy changes for these processes are called the heats of fusion and vaporization, respectively:

$$A(s) \rightleftharpoons A(l) \qquad \Delta H°_{fus}$$

$$A(l) \rightleftharpoons A(g) \qquad \Delta H°_{vap}$$

Heats of fusion and vaporization are always positive. Values of $\Delta H°_{fus}$ are much smaller than $\Delta H°_{vap}$ values, because the forces holding liquids together are only slightly weaker than the lattice forces in solids. Solids that do not melt when heated, but vaporize directly, are said to sublime. The heat of sublimation, $\Delta H°_{sub}$, is the enthalpy change for the process

$$A(s) \rightleftharpoons A(g)$$

Entropy changes for these processes are designated $\Delta S^\circ_{fus}$, $\Delta S^\circ_{vap}$, and $\Delta S^\circ_{sub}$, respectively. Entropy changes for vaporization and sublimation are much larger than those for fusion, since gases are completely disordered, while solids are highly structured, and liquids only slightly less so. Trouton's rule is an empirical, or experimentally derived, rule of thumb that gives the entropy of vaporization of most liquids as ∿90 J/K or 90 e.u. Exceptions to Trouton's rule indicate an unusual degree of order in a liquid, such as from hydrogen bonding.

Example 1

Calculate the standard enthalpy and entropy of vaporization for formic acid, HCOOH. Does formic acid obey Trouton's rule?

Solution: Vaporization is just the equilibrium process

$$HCOOH(l) \rightleftharpoons HCOOH(g)$$

$\Delta H^\circ_{vap}$ and $\Delta S^\circ_{vap}$ can be calculated from the appropriate heats of formation and absolute entropies, as tabulated in Appendix 2.

$$\Delta H^\circ_{vap} = \Delta H^\circ_f(HCOOH(g)) - \Delta H^\circ_f(HCOOH(l))$$

$$\Delta H^\circ_{vap} = -362.6 \text{ kJ mol}^{-1} - (-409.2 \text{ kJ mol}^{-1}) = 46.6 \text{ kJ mol}^{-1}$$

$$\Delta S^\circ_{vap} = S^\circ(HCOOH(g)) - S^\circ(HCOOH(l))$$

$$\Delta S^\circ_{vap} = 251 \text{ e.u./mol} - 129.0 \text{ e.u./mol}$$

$$\Delta S^\circ_{vap} = 122 \text{ e.u./mol}$$

The standard entropy of vaporization can be estimated from

$$\Delta H^\circ_{vap} \,/\, T_b = \Delta S^\circ_{vap}$$

where $T_b$ = boiling point, since enthalpy and entropy changes do not vary much with temperature. Calculated in this manner, $\Delta S^\circ_{vap}$ is $(46.6 \times 10^3 \text{ J mol}^{-1})/373.8 \text{ K} = 125$ e.u./mol, so the estimation is a good one.

Trouton's rule predicts ∿90 e.u./mol for the entropy of vaporization. Since the value calculated from absolute entropies is significantly higher, it indicates that the liquid phase must be very highly structured. Examining the electronic structure of formic acid, we find

```
           _
           O|
          //
     H — C
          \
           O — H
           ‾
```

Hydrogen bonding would account for the extra order in liquid formic acid.

## SECTION 17-2: FREE ENERGY OF VAPORIZATION AND VAPOR PRESSURE

While $\Delta H^\circ_{vap}$ and $\Delta S^\circ_{vap}$ are relatively insensitive to temperature, the free energy of vaporization varies enormously because of the $T\Delta S$ term.

$$\Delta G^\circ_{vap} = \Delta H^\circ_{vap} - T\Delta S^\circ_{vap}$$

The chemical equation describing vaporization,

$$X(l) \rightleftharpoons X(g)$$

says that liquid $X$ is in equilibrium with gaseous $X$ and thus $\Delta G = 0$. When the vapor pressure ($p_v$) of $X$ is 1 atmosphere, then $\Delta G = \Delta G^\circ$ and the temperature of the system is called the normal, or sea-level, boiling point, $T_b$. The normal boiling point can be estimated from

$$T_b = \Delta H^\circ_{vap}/\Delta S^\circ_{vap}$$

To find the vapor pressure of a liquid at any temperature, use the general expression

$$\Delta G = \Delta G^\circ + RT \ln Q = \Delta G^\circ + RT \ln \frac{a_{(g)}}{a_{(l)}} = \Delta G^\circ + RT \ln \frac{p_{(g)}}{1}$$

Since vapor pressure is defined for equilibrium conditions, $\Delta G = 0$, $p_{(g)} = p_v$ and $\Delta G^\circ_{vap} = -RT \ln p_v$. Vapor pressure at any temperature can be calculated from $\Delta G^\circ_{vap}$. Conversely, the boiling point at any pressure can be obtained from this expression. Boiling occurs when vapor pressure equals atmospheric pressure.

Now we can predict whether condensation or evaporation will occur at a specified temperature, by comparing $Q$, or $p_{(g)}$ -- if the liquid phase is pure -- with $p_v$:

If $Q$ or $p_{(g)} > p_v$, net condensation occurs.

If $Q$ or $p_{(g)} < p_v$, net evaporation occurs.

If $Q = p_v$, there is equilibrium.

If $Q = p_v = 1$ atm, the system is at the normal boiling point.

Example 2

How can the relative humidity of the air be 100% if no rain is falling?

Solution: Relative humidity of the air is the ratio of the partial pressure of water vapor to the maximum partial pressure possible at a given temperature (the equilibrium vapor pressure), or $p_{(g)}/p_v$. At 100% humidity, $p_{(g)} = p_v$. For rain to fall, there must be net condensation. One way this happens is for the air temperature to drop slightly, decreasing $p_v$. Then, $p_{(g)} > p_v$ and some water vapor condenses to rain.

## SECTION 17-3: THE CRITICAL POINT

If a liquid in a closed container is heated, $p_v$ increases, increasing the density of the vapor. Simultaneously, the density of the remianing liquid decreases. At sufficiently high temperature -- the critical temperature -- the densities of gas and liquid become equal, and only one phase is present. There is no longer a gas-liquid boundary. Once a substance has reached its critical temperature, it cannot be liquified, no matter how much pressure is applied to it. The critical point for a substance is described by the critical temperature ($T_c$), pressure ($P_c$), and molar volume ($\overline{V}_c$). Another way to think about the critical point is that both liquid and gas exist, but they cannot be distinguished from one another.

## SECTION 17-4: PHASE DIAGRAMS

A phase diagram summarizes conditions of pressure and temperature for which a substance can exist in one phase -- solid, liquid, or gas -- or be in equilibrium with two or three phases. Phase diagrams of pure substances and mixtures are used extensively by such people as geologists, mechanical and structural engineers, and others who study materials in their day-to-day work.

Study Figures 17-6 and 17-7 carefully and note these features:

- lines separating the gas, liquid, and solid phases: two-phase equilibria exist at values of $T$ and $P$ on these lines;
- areas between the phase equilibria lines: a single phase, solid, liquid, or gas, exists in these regions;
- triple point: a unique $P$ and $T$ for a substance at which all three phases coexist in equilibrium;
- critical point: another unique point, at which liquid and gas are indistinguishable from one another;
- slope of the solid-liquid equilibrium line: positive slope indicates normal contraction of a substance upon freezing; negative slope, as for water and some metal alloys, indicates expansion of substance upon freezing (liquid is favored at high pressures, being more dense).

The Gibbs phase rule is useful for predicting the number of degrees of freedom, or independent variables such as $T$ and $P$, one has in a system under given conditions:

$$f = 2 + c - p$$

where

$f$ = number of degrees of freedom

$c$ = number of components in the system

$p$ = number of phases present

For a pure substance, $c = 1$. Along a phase equilibrium boundary, $p = 2$. Then, $f = 2 + 1 - 2 = 1$. That is, either temperature or pressure, but not both, may be independently varied. If both are changed independently, one of the phases will disappear, i.e., you have moved off the line and into a single-phase region of the diagram.

## SECTION 17-5: SOLUTIONS AND RAOULT'S LAW

The equilibrium vapor pressure of a liquid, which measures the tendency of molecules to escape into the gas phase, is decreased when a solute is dissolved in the liquid. It is the presence of solute itself, not its nature, which produces this phenomenon. In a pure liquid, call it $A$, all the molecules with sufficient kinetic energy to vaporize are $A$ molecules. In a solution of $A$, some of the molecules with that kinetic energy are $A$, while the rest are solute molecules or ions. Thus, the vapor pressure of *A* over the solution is less than it is over pure liquid *A*, at a given temperature.

For an ideal solution, this decrease in escaping tendency is expressed as Raoult's law,

$$p_A = X_A p_A^{\bullet},$$

where $p_A$ = vapor pressure of liquid *A* over a solution

$X_A$ = mole fraction of *A* in the liquid

$p_A^{\bullet}$ = vapor pressure over pure liquid *A*

An ideal solution is one in which intermolecular forces between all components are equal. In other words, in an ideal solution of substances *A* and *B*, the *A*-*A*, *A*-*B*, and *B*-*B* interactions are all equal. As you might suppose, not all substances form ideal solutions. In many instances, however, ideal behavior is approximated in very dilute solutions.

For an ideal solution of two volatile components, the total vapor pressure is given by

$$P_{total} = p_A + p_B = X_A p_A^{\bullet} + X_B p_B^{\bullet}$$

The mole fractions of *A* and *B* in the vapor can be calculated from Dalton's law of partial pressures:

$$X_{A,vap} = p_A / P_{total}$$

$$X_{B,vap} = p_B / P_{total} = 1 - X_{A,vap}$$

Calculate the mole fractions of *A* and *B* in the vapor, using your answer to problem 11 in the text. The interesting result forms the basis for fractional distillation, a method of separating mixtures of liquids.

Liquids which do not obey Raoult's law exhibit positive or negative deviations from ideality. If *A* and *B* attract each other more than molecules of their own kind, such as ethanol and water do, the deviation is negative, as illustrated in Figure 17-10. Other indicators of this kind of nonideality are an exothermic heat of mixing and volume shrinkage when the liquids are mixed. Liquids which repel each other when mixed exhibit positive deviation from Raoult's law, as shown in Figure 17-9. Ideal behavior, which follows Raoult's law exactly at all concentrations, is plotted in Figure 17-8.

## SECTION 17-6: COLLIGATIVE PROPERTIES

Colligative properties of dilute solutions are those which depend on the number of nonvolatile solute particles but not on their nature. We are all familiar with at least one of them, freezing-point depression, because it is applied to formulating antifreeze for automobile radiators. The other three are vapor-pressure lowering, boiling-point elevation, and osmotic pressure. In research laboratories the colligative properties are used for determining molecular weights.

The vapor pressure of a solvent is lowered by the presence of a nonvolatile solute because the molecules that have sufficient kinetic energy to escape into the gas phase are a mixture of solvent and solute. Hence, the number of energetic solvent molecules is less, relative to pure solvent at the same temperature. One speaks of the free energy, or escaping tendency, of the solvent being lowered by the presence of solute. The vapor pressure of solvent is given by Raoult's law,

$$p_B = X_B p_B^{\bullet}$$

and vapor-pressure lowering, $p_B^{\bullet} - p_B$, is expressed as

$$\Delta p = X_A p_B^{\bullet}$$

Boiling-point elevation is a consequence of vapor-pressure lowering. Figure 17-12, a plot of equilibrium vapor pressure as a function of temperature for a pure liquid and a solution of the liquid, illustrates the phenomenon. For dilute solutions, the difference in boiling points of pure solvent and solution is given by

$$\Delta T_b = k_b m_A$$

where $k_b$ = boiling-point elevation constant of the solvent

$m_A$ = total concentration of solute particles, expressed as molality

The boiling-point elevation constant, $k_b$, depends only on the nature of the solvent and has nothing to do with the nature of the solute.

The overall physical effect of a nonvolatile solute is to extend the liquid range of the solvent. Just as the escaping tendency of solvent molecules from liquid to vapor is lowered by the solute, so also is the escaping tendency from liquid to solid. The solid-liquid equilibrium at a given temperature is perturbed by the presence of solute because, while the number of molecules of sufficiently low energy to crystallize remains the same, not all of these molecules are solvent. The result is a shift of equilibrium toward the liquid phase, or net melting.

Example 3

At what temperature will aqueous antifreeze that is 20% ethylene glycol by weight begin to freeze?

Solution: An approximate freezing point can be calculated using the formula

$$\Delta T_f = -k_f m$$

A 20% solution is not dilute, to be sure, but a more accurate value would require having an experimentally obtained plot of freezing point as a function of composition of glycol-water mixtures.

Before the relationship above can be used, weight percent glycol must be converted to molality. Recall that

$$m = \frac{\text{moles solute}}{\text{kilograms of solvent}}$$

Moles of solute can be calculated from the mass of solute and molecular weight. The mass of the solvent can be obtained by arbitrarily choosing some quantity of solution and then recognizing that 100% - 20% = 80% of it is solvent, since the system has only two components. Taking 100 g of solution,

mass solute = (0.20)(100 g) = 20 g

mass solvent = (0.80)(100 g) = 80 g

moles solute = 20 g/MW glycol

moles solute = 20 g/62.07 g $mol^{-1}$ = 0.32 mol

molality = 0.32 mol/0.080 kg = 4.0 m

Now the freezing point can be calculated.

$\Delta T_f = -k_f m = -(1.86 \text{ deg/molal})(4.0 \text{ m}) = -7.4°$

The freezing-point lowering is -7.4°. The freezing point of this solution is found by adding $\Delta T_f$ to the freezing point of pure water, 0.00°C. Thus, $T_f$ for the solution is -7.4°C.

When a concentration gradient, or difference, across a semipermeable membrane exists, osmosis of solvent takes place until the concentrations on both sides of the membrane are equal. Osmotic pressure is the pressure on the solution which will prevent osmosis. Trees use osmotic pressure to pump sap to their uppermost branches. Reverse-osmosis processes, in which water is pumped out of a solution, are used to purify water and, recently, to make maple syrup.

Osmotic pressure is a particularly useful technique for measuring molecular weights of macromolecules, because large pressures are produced by very dilute solutions. Large effects are generally easier to measure accurately than are small ones, a fact that must be borne in mind when designing experiments.

The osmotic pressure expression,

$$\pi V = nRT$$

can be rearranged to include the molecular weight of the solvent explicitly:

$$\pi V = \frac{\text{mass}}{\text{MW}} RT \qquad \text{or} \qquad \text{MW} = \frac{(\text{mass})RT}{\pi V}$$

Example 4

A 0.250 g sample of a biological material, when dissolved in 100.0 mL of water at 25°C, produces an osmotic pressure of 129 torr. What is the molecular weight of this compound?

Solution: Molecular weight can be obtained using the expression above. Note that it contains $R$, the gas constant, which determines permissable units for $\pi$, $V$, and $T$ of atmospheres, liters, and kelvin, respectively.

$$\text{MW} = \frac{(0.250 \text{ g})(0.08206 \text{ L}\cdot\text{atm/mol}\cdot\text{K})(298 \text{ K})(760 \text{ torr/atm})}{(129 \text{ torr})(0.1000 \text{ L})}$$

$$\text{MW} = 360 \text{ g/mol}$$

## Terms to Know

boiling point
boiling-point elevation
colligative properties
critical point
critical pressure

critical temperature
equilibrium vapor pressure
freezing-point depression
fusion
heat of fusion
heat of sublimation
heat of vaporization
ideal solution
negative deviation from ideality
normal boiling point
osmotic pressure
phase diagram
phase rule
positive deviation from ideality
Raoult's law
sublimation
triple point
Trouton's rule
vapor-pressure lowering

## Test Yourself

1. Calculate the enthalpy, entropy, and free energy of vaporization of bromine molecules at 298 K, using data from Appendix 2. Calculate the normal boiling point and compare it to the true boiling point, listed in the Handbook of Chemistry and Physics. What is the percent error?

2. Calculate the enthalpy, entropy, and free energy of vaporization of ethanol, $CH_3CH_2OH$, at 298 K, using data from Appendix 2. Calculate the vapor pressure of ethanol at 298 K. The true normal boiling point of ethanol is 78.5°C. Does ethanol obey Trouton's rule? Give a molecular interpretation of your answer.

3. Sketch a pressure-temperature phase diagram for tetrafluorosilane, $SiF_4$. The normal boiling point is -86°C, the melting point is -90.2°C, and the critical point is -14.06°C, 36.7 atm. Predict whether $SiF_4$ will expand or contract upon freezing and use your prediction in the diagram.

4. The vapor pressures of water and ethanol at 25°C are 23.6 torr and 54.2 torr, respectively. What is the total vapor pressure above a solution that is 40% ethanol by weight? What is the mole fraction of ethanol in the vapor?

5. Arrange the following aqueous solutions in order of decreasing freezing point: 0.2 m $BaCl_2$, 0.1 m galactose ($C_6H_{12}O_6$), and 0.1 m $Cr(NO_3)_3$. Assume complete dissociation of ionic compounds.

6. The boiling point of a solution prepared from 12.884 g of a compound of unknown molecular weight dissolved in 100.0 mL of chloroform is 62.5°C. What is the molecular weight of the compound? The density of chloroform is 1.4832 g/cm$^3$ at 20°C.

7. What concentration of nutrients in sap is necessary to drive the sap to the top of a 30-ft oak tree by osmotic pressure at 20°C? Take the density of sap to be 1.00 g/cm$^3$. (Hint: One atmosphere pressure = 76.0 cm of mercury. The density of mercury is 13.6 g/cm$^3$.)

8. How many degrees of freedom does water have at 75°C and 1 atm pressure?

9. Calculate the weight percent of ethylene glycol, $C_2H_6O_2$, in an antifreeze solution that will protect an automobile from freezing at temperatures above -10°F.

10. The vapor pressure of carbon tetrachloride is 100.0 mm Hg at 23°C. What mass of iodine must be dissolved in 500 mL of $CCl_4$ to lower its vapor pressure to 75.0 torr? The density of $CCl_4$ is 1.5940 g/cm$^3$.

11. Use your results from question 4 to suggest a method of separating ethanol and water from mixtures of the two.

# 18 Oxidation-Reduction Equilibria and Electrochemistry

## CHAPTER OVERVIEW AND OBJECTIVES

Harnessing electron-transfer, or redox, reactions to do useful work and using electrical energy to drive desirable, but nonspontaneous, reactions are the main topics of this chapter. You may want to review portions of Chapters 14 and 15, because electrochemistry is a form of applied thermodynamics.

When you finish this chapter you should be able to:

1. Relate maximum useful work available from a chemical process to free energy and cell potential;

2. Design an electrochemical cell, given the cell reaction;

3. Deduce the cell reaction and potential, given the design of a cell;

4. Use shorthand cell notation;

5. Predict the direction of spontaneous cell reaction, given the oxidation and reduction half-cells;

6. Calculate the potential of a half-reaction by manipulating related half-reactions and their potentials;

7. Calculate half-cell and cell potentials under nonstandard conditions;

8. Describe some corrosion processes and some methods for combatting corrosion.

## SECTION 18-1: HARNESSING SPONTANEOUS REACTIONS

In Chapter 15 we saw that the maximum amount of useful work that can be obtained from a process is given by its free energy change. Read the portion of section 15-5 headed "Free Energy Changes When External Work is Done" to refresh your memory. One method for utilizing free energy to do useful, or external, work is to adapt the process to an electrochemical cell. This is analogous to using falling water to generate electricity by driving a turbine, rather than allowing it to fall freely.

The simplest type of voltage-generating electrochemical cell is a concentration cell. Instead of allowing two solutions of different concentrations to mix spontaneously, they are placed in an apparatus such as that depicted in Figure 18-3. The maximum free energy obtainable from such a cell is

$$\Delta G = \Delta G^\circ + RT \ln(c_2/c_1)$$

Example 1

A concentration cell is designed using nickel electrodes and $Ni^{2+}$ solutions of 1.0 M and $1.0 \times 10^{-3}$ M.

a. Identify the anode and cathode of this cell, and calculate free energy available from it at 25°C.

Solution: The overall cell reaction is

$$Ni^{2+}(1.0\ M) \rightleftharpoons Ni^{2+}(1.0 \times 10^{-3}\ M)$$

The reaction proceeds so as to equalize the concentration of $Ni^{2+}$ in the two compartments. Thus, $Ni^{2+}$ is reduced in one, and Ni is oxidized in the other. The cathode is the electrode at which reduction takes place; oxidation occurs at the anode. The reactions are

cathode: $Ni^{2+}(1.0\ M) + 2\bar{e} \longrightarrow Ni(s)$

anode: $Ni(s) \longrightarrow Ni^{2+}(1.0 \times 10^{-3}\ M) + 2\bar{e}$

The free energy change for the cell is

$$\Delta G = RT\ \ln(1.0 \times 10^{-3}/1.0)$$

$$\Delta G = (8.314\ J\ mol^{-1}\ K^{-1})(298)(2.303)\log 10^{-3}$$

$$\Delta G = (8.314)(298)(2.303)(-3)\ J\ mol^{-1} = -17.1\ kJ\ mol^{-1}$$

As the reaction proceeds, the free energy will decrease until it is zero when the concentrations become equal. Then the cell is at equilibrium and has run down.

b. How could this cell be modified to make more free energy available?

Solution: Look at the free-energy calculation above. Notice that the only variable is the log of the concentration ratio. Thus, the larger the concentration differential, the larger the free-energy change will be. Make the dilute solution more so.

## SECTION 18-2: ELECTROCHEMICAL CELLS--GALVANIC

Galvanic cells are those that produce electrical energy from spontaneous processes. Several of these cells connected together make a battery. On the other hand, electrolytic cells use externally supplied electrical energy to drive chemical reactions to make desired products, such as aluminum or chlorine. Several types of galvanic cells are described in this section. They have these features in common:

- the overall cell reaction is spontaneous, so free energy is released;
- the two half-reactions are physically separated: electrons must be transferred through an external wire and ions may pass through a salt bridge or some other interface to maintain electrical neutrality;
- potentials, $E$, for galvanic cells are positive, because the reactions are spontaneous.

Note that potential, $E$, is designated as $E^0$ when all reactants and products are in their standard states. You may want to review standard states of materials in Chapter 14. Solute concentrations must be 1 M and gas pressures, 1 atm.

Note also that potentials may be added just as reactions are, as long as their sum isn't a half-reaction.

## SECTION 18-3: ELECTROCHEMICAL CELLS--ELECTROLYTIC

These cells produce materials by using electricity to drive a nonspontaneous chemical process. Faraday's laws of electrolysis state the quantitative relationship between the amount of electricity provided to the cell and the amount of product liberated at an electrode. They are

1. The mass of a material produced at an electrode is proportional to the quantity of electricity that has passed through the cell.

2. For each mole of electrons lost or gained as a result of an electrolysis reaction, 96,485 coulombs of electricity must be supplied.

One faraday, $\mathcal{F}$, of electricity is 96,485 coulombs and equals the charge on one mole of electrons.

### Example 2

Aqueous $NiSO_4$ is to be electrolyzed to produce nickel metal. How long must a current of 20,000 amperes be passed through the solution to plate out one kilogram of nickel?

Given: $NiSO_4$ to produce 1 kg Ni(*s*)
$i$ = 20,000 amperes

Find: time required

Solution: Start by writing the half-reaction for the reduction of $Ni^{2+}$:

$$Ni^{2+}(aq) + 2\bar{e} \longrightarrow Ni(s)$$

This tells us that two electrons per $Ni^{2+}$, or $2\mathcal{F}$ per mole $Ni^{2+}$, are required. The time required to carry out this reduction reaction depends on the current available and the charge required, or

$$q = it$$

where

$q$ = charge (coulombs)

$i$ = current (amperes, A)

$t$ = time (seconds)

Current, $i$, is given, but charge, $q$, must be calculated first.

$$q = \frac{2\mathcal{F}}{\text{mol Ni}} \times \frac{1\text{ kg Ni}}{58.70\text{ g mol}^{-1}} \times \frac{10^3\text{ g}}{\text{kg}} \times \frac{96{,}485\text{ coul}}{\mathcal{F}}$$

$$q = 3.287 \times 10^6\text{ coulombs}$$

Time can now be calculated:

$$t = q/i$$

$$t = 3.287 \times 10^6 \text{ coul}/20{,}000\text{A} = 1.64 \times 10^2 \text{ s, or } 2.73 \text{ min}$$

## SECTION 18-4: CELL emf AND FREE ENERGY

The free energy, or maximum useful work, available from a spontaneous reaction is related to cell potential, $E$, as follows:

$$\Delta G = -nFE = -w_{ext}$$

where $n$ = number of moles of electrons transferred in the cell reaction. The units of $E$ are volts; for $F$, they are coulombs/mol; and for $\Delta G$, they are joules. One joule equals one volt · coulomb.

### Example 3

Calculate the standard free-energy change for a cell whose reaction is

$$Cu(s) + 2Ag^+(aq) \longrightarrow Cu^{2+}(aq) + 2Ag(s)$$

All materials in the cell are in their standard states. The cell potential is 0.46 V.

Solution: Free energy is calculated directly from cell potential:

$$\Delta G = -nFE$$

Dividing the equation into half-reactions gives

$$Ag^+(aq) + \bar{e} \longrightarrow Ag(s) \qquad \text{(cathode)}$$

$$Cu(s) \longrightarrow Cu^{2+} + 2\bar{e} \qquad \text{(anode)}$$

For each half-reaction, you can write

$$\Delta G_{cathode} = -nFE_{cathode}$$

$$\Delta G_{anode} = -nFE_{anode}$$

Before the half-reactions and their corresponding free energies can be added together, the cathode reaction must be doubled in order to balance electrons. This will double $\Delta G$ as well, by doubling $n$. $E_{cathode}$ remains the same. Its value is characteristic of the half-cell, not of how large the half-cell is. Thus, $n = 2$ for the overall reaction.

$$\Delta G = -(2 \text{ mol})(96{,}485 \text{ coul/mol})(0.46 \text{ V})$$

$$\Delta G = -89 \text{ kJ}$$

Note that this sizeable free-energy change corresponds to a cell potential of only half a volt.

## SECTION 18-5: HALF-REACTIONS AND REDUCTION POTENTIALS

Potentials for half-reactions are evaluated by constructing a cell in which one electrode is a standard hydrogen electrode,

$$H_2(g) \longrightarrow 2H^+(aq) + 2\bar{e}$$

and the other is the electrode for the half-reaction of interest. The potential for the standard hydrogen electrode has been arbitrarily designated as zero volts. The potential for the entire cell is then assigned to the other half-reaction. The reason for doing this is that a half-reaction cannot run by itself, so half-cell potentials can't be measured directly.

Using the standard hydrogen electrode as a reference point for all other half-cell potentials is similar to using carbon-12 as the reference point for the atomic weight scale. It, too, is a relative scale.

The half-reactions and their standard electrode potentials listed in Tables 18-2 and 18-3 can be used in a variety of ways. Note that, by convention, they are all written as reductions. The sign of $E°$ indicates whether reduction is favored. Positive $E°$ values indicate that reduction is spontaneous when coupled with the oxidation of hydrogen. Conversely, negative $E°$ values signal that the reverse reaction, oxidation, is favored.

Example 4

Choose three good reducing agents and three good oxidizing agents from the list in Table 18-2.

Solution: Recall that a good oxidizing agent is easily reduced, and that a good reducing agent is easily oxidized. Thus, the best oxidizing agents should have large positive $E°$ values. Examples are $F_2(g)$, $H_2O_2$ in acidic solution, and $MnO_4^-$ in acidic solution. Conversely, excellent reducing agents are expected to have large negative $E°$ values. Such materials are the alkali and alkaline earth metals, hydride ion ($H^-$), and aluminum metal.

Standard electrode potentials can also be used to predict in which direction a cell will run spontaneously, whether a given reaction is spontaneous, the standard free energy of a reaction, and equilibrium constants. The following examples illustrate the great utility of electrode potentials.

Example 5

Given the reaction

$$Cd^{2+}(aq) + Ni(s) \longrightarrow Cd(s) + Ni^{2+}(aq)$$

a. Calculate the standard potential, $E°$.

Solution: Divide the reaction into half-reactions:

$$Cd^{2+} + 2\bar{e} \longrightarrow Cd \qquad \text{(reduction)}$$

$$Ni \longrightarrow Ni^{2+} + 2\bar{e} \qquad \text{(oxidation)}$$

Now consult Table 18-2 for the half-cell potentials. The sign of $E°$ for the oxidation half-reaction will be opposite to that listed in the table, since the tabulated values all correspond to reductions.

$$Cd^{2+} + 2\bar{e} \longrightarrow Cd \qquad E° = -0.40\ V$$

$$Ni \longrightarrow Ni^{2+} + 2\bar{e} \qquad E° = +0.23\ V$$

Adding the half-cell potentials gives $E°$ for the cell, -0.17 V.

b. Is the reaction spontaneous?

Solution: Under standard conditions the reaction is not spontaneous, because $E°$ is negative. The reaction will run spontaneously in the opposite direction, however.

c. If a cell were constructed from a Cd electrode in 1 M $CdSO_4$ and a Ni electrode in 1 M $NiSO_4$, which electrode would be the cathode? Write the shorthand notation for this cell.

Solution: We know from our calculation in part a that the spontaneous cell reaction is

$$Ni^{2+}(aq) + Cd(s) \longrightarrow Ni(s) + Cd^{2+}$$

Thus, the cathode reaction is

$$Ni^{2+}(aq) + 2\bar{e} \longrightarrow Ni(s)$$

Using shorthand notation one writes the cathode on the right:

$$Cd \mid Cd^{2+}(1\ M) \parallel Ni^{2+}(1\ M) \mid Ni$$

d. What is the equilibrium constant for this reaction?

Solution: We know that

$$\Delta G° = -RT \ln K = -n\mathcal{F}E°$$

Thus,

$$\ln K = \frac{n\mathcal{F}E°}{RT}$$

$$\log K = \frac{(2\ mol)(96{,}485\ coul/mol)(0.17\ V)}{(2.303)(8.314\ J\ mol^{-1}\ K^{-1})(298\ K)}$$

Since $E°$ is the standard potential, $T$ is 298 K, the temperature at which $E°$ is defined.

$$\log K = 5.749$$

$$K = 5.6 \times 10^5$$

Example 6

What is the standard potential for the cell

$$Al \mid Al^{3+}(1\ M) \parallel Sn^{2+}(1\ M) \mid Sn \qquad ?$$

The half-cell reactions are

anode: $Al(s) \longrightarrow Al^{3+}(aq) + 3\bar{e}$ $E° = 1.71$ V

cathode: $Sn^{2+}(aq) + 2\bar{e} \longrightarrow Sn(s)$ $E° = -0.14$ V

(Remember to reverse the sign of the tabulated $E°$ value for oxidation reactions.)

Solution: To get the overall cell reaction, we must first balance electrons by doubling the anode reaction and tripling the cathode one. This is equivalent to changing $n$, and thus $\Delta G$, in the expressions

$$\Delta G_{anode} = -nFE°_{anode}$$

$$\Delta G_{cathode} = -nFE°_{cathode}$$

The $E°$ values are not multiplied by the factors used to balance the electrons; $n$ values are changed, $E°$ values remain the same, characteristic of their half-cells. The overall cell reaction is thus

$$2Al(s) + 3Sn^{2+}(aq) \longrightarrow 2Al^{3+}(aq) + 3Sn(s)$$

and

$$E° = 1.71 \text{ V} + (-0.14 \text{ V}) = 1.57 \text{ V}$$

Verify, using $\Delta G° = -nFE°$.

$$\Delta G°_{cell} = 2(\Delta G°)_{anode\ reaction} + 3(\Delta G°)_{cathode\ reaction}$$

$$\Delta G°_{cell} = 2(-3FE°_{anode}) + 3(-2FE°_{cathode})$$

$$-6FE°_{cell} = -6F(E°_{anode} + E°_{cathode})$$

$$E°_{cell} = E°_{anode} + E°_{cathode}$$

Example 7

Given the standard potentials

(1) $Sn^{2+} + 2\bar{e} \longrightarrow Sn$ $E° = -0.14$ V

(2) $Sn^{4+} + 2\bar{e} \longrightarrow Sn^{2+}$ $E° = 0.15$ V

calculate the standard electrode potential for

(3) $Sn^{4+} + 4\bar{e} \longrightarrow Sn$

Solution: Half-cell potentials can be directly added together only for combinations of oxidation and reduction half-reactions. Otherwise, the free-energy route is the only safe one to take. Thus,

$$\Delta G°(3) = \Delta G°(1) + \Delta G°(2)$$

$$\Delta G°(3) = -2F(-0.14) - 2F(0.15)$$

$$\Delta G°(3) = -2F(0.15 - 0.14) = -2F(0.01)$$

$$-4FE°(3) = -2F(0.01)$$

$$E°(3) = 0.01/2 = 0.005 \text{ V}$$

Compare this with what we would have obtained by adding $E°(1)$ with $E°(2)$ directly, just as reactions (1) and (2) add to give reaction (3):

$$-0.14 \text{ V} + 0.15 \text{ V} = 0.01 \text{ V}$$

This does not agree with the answer obtained from free energies. You can check this by calculating the numerical values of the three free energies, and then calculating $E°(3)$ from $\Delta G°(3)$.

## SECTION 18-6: THE EFFECT OF CONCENTRATION ON CELL VOLTAGE: THE NERNST EQUATION

Because free energy varies with concentration, cell potential varies as well. The general free-energy relationship

$$\Delta G = \Delta G° + 2.303\ RT \log Q$$

becomes

$$-nFE = -nFE° + 2.303\ RT \log Q$$

or

$$E = E° - \frac{2.303\ RT}{nF} \log Q, \text{ the Nernst equation.}$$

This equation is useful for calculating cell potentials and electrode potentials for conditions other than standard, and for determining how concentrations in a cell should be adjusted to obtain maximum voltage from the cell.

Example 8

Calculate the potential at 298 K for the cell

$$Al \mid Al^{3+}(0.01\ M) \mid\mid Sn^{2+}(1\ M) \mid Sn$$

Solution: This is similar to the cell in Example 6, for which $E° = 1.57$ V and $n = 6$. The cell reaction is

$$2Al(s) + 3Sn^{2+}(aq) \longrightarrow 2Al^{3+}(aq) + 3Sn(s)$$

$$E = E° - \frac{2.303\ RT}{nF} \log Q$$

at 298 K, $2.303\ RT/F = 0.0592$ V·mol

$$E = 1.57 \text{ V} - \frac{0.0592}{6} \log \frac{[Al^{3+}]^2}{[Sn^{2+}]^3}$$

$$E = 1.57 \text{ V} - \frac{0.0592}{6} \log \frac{(0.01)^2}{1}$$

$$E = 1.57 \text{ V} - \frac{0.0592}{6} \log 10^{-4} = 1.57 \text{ V} - \frac{0.0592}{6} (-4) \text{ V}$$

$$E = 1.57 \text{ V} + 0.039 \text{ V} = 1.61 \text{ V}$$

Thus the cell potential is increased by having less product ($Al^{3+}$) present than reactant ($Sn^{2+}$), i.e., $Q < 1$.

If no product were present, one might think that cell potential would be maximized. This is not practical, however, because there would be no ions in the anode compartment to conduct current. Some $Al^{3+}$ ions are needed.

Conversely, as product concentration builds up, $Q$ becomes larger, log $Q$ becomes positive, and the potential decreases. Eventually the cell runs down, and $E = 0$, the condition of equilibrium.

Example 9

Calculate the potential for the half-cell

$$Sn^{2+}(10^{-4}M) + 2\bar{e} \longrightarrow Sn$$

Solution: The Nernst equation is also applicable to half-reactions.

$$E = -0.14 - \frac{0.0592}{2} \log \frac{1}{[Sn^{2+}]} = -0.14 - \frac{0.0592}{2} \log \frac{1}{10^{-4}}$$

$$E = -0.14 - \frac{0.0592}{2} (+4) = -0.14 - 0.1184$$

$$E = -0.25 \text{ V}$$

As the concentration of $Sn^{2+}$, the reactant, increases, potential drops.

## SECTION 18-7: SOLUBILITY EQUILIBRIA AND POTENTIALS

Electrochemical cells offer an extremely convenient method for determining solubility product constants, because accurately measured voltages can be obtained for extremely small concentrations. Cells are also useful for studying equilibria involving complex ions.

Example 10

Calculate $K_{sp}$ for $Cr(OH)_3$.

Solution: The overall cell reaction is just the dissociation of $Cr(OH)_3$ into ions:

$$Cr(OH)_3(s) \rightleftharpoons Cr^{3+}(aq) + 3OH^-(aq)$$

This can be separated into half-reactions:

$$Cr(OH)_3 + 3\bar{e} \longrightarrow Cr + 3OH^- \qquad E° = -1.3 \text{ V}$$

$$Cr \longrightarrow Cr^{3+} + 3\bar{e} \qquad E° = 0.74 \text{ V}$$

$E°$ for the cell is $(-1.3 + 0.74)$ V = $-0.6$ V.

At equilibrium $E = 0$, $Q = K$, and the Nernst equation becomes

$$E° = \frac{0.0592}{n} \log K$$

$$-0.6 = \frac{0.0592}{3} \log K$$

$$\log K = -(0.6)(3)/(0.0592) = -30.405 = 0.595 - 31$$

$$K = 4 \times 10^{-31}$$

## SECTION 18-8: REDOX CHEMISTRY GONE ASTRAY: CORROSION

Practical application of redox chemistry is the topic of this section. Cell potentials predict what can and cannot happen chemically. They say nothing about rates. If an undesirable reaction, such as corrosion, can be predicted, steps can be taken to prevent it from occurring or at least to slow it down.

Corrosion can be slowed by surface coating, a familiar technique. In some cases, it can be prevented by coupling one of the corrosion half-reactions with a different half-reaction. The use of a sacrificial anode is an example of this approach.

### Terms to Know

anode
battery
cathode
concentration cell
corrosion
electrochemical cell
electrolytic cell
electromotive force
faraday
Faraday's laws of electrolysis
galvanic cell
Nernst equation
reduction potential
sacrificial metal
standard hydrogen electrode
standard potential

### Test Yourself

1. Which pairs of substances will react together in a redox process?

   a. $F_2(g) + Cl^-(aq)$

   b. $Br_2(l) + Cl^-(aq)$

   c. $Cl_2(g) + I^-(aq)$

   d. $I_2(s) + Br^-(aq)$

   e. $I_2(s) + F^-(aq)$

2. Design an electrochemical cell which runs by the process

$$3Cu(s) + 8HNO_3(aq) \longrightarrow 3Cu(NO_3)_2(aq) + 2NO(g) + 4H_2O(l)$$

Write shorthand notation for the cell and calculate $E°$ at 298 K.

3. An electrochemical cell is constructed from the following half-cells:

$$MnO_2(s) + 4H^+(aq) + 2\bar{e} \longrightarrow Mn^{2+}(aq) + 2H_2O(l)$$

$$Cl_2(g) + 2\bar{e} \longrightarrow 2Cl^-(aq)$$

Calculate $E°$ for the cell, write the spontaneous cell reaction, and make a drawing of the cell in operation. The drawing should include the type of electrodes used, identity of anode and cathode, direction of electron flow, direction of ion movement, and products formed at each electrode.

4. Elemental bromine is prepared by the electrolysis of natural brines, e.g., $NaBr(aq)$. How many kilograms of liquid bromine can be produced by electrolyzing a solution of sodium bromide for 8.0 hours at a current of 5000 amperes?

5. An automobile bumper is to be plated with chromium. How long must a solution of $Cr^{3+}(aq)$ be electrolyzed at 500 amps to plate out one-half pound (227 g) of chromium metal?

6. Design a cell to measure the solubility product for $Ag_2CrO_4$ and calculate $K_{sp}$ at 25°C. The standard potential for the half-cell

$$Ag_2CrO_4 + 2\bar{e} \longrightarrow 2Ag + CrO_4^-$$

is 0.4463 volt.

7. Calculate the standard potential for the reaction between aluminum metal and water. The standard potential for the reduction of water

$$2H_2O + 2\bar{e} \longrightarrow H_2 + 2OH^-$$

is -0.8277 volt. Explain why unpainted aluminum canoes don't dissolve in lakes and rivers.

8. What is $E$ at 25°C for the cell

$$Cd \mid CdSO_4(0.75\ M) \parallel NiSO_4(1.5\ M) \mid Ni \qquad ?$$

9. Calculate the electrode potential for the half-cell

$$Au \mid AuCl_4^-(0.10\ M),\ Cl^-(2\ M)$$

10. Consider a copper-silver cell:

$$Cu \mid CuSO_4(aq) \parallel AgNO_3(aq) \mid Ag$$

a. Calculate $E°$ for the cell.

b. How could conditions in the cell be changed to increase the potential above $E°$?

c. As the cell generates electricity, how does $E°$ change? How do the concentrations of $Cu^{2+}$ and $Ag^{+}$ change? How do the masses of the electrodes change?

d. When the cell runs down, and $E = 0$, what will be the relative concentrations of $Ag^{+}$ and $Cu^{2+}$?

# 19 Coordination Chemistry

## CHAPTER OVERVIEW AND OBJECTIVES

The chemistry of transition metals functioning as Lewis acids is the topic of this chapter. Transition-metal complexes are frequently brightly colored and can have unusual structures. They are interesting in and of themselves, but also because they are a prominent feature of biological systems.

When you finish this chapter you should be able to:

1. Relate experimental observations to properties of complexes such as color, isomerism, magnetism, lability, and oxidation number of the metal;

2. Given the formula of a complex,

   o name it
   o predict its structure
   o predict the number and types of isomers it has
   o write the electronic configuration if it is octahedral, tetrahedral, or square-planar
   o predict the number of unpaired electrons
   o predict the relative energy of radiation required to cause electronic transitions in the complex, which is related to color;

3. Compare and evaluate four theories of bonding in transition-metal complexes: simple electrostatic, valence bond, crystal field, and ligand field;

4. Do equilibrium calculations using formation constants of complexes, alone and in combination with other equilibria.

## SECTION 19-1: PROPERTIES OF TRANSITION-METAL COMPLEXES

Coordination compounds are so named because the bonds between the central atom and the ligands are coordinate covalent ones. Both electrons in such a bond originally come from the ligand, which is a Lewis base. Transition-metal complexes, then, are Lewis acid-base adducts. This first section is a survey of six characteristic properties of complexes: color, geometry and isomerism, magnetism, lability and inertness, structure related to oxidation number, and number of *d* electrons. Some important features of each of these properties are summarized here. The text provides more details and examples.

Color of transition-metal complexes varies in both hue and intensity. The most intense colors usually are observed when the metal atom is in a high oxidation state, although there are some notable exceptions. High intensity, whatever the oxidation state of the metal, comes from charge transfer between ligand and metal; ligand electrons are transferred to empty metal orbitals. Colors arising from other types of electronic transitions are much less intense. Metal-ligand interactions, not the metal itself, produce color. The observed hue is the complement of the one that is absorbed.

Example 1

Aqueous solutions of $Ni^{2+}$ are green. Adding ammonia changes the color to dark blue, and then adding dimethylglyoxime (DMG, $C_4H_8N_2O_2$) produces a strawberry-red precipitate. Which colors are absorbed by the complexes in these mixtures?

Solution: The complement of green is purple-red, the color absorbed by $[Ni(H_2O)_6]^{2+}$. Blue is complemented by orange, which is the light absorbed by $[Ni(NH_3)_6]^{2+}$. The complex $[Ni(DMG)_2]^0$, which is a strawberry-red solid, absorbs blue-green. Colors and their complements are listed in Table 19-3.

The most common coordination numbers in transition-metal complexes are 6 and 4. Two geometries are possible for CN = 4, square planar and tetrahedral. A tetrahedral molecule can have no geometrical, or cis-trans, isomers, but square-planar and octahedral ones can. Structure can often be inferred from the existence of isomers.

Example 2

Draw all geometrical isomers for $[Ni(NH_3)_4(H_2O)_4]^{2+}$.

Solution: The coordination number of nickel is 6, so the geometry is approximately octahedral. Two isomers, cis and trans, are possible:

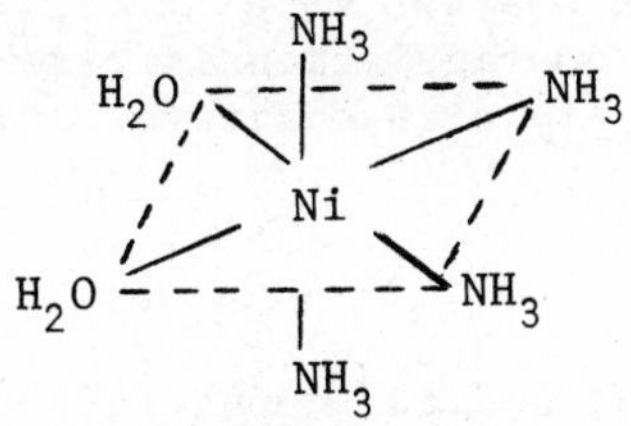

$NH_3$ / $H_2O$, $NH_3$ / Ni / $H_2O$, $NH_3$ / $NH_3$

cis

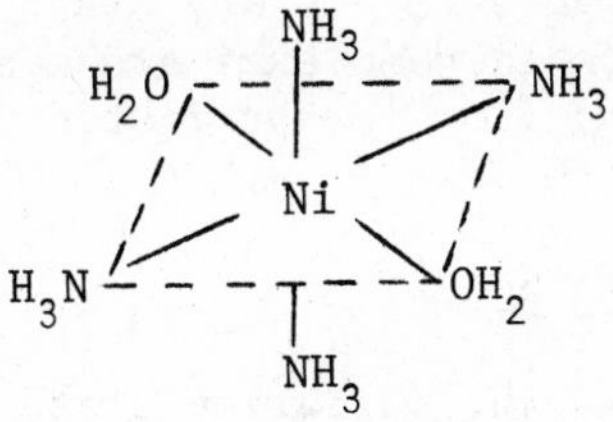

$NH_3$ / $H_2O$, $NH_3$ / Ni / $H_3N$, $OH_2$ / $NH_3$

trans

Note: The trans isomer above is the same as this one, but has a different orientation:

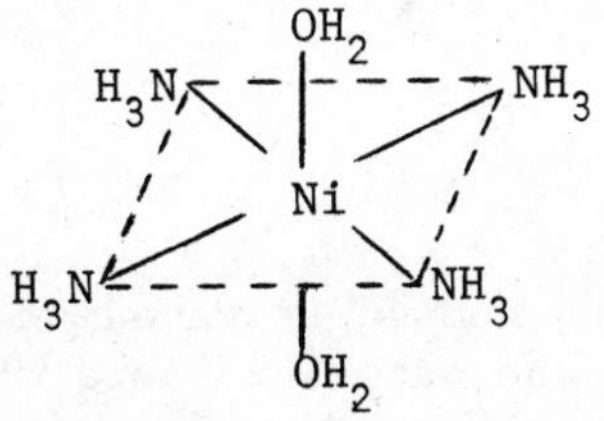

$OH_2$ / $H_3N$, $NH_3$ / Ni / $H_3N$, $NH_3$ / $OH_2$

To get from one drawing to the other, rotate the first trans figure 90°, so that the back left $H_2O$ moves to the top, and the front right $H_2O$ moves to the bottom of the octahedron:

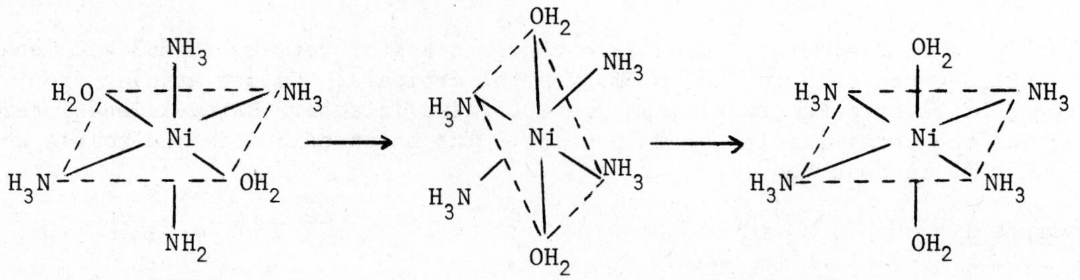

Magnetism, or its absence, in transition-metal complexes gives clues to electronic configuration in the ion. All electrons are paired in diamagnetic materials. The number of unpaired electrons in a paramagnetic substance can be determined by measuring the magnetic moment of the compound. The relationship between magnetic properties, electronic configuration, and structure is discussed in section 3 of this chapter.

Complexes which readily exchange ligands are labile; those which do not are inert. These terms should not be confused with thermodynamic stability and instability. Tripositive cations with three or six *d* electrons, such as $Co^{3+}$ and $Cr^{3+}$, are especially inert.

The oxidation state of the metal atom correlates with coordination number. The majority of complexes of +2 and +3 metal ions are six-coordinate, although there are many examples of coordination numbers 4 and 5. Unipositive ions usually exhibit coordination number 2, unless the ligand can form $\pi$ as well as $\sigma$ bonds, as do $CN^-$ and CO. Higher oxidation states are found in complexes with $O^{2-}$ and $F^-$ ligands, such as $SO_4^{2-}$, $ReO_4^-$, $NiF_6^{3-}$ and $AgF_4^-$.

Just as chemical behavior in general is organized around valence electronic configuration, the chemistry of the transition metals is intimately tied to the number of their *d* electrons. Metal ions of oxidation state +2 and +3, and valence configuration $d^0$, $d^5$, and $d^{10}$, are most favored. Configuration $d^0$, a noble-gas configuration, is achieved by free +3 ions such as $Y^{3+}$ and oxo ions in which the oxidation state of the metal is very high, such as $WO_4^{2-}$. Filled ($d^{10}$) and half-filled ($d^5$) *d* orbitals are stable configurations for metal ions, but the metal-ligand bonds in complexes are weak. The $d^4$ configuration is rare and unstable. Chromous ion ($Cr^{2+}$), for instance, is extremely air-sensitive, and is rapidly oxidized to $Cr^{3+}$.

Example 3

What is the oxidation state of the metal and the number of *d* electrons in each of the following complexes?

a. $VO_3^-$

b. $[Ru(H_2O)_3Cl_3]$

c. $AuCl_4^-$

d. $[Ni(CN)_5]^{3-}$

Solution:

a. The oxidation number of vanadium in vanadate ion is +5. V can formally be described as a $d^0$ metal, even though it does not exist as a +5 ion.

b. Ruthenium, in the same group as iron, has a +3 charge and 5 *d* electrons.

c. Gold has oxidation number +3 and 8 *d* electrons in this square-planar complex.

d. Nickel in its most common oxidation state, +2, is a $d^8$ metal ion.

## SECTION 19-2: NOMENCLATURE

The seven rules of systematic (IUPAC) nomenclature should be learned if your instructor so designates, along with the contents of Tables 19-5 and 19-6. Learning nomenclature is a memory exercise, so use whatever study aids work best for you. Keep in mind that practice makes perfect!

Isomerism is of three major types: structural, geometrical, and optical. Structural isomerism is primarily concerned with which Lewis bases in a compound are coordinated to the metal. Geometrical, or cis-trans, isomerism was just discussed in section 19-1. Optical isomerism has to do with the interaction of coordination compounds with plane-polarized light. Such compounds are said to be optically active.

### Example 4

Name these compounds and draw all their isomers, indicating whether they are structural, geometrical or optical.

a. $Ni(H_2O)_6(SCN)_2$

b. $Na_3[CrCl_2(ox)_2]$

Solution: a. This compound cannot be named as it is written, because it is not clear which ligands are coordinated to the metal atom. Three structural isomers are possible:

$[Ni(H_2O)_6](SCN)_2$ -- hexaaquonickel(II) thiocyanate

$[Ni(SCN)_2(H_2O)_4]\cdot 2H_2O$ -- bis(thiocyanato)tetraaquonickel(II) dihydrate

$[Ni(SCN)(H_2O)_5](SCN)\cdot H_2O$ -- thiocyanatopentaaquonickel(II) thiocyanate hydrate

Note that the name of the metal without a suffix is used in cationic and neutral complexes. Note also the difference between water as ligand, water as hydrate, and between $SCN^-$ as ligand and $SCN^-$ as counterion.

b. The chromium complex exhibits both geometrical and optical isomerism. The symbol "ox" stands for the bidentate chelating ligand oxalate ion, $C_2O_4^{2-}$. In the drawings, a curved line, ⌒, stands for oxalate.

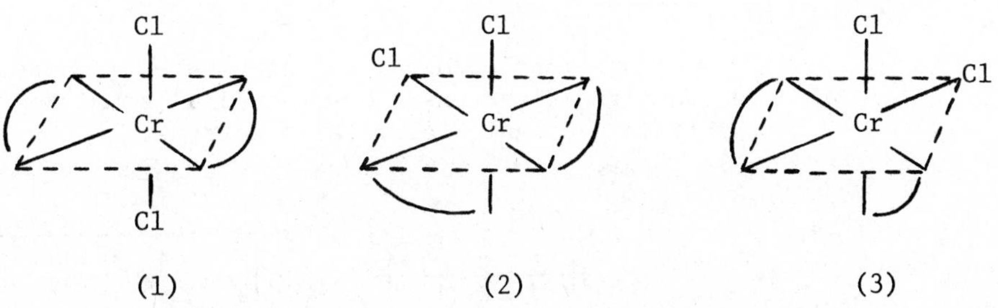


(1) sodium trans-dichlorobis(oxalato)chromate(III)

(2) & (3) sodium cis-dichlorobis(oxalato)chromate(III)

Isomer 1 is not optically active, because there is a mirror plane through the center of the compound. Isomers 2 and 3 are enantiomers; they are nonsuperimposable mirror images, and are thus optically active.

## SECTION 19-3: THEORIES OF BONDING IN COORDINATION COMPLEXES

Four theories of bonding in transition-metal complexes are examined in this section and evaluated in light of observed properties. The criteria used to judge the usefulness of the theories are color, magnetism, stability of $d^3$ and $d^6$ configurations, and existence of square-planar complexes.

The simple electrostatic theory, which is the oldest, only accounts for anionic ligands and does not meet any of the criteria for validity. It is not a useful theory and has been discarded.

Valence bond (VB) theory was the first one to offer any explanation for the observed properties of complexes. It is very good for rationalizing observed magnetic properties, but not for predicting those of new complexes. It does not meet the other three criteria we are using to evaluate bonding theories. VB theory is a localized molecular-orbital approach in which octahedral complexes are held together by sigma bonds, in which the metal uses $d^2sp^3$ (or $sp^3d^2$) hybrid orbitals.

### Example 5

Use valence bond theory to predict the number of unpaired electrons in an inner-orbital and in an outer-orbital complex of $Fe^{2+}$.

Solution: The valence configuration of $Fe^{2+}$ is $d^6$. The configuration of the free ion is

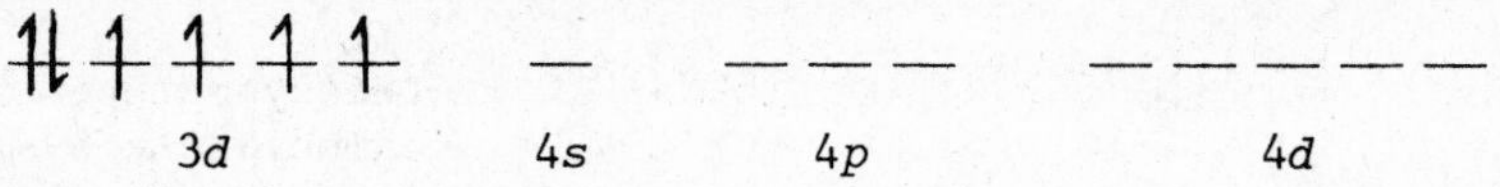

⥮ ↿ ↿ ↿ ↿ — ——— —————
3*d* 4*s* 4*p* 4*d*

It is paramagnetic with four unpaired electrons. An inner-orbital complex uses $d^2sp^3$ hybrid orbitals in which two 3*d* orbitals are mixed with 4*s* and 4*p*. The metal electrons must fit into the three leftover 3*d* orbitals.

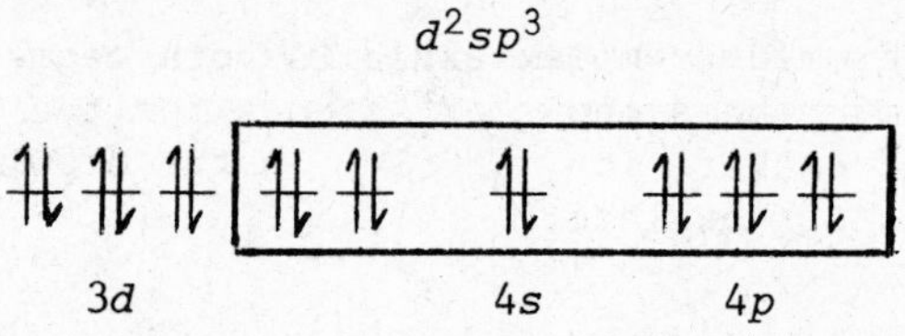

$d^2sp^3$

⥮ ⥮ ⥮ [⥮ ⥮ ⥮ ⥮ ⥮ ⥮]
3*d* 4*s* 4*p*

Thus, inner-orbital complexes are diamagnetic, since there are no unpaired electrons. Outer-orbital complexes have all the 3*d* orbitals available for metal electrons.

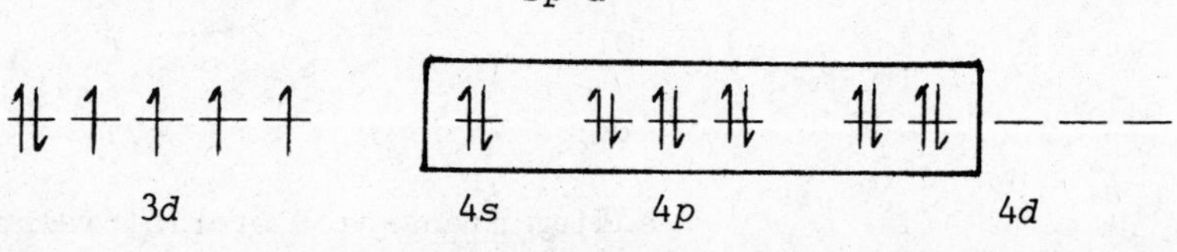

$sp^3d^2$

⥮ ↿ ↿ ↿ ↿ [⥮ ⥮ ⥮ ⥮ ⥮ ⥮] — — —
3*d* 4*s* 4*p* 4*d*

These complexes are paramagnetic with four unpaired electrons, just as the free $Fe^{2+}$ ion is.

The third theory to be proposed is crystal field theory. Its model is an electrostatic one, in which there are no ligand-metal covalent bonds. The presence of six ligands octahedrally arranged around a metal ion causes the originally degenerate *d* orbitals to split into two sets, $t_{2g}$ and $e_g$, separated by an energy $\Delta_o$. magnitude of $\Delta_o$ depends on the ligands. Strong-field ligands produce large splittings, while weak-field ligands produce small $\Delta_o$ values.

Crystal field theory both explains and predicts magnetic properties of complexes, and it explains color in these compounds. The spectrochemical series is an empirical ordering of ligands from weakest field to strongest. It can be used to predict magnetic properties, and, to some extent, colors of simple complexes. Crystal field theory cannot, however, account for the order of ligands in the spectrochemical series.

Example 6

Using the crystal field formalism, write electronic configurations for $[Fe(H_2O)_6]^{2+}$ and $[Fe(CN)_6]^{4-}$.

Solution: The energy-level diagrams for these octahedral complexes differ only in the relative values of $\Delta_o$, which is larger for $CN^-$ than $H_2O$. $Fe^{2+}$ is a $d^6$ ion.

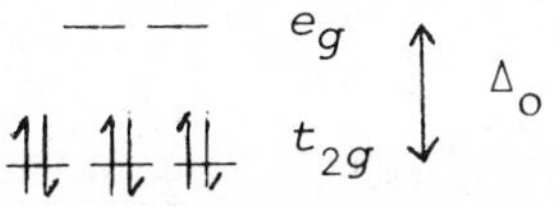

— — $e_g$ ↕ $\Delta_o$
⇅ ⇅ ⇅ $t_{2g}$
$[Fe(CN)_6]^{4-}$

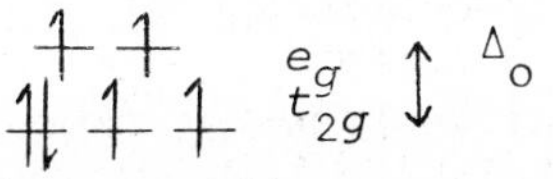

↑ ↑ $e_g$ ↕ $\Delta_o$
⇅ ↑ ↑ $t_{2g}$
$[Fe(H_2O)_6]^{2+}$

Ferrocyanide ion, $[Fe(CN)_6]^{4-}$, should be low-spin and diamagnetic because $\Delta_o$ is larger than the pairing energy, *P*, required to pair two electrons in an orbital. On the other hand, $\Delta_o$ for hexaaquoiron (II) is small relative to *P*, so this ion is high-spin with four unpaired electrons. Moreover, $[Fe(CN)_6]^{4-}$ is expected to be colorless or nearly so because high-energy photons are required to excite an electron from the $t_{2g}$ to the $e_g$ level. It is, in fact, pale yellow, so it absorbs violet light. $[Fe(H_2O)_6]^{2+}$, which requires much less energetic light for electronic excitation, is pale green and absorbs purple-red light.

The most modern theory of the four is ligand field theory. It is a delocalized molecular-orbital treatment of complexes, but gives results that are essentially the same as those of crystal field theory.

Ligand field theory recognizes that there really are bonds between the metal and the ligands. The crystal field theory is not accurate in that respect, but even so, it works quite well for most complexes. Just as one can make an MO diagram for ionic compounds, crystal field theory can be viewed as the ionic extreme of MO theory for complexes. Ligand field theory, however, explains the order of ligands in the spectrochemical series based on their ability to form $\pi$ bonds with the metal, something crystal field theory cannot do.

## SECTION 19-4: TETRAHEDRAL AND SQUARE PLANAR COORDINATION

In this section ligand field theory is applied to four-coordinate complexes. Only octahedral geometry was considered in section 19-3. Note that Figure 19-7 represents only a small portion of a complete MO diagram for a complex. This section of the diagram looks just like the crystal field diagram, and the terminology is the same. You should demonstrate this similarity for yourself.

## SECTION 19-5: EQUILIBRIA INVOLVING COMPLEX IONS

The principles governing equilibrium systems are the same for complex ions as for any other type of equilibrium. Equilibrium constants for reactions of the type

metal + ligands $\rightleftharpoons$ complex

are called formation constants, $K_f$. Equilibrium constants for the dissociation of a complex are referred to as instability constants, $K_{inst}$. Be sure to study the example in this section and work problems 24-32.

Complex-ion equilibria can often be combined with solubility-product equilibria to quantitatively predict enhancement of solubility through complex formation. The appropriate chemical equations and equilibrium-constant expressions are combined in these situations, just as you have done before in Chapters 4, 5, and 16.

### Terms to Know

asymmetric center
bidentate
charge transfer process
chelate
chelate effect
chelating agent
chiral center
cis
complementary color
coordination compound
crystal-field splitting energy
crystal field theory
enantiomers
formation constant
geometrical isomers
high-spin complex
hygroscopic
inert
inner-orbital complex
labile
ligand
ligand field theory
low-spin complex
optical isomers
outer-orbital complex
$\pi$ back bonding
spectrochemical series
strong-field ligand
trans
transition-metal complex
valence bond theory
weak-field ligand

Test Yourself

1. Name the following compounds:

   a. $[Cr(NH_3)_6][CuCl_5]$
   b. $Fe(CO)_5$
   c. $[Co(NCS)(NH_3)_5]Cl_2$
   d. $K_2[Pt(NO_2)_4]$
   e. $[Ni(en)_3](NO_3)_2$
   f. $[Cr(H_2O)_5F]SO_4$

2. Write the formulas of these compounds:

   a. tetramminecopper(II) sulfate
   b. sodium tetrafluoroferrate(III)
   c. bromochlorodiammineplatinum(II)
   d. tris(ethylenediammine)cobalt(III) hexacyanochromate(III)
   e. potassium dichlorobis(oxalato)chromate(III)
   f. potassium octacyanotungstate(V)

3. Identify the complexes in problems 1 and 2 that have isomers.

   a. Write formulas for all the isomers and classify them as geometrical or optical.
   b. Locate any mirror planes within these compounds.

4. How many unpaired electrons does each of the following complexes have?

   a. $[Cr(NH_3)_6]^{3+}$
   b. $[Ni(en)_3]^{2+}$
   c. $[Pt(NO_2)_4]^{2-}$ (square planar)
   d. $[Co(NCS)(NH_3)_5]^{2+}$
   e. $FeCl_4^-$ (tetrahedral)

5. The compounds $Co(NH_3)_5(NO_3)_2SO_4$ and $Co(en)_2Cl(NO_2)_2$ have structural isomers in which one anion does not act as a ligand. Write the formulas for these isomers and name them.

6. Arrange the following complexes in order of increasing crystal field energy, $\Delta_0$: $[CrCl_6]^{3-}$, $[Cr(NH_3)_6]^{3+}$, $[Cr(H_2O)_6]^{3+}$, $[Cr(CN)_6]^{3-}$, $CrF_6^{3-}$, $[Cr(NCS)_6]^{3-}$.

7. Do you think it is possible for diamagnetic Ni(II) complexes to exist? If so, what geometry would such a complex have? Use energy-level diagrams to illustrate your answer.

8. The $NO_2^-$ ligand can coordinate through two different atoms. This phenomenon gives rise to a type of structural isomerism known as linkage isomerism. Sketch the structures of the isomers of the complex between Ir(III), five $NH_3$ molecules, and one $NO_2^-$ ion. Name the isomers.

9. Fe(III) and Co(II) can be identified in each other's presence in aqueous solution by converting them to thiocyanate complexes. The cobalt complex, $[Co(NCS)_4]^{2-}$, is blue. Iron(III) forms several complexes of the general formula $[Fe(NCS)_x(H_2O)_{6-x}]^{3-x}$, where $x$, the number of -NCS ligands, varies between one and six. These complexes are intensely red, so that extremely low concentrations of Fe(III) can be detected visually. The red color of the iron-thiocyanate complex masks the blue of the cobalt complex. When testing for Co(II), the solution is first saturated with NaF to convert the Fe(III) to $FeF_4^-$, which is colorless. Subsequent addition of an alcoholic solution of $NH_4$ NCS results in formation of $[Co(NCS)_4]^{2-}$, with no interference from Fe(III).

   a. Diagram the electronic configuration of the *d*-like orbitals for each of the three complexes, $[Co(NCS)_4]^{2-}$ (tetrahedral), $FeF_4^-$ (tetrahedral), and $[Fe(NCS)_6]^{3-}$.

   b. Explain why $FeF_4^-$ is colorless, while the $[Fe(NCS)_x(H_2O)_{6-x}]^{3-x}$ complexes are intensely red.

   c. How many unpaired electrons does each complex in part a contain?

10. Consider the complexes $[Mn(H_2O)_6]^{2+}$ and $[Mn(CN)_6]^{4-}$.

   a. Describe the ligands as weak- or strong-field, and the complexes as low- or high-spin.

   b. Compare the electronic structures of these complexes using the valence-bond formalism.

11. Lead(II) forms a soluble complex, $PbCl_4^{2-}$, in the presence of excess chloride ion. This is why $Pb^{2+}$ is not completely precipitated as its chloride, along with $Ag^+$ and $Hg_2^{2+}$, in the qualitative analysis scheme. In a solution originally 0.010 M in $Pb^{2+}$, what must the concentration of $Cl^-$ be so that only 0.10% of the $Pb^{2+}$ remains uncomplexed?

# 20 Rates and Mechanisms of Chemical Reactions

## CHAPTER OVERVIEW AND OBJECTIVES

The question "Will it react?" can be answered, as we have seen, by thermodynamics. But thermodynamics, as useful as it is, cannot answer any questions about reaction speed. Chemical kinetics is the study of reaction rates and mechanisms. Kinetics has some very practical applications. Reactions can be made to speed up or slow down, as desired, if the factors affecting the rate are known. Moreover, knowledge of the detailed mechanism of a reaction can be used to design catalysts, which increase reaction rate without being consumed.

Reaction mechanisms are one of the most interesting aspects of chemical kinetics. As Morton Z. Hoffman, professor of chemistry at Boston University, has put it, "It's like being in a helicopter above a tunnel and seeing red and yellow Volkswagens going in one end, while green trucks come out the other end. The question is, what's going on inside that tunnel?" Mechanisms are proposed on the basis of observed quantitative rate expressions.

When you finish this chapter you should be able to:

1. State the order of a reaction, both overall and in each reactant, from inspection of the rate law;

2. List various factors which influence reaction rate;

3. Use the first-order rate law in both its differential and integrated forms;

4. Apply the concept of half-life to reactions of any order, and calculate the half-life of a first-order reaction from its rate constant;

5. Explain the collision theory of chemical kinetics;

6. Explain activation energy and use the Arrhenius equation;

7. Explain how a catalyst functions to increase reaction rate.

## SECTION 20-1: EXPERIMENTAL RATE LAWS

Reaction rate is mathematically described by the rate law, which is always determined experimentally. The rate law states how fast products are formed, or reactants used, in terms of the concentrations of reacting species. Reaction rate has dimensions of concentration per unit time; therefore, it is high at the beginning of a reaction and decreases with time, as the concentrations of reactants decrease. Reaction rate is also affected by temperature, contact between the reactants, and catalysts.

A rate law <u>cannot</u> be determined from the stoichiometry of the reaction; any resemblance between them is purely coincidental. Moreover, a reaction mechanism, or detailed, stepwise description of the reaction, cannot be directly inferred from the rate law. The order of a reaction is given by the sum of the exponents in the rate law. First- and second-order reactions are the most common, but there are some reactions of third, zeroth, fractional and other orders. One can also speak of the order of a reaction in a particular component, given by the power to which its concentration is raised in the rate law.

<u>Example 1</u>

For the reaction

$$2SO_2(g) + O_2(g) \longrightarrow 2SO_3(g)$$

write expressions for the relative rates of appearance of product and disappearance of reactants.

<u>Solution:</u> Inspection of the reaction stoichiometry reveals that $SO_3$ must be formed at the same rate $SO_2$ is used up; they have identical coefficients in the balanced equation. Moreover, $SO_2$ disappears twice as fast as $O_2$; two $SO_2$ molecules must react with every $O_2$ molecule consumed. Thus,

$$\text{rate} = \frac{d[SO_3]}{dt} = -\frac{2d[O_2]}{dt} = -\frac{d[SO_2]}{dt}$$

Note that rates of appearance of products are positive, while rates of use of reactants are negative.

<u>Example 2</u>

The experimental rate law for the catalysis of styrene polymerization by Lewis acids,

$$\underset{\text{styrene}}{n\ C_6H_5\text{-}CH\text{=}CH_2} \xrightarrow{AlCl_3} (\text{-}\underset{\substack{|\\ C_6H_5}}{CH}\text{-}CH_2\text{-})_n$$

is

$$\frac{-d[\text{styrene}]}{dt} = k[AlCl_3][\text{styrene}]^3$$

where $k$ = the rate constant, or specific rate. What is the order of this reaction in $AlCl_3$, in styrene, and overall?

<u>Solution:</u> The overall order of the reaction is just the sum of the exponents in the rate law: 1 + 3 = 4. The order in $AlCl_3$ is its exponent, one, while that in styrene is its exponent, three.

<u>Example 3</u>

Determine the order of the reaction

$$2ICl(g) + H_2(g) \longrightarrow I_2(g) + 2HCl(g)$$

using the initial-rate data displayed below.

| Trial | $[ICl]_0$ | $[H_2]_0$ | Rate (L mol$^{-1}$ s$^{-1}$) |
|---|---|---|---|
| 1 | 0.040 | 0.020 | $0.378 \times 10^{-4}$ |
| 2 | 0.060 | 0.020 | $0.566 \times 10^{-4}$ |
| 3 | 0.060 | 0.060 | $1.70 \times 10^{-4}$ |
| 4 | 0.080 | 0.020 | $0.755 \times 10^{-4}$ |

Solution: The method of initial rates for determining rate laws requires that the initial concentrations of the reactants be systematically varied. Rates at the beginning of the reaction can then be compared directly to find the influence of each reactant individually.

To find the order of the reaction in ICl, hold the concentration of $H_2$ constant and compare rates as $[ICl]_0$ varies. Trials 1, 2, and 4 are used. Trials 1 and 2: $[ICl]_0$ increases by a factor of $0.060/0.040 = 1.5$; the rate increases by $(0.566 \times 10^{-4})/(0.378 \times 10^{-4}) = 1.5$. Thus, rate varies directly, to the first power, with ICl concentration. Trials 1 and 4: $[ICl]_0$ increases by a factor of $0.080/0.040 = 2$; rate increases by $(0.755 \times 10^{-4})/(0.378 \times 10^{-4}) = 2$. These results agree with those of trials 1 and 2. The reaction is first-order in ICl.

Applying the same reasoning to $H_2$, we compare trials 2 and 3. $[ICl]_0$ is constant. $[H_2]_0$ increases by a factor of $0.060/0.020 = 3$, and rate increases by $(1.70 \times 10^{-4})/(0.566 \times 10^{-4}) = 3$. Thus, the order in $H_2$ is one. The rate law is then

$$-\frac{d[ICl]}{dt} = k[ICl][H_2]$$

Note that the rate law does <u>not</u> agree with the reaction stoichiometry.

## SECTION 20-2: FIRST-ORDER KINETICS

The integrated form of a rate law allows one to calculate reactant concentration at a given time during the reaction or the time required for reaction concentration to decline to a given level. For a first-order reaction, the rate law is

$$\ln(C_0/C) = kt$$

where $C_0$ and C refer to concentrations at time zero and $t$, respectively. The rate constant, $k$, is also called the specific rate, because the rate is equal to $k$ when the concentration is one. A plot of lnC vs. $t$ is a straight line of slope $-k$ and intercept $\ln C_0$.

Rates of different reactions can be compared by comparing rate constants; the larger the value of $k$, the faster the reaction. First-order reactions can also be compared on the basis of half-life, $t_{1/2}$, the time required for half the reactant originally present to be converted to product. Half-life is given by

$$t_{1/2} = \frac{\ln 2}{k}$$

Half-life depends only on the rate constant, and not on the concentration of reactant or product.

Example 4

Strontium-90 is present in the fallout from nuclear-bomb explosions. Because of its chemical similarity to calcium, it is absorbed by the body, settling in bones and teeth, where it emits beta-particles.

a. The half-life of $^{90}Sr$ is 28.1 years. What is the specific rate of its decomposition?

Solution: Half-life and specific rate, *k*, are related by

$$t_{1/2} = (\ln 2)/k$$

$$k = (0.693)/(28.1 \text{ yr}) = 0.0247 \text{ yr}^{-1}$$

b. If a mole of $^{90}Sr$ decays through ten half-lives, how much of it remains?

Solution: Two approaches can be taken here. (1) Because the reaction time is an integral number of half-lives, the integrated rate law need not be used. You work backward from one mole, using the appropriate number of half-lives, as follows:

| Fraction $^{90}Sr$ left | No. half-lives |
|---|---|
| 1/2 | 1 |
| 1/4 | 2 |
| 1/8 | 3 |
| 1/16 | 4 |
| 1/32 | 5 |
| 1/64 | 6 |
| 1/128 | 7 |
| 1/256 | 8 |
| 1/512 | 9 |
| 1/1024 | 10 |

The number of atoms remaining from the original mole of $^{90}Sr$ are

$$(1/1024 \text{ mol})(6.023 \times 10^{23} \text{ atoms/mol}) = 5.88 \times 10^{20} \text{ atoms},$$

still a huge number. The percentage of the mole remaining is

$$1/1024 = 9.76 \times 10^{-4} = 0.0976\%$$

The percent looks extremely small, until one considers the actual number of radioactive atoms still present after 281 years.
(2) Alternately, you can use the integrated rate law.

$$\ln(C_0/C) = kt$$

or $\ln(C/C_0) = -kt$

$\ln C = \ln C_0 - kt$

Let $C_0 = 1$ mol

$\ln C = \ln(1) - (0.0247\ yr^{-1})(281\ yr)$

$\ln C = 0 - 6.9407$

$C = 9.68 \times 10^{-4}$ mol

$C = (9.68 \times 10^{-4}\ mol)(6.023 \times 10^{23}\ atoms/mol)$

$= 5.83 \times 10^{20}$ atoms

In a given problem, select the easier method. Counting half-lives is simple if there aren't many of them.

c. How many years are required for only one million $^{90}Sr$ atoms to remain out of the original mole?

Solution: Solve the integrated rate law for time:

$$t = \frac{\ln(C_0/C)}{k}$$

$$t = \frac{\ln(6.023 \times 10^{23}\ atoms/10^6\ atoms)}{0.0247\ yr^{-1}}$$

$$t = (\ln 6.023 \times 10^{17})/0.0247\ yr^{-1}$$

$$t = 40.9395/0.0247\ yr^{-1} = 1{,}660 \text{ years}$$

This is 24 times our average life expectancy.

## SECTION 20-3: HIGHER-ORDER RATE EQUATIONS

A reaction that is second-order in one reactant and second-order overall follows the integrated rate law $1/C - 1/C_0 = kt$. Plotting $1/C$ vs. $t$ gives a straight line of slope $k$ and intercept $1/C_0$. Rates of second-order reactions can be compared by using rate constants. Half-life is not a useful comparison in these reactions, because it depends on $C_0$.

Be sure to study Figures 20-3 and 20-4 and Table 20-3, which give information about plotting data for reactions of various orders. Graphs are extremely useful in helping to determine reaction order.

## SECTION 20-4: REACTION MECHANISMS: COLLISIONS AND MOLECULARITY

Most reactions proceed in stepwise, rather than concerted, fashion. The series of steps which describe the intimate details of a reaction are called its mechanism. The steps in the mechanism add up to give the stoichiometric equation. They are also fully consistent with the experimental rate law.

The molecularity of a step in a reaction mechanism, or elementary process, is just the number of moieties which participate in that step. Nearly every elementary process is bimolecular or unimolecular. Trimolecular processes are rare. The slowest step in a mechanism is rate-limiting. Any steps following the slow step have no effect on reaction rate, although they do, of course, contribute to the reaction stoichiometry.

Any proposed reaction mechanism must be consistent with the observed rate law. Often several such mechanisms can be formulated. Choosing the true mechanism requires additional experimentation designed to detect the presence of transient species which are formed in one step and then consumed in a subsequent one.

Example 5

The experimental rate law for the reaction in Example 3,

$$2ICl(g) + H_2(g) \longrightarrow I_2(g) + 2HCl(g)$$

is

$$\text{rate} = k[ICl][H_2]$$

A suggested mechanism for this reaction is

$$ICl + H_2 \xrightarrow{k_1} HI + HCl \qquad \text{(slow)}$$

$$HI + ICl \xrightarrow{k_2} HCl + I_2 \qquad \text{(fast)}$$

a. Show that the mechanistic steps add up to give the stoichiometric equation.

Solution: Adding the above steps yields

$$ICl + H_2 + HI + ICl \longrightarrow HI + HCl + HCl + I_2$$

Simplifying the equation gives

$$2ICl + H_2 \longrightarrow 2HCl + I_2$$

b. Show that the proposed mechanism is consistent with the observed rate law.

Solution: The rate can proceed only as fast as the slow step. Thus, the second step has no influence on the reaction rate and need not be considered when deriving the rate law from the mechanism. The rate of an elementary process, i.e., a step in a mechanism, can be written directly from its equation. The rate of the slow step in this mechanism is then

$$\text{rate} = k_1[ICl][H_2]$$

where $k_1$ is the rate constant only for that step. Because the second step has no effect on the rate, the rate law for the slow step is the rate law for the overall reaction, and $k_1 = k$. It is in agreement with the experimental rate law.

## SECTION 20-5: RATE-LIMITING PROCESSES WITH PRE-EQUILIBRIUM STEPS

Fast steps which precede the rate-determining step do appear in the rate law. Because the reaction proceeds no faster than the rate-determining step, all steps prior to it achieve equilibrium. The following example shows how to derive a rate law from such a mechanism, in order to demonstrate whether the mechanism is consistent with the observed rate law.

Example 6

Consider the acid hydrolysis of the ester ethylbenzoate, $C_6H_5\overset{O}{\overset{\|}{C}}-OC_2H_5$, a derivative of benzoic acid:

$$C_6H_5\overset{O}{\overset{\|}{C}}-OC_2H_5 + H_2O \xrightarrow{H^+} C_6H_5COOH + C_2H_5OH$$

The observed rate law is rate = $k$[ester][$H^+$], where [ester] = concentration of ethyl benzoate.

Two mechanisms have been proposed. One of them is

$$C_6H_5\overset{O}{\overset{\|}{C}}-OC_2H_5 + H^+ \underset{}{\overset{K}{\rightleftharpoons}} C_6H_5\overset{O\ H}{\overset{\|\ \ |}{C-\underset{\oplus}{O}}}-C_2H_5$$

$$C_6H_5\overset{O\ H}{\overset{\|\ \ |}{C-\underset{\oplus}{O}}}-C_2H_5 + H_2O \xrightarrow{k_2} C_2H_5OH + C_6H_5\overset{O\ H}{\overset{\|\ \ |}{C-\underset{\oplus}{O}}}-H \qquad \text{(slow)}$$

$$C_6H_5\overset{O\ H}{\overset{\|\ \ |}{C-\underset{\oplus}{O}}}-H \xrightarrow{k_3} C_6H_5\overset{O}{\overset{\|}{C}}-OH + H^+$$

Derive a rate law from this mechanism.

Solution: Start with the concept of the rate-determining step, and write its rate first. Let "ester $H^+$" stand for the protonated ester.

$$\text{rate} = k_2[\text{ester } H^+][H_2O]$$

Because water is the solvent, its concentration does not change, and

$$\text{rate} = k_2'[\text{ester } H^+]$$

Now, transient species such as ester $H^+$ do not appear in experimental rate laws, because they aren't initial reactants. Thus, the pre-equilibrium step is incorporated into the rate law so that the rate is expressed only in terms of reactants initially present.

$$K = \frac{[\text{ester } H^+]}{[\text{ester}][H^+]}$$

Solving for [ester $H^+$]:

$$[\text{ester } H^+] = K[\text{ester}][H^+]$$

Substituting in the rate expression:

$$\text{rate} = k_2'K[\text{ester}][H^+] = k[\text{ester}][H^+]$$

This mechanism is thus consistent with the observed rate law,

$$\text{rate} = k[\text{ester}][H^+]$$

Another mechanism which is consistent with the experimental rate law is

$$\text{ester} + H^+ \rightleftharpoons \text{ester } H^+$$

$$\text{ester } H^+ \longrightarrow C_6H_5\overset{+}{C}{=}O + C_2H_5OH \qquad \text{(slow)}$$

$$C_6H_5\overset{+}{C}{=}O + H_2O \longrightarrow C_6H_5COOH + H^+$$

To choose between these mechanisms, one would have to conduct additional experiments. These experiments should be designed to detect the presence of the intermediate species formed in the slow step. In the first mechanism, it is the highly polar $C_6H_5COOH_2^+$, while in the second it is the less polar $C_6H_5CO^+$. Further experimentation has shown that the first mechanism is the better one.

## SECTION 20-6: COLLISION THEORY OF BIMOLECULAR GAS PHASE REACTIONS

There are several theoretical treatments of chemical kinetics. Collision theory is an extension of the kinetic molecular theory of gases and uses a model with which you are already familiar, the ideal gas. Before studying this section you will want to review the material on the kinetic molecular theory in Chapter 3.

The purpose of collision theory is to calculate, or predict, rate constants. If the calculated rate constants agree with the true, or experimental, ones, then the theory is successful. Starting with the ideal-gas model, in which the molecules are hard spheres, one can calculate a collision frequency, $Zc_Ac_B$. The factor $Z$ depends on temperature, molecular size, and molecular mass. However, not all collisions result in reaction, because the molecules do not possess sufficient energy. The minimum energy necessary for reaction is the Arrhenius activation energy, $E_a$. Molecules must be able to overcome this energy barrier for a collision to be successful, that is, to lead to products. The fraction of molecules which have at least $E_a$ is $e^{-E_a/RT}$. The rate constant is given by

$$k = Ze^{-E_a/RT}$$

As temperature increases, the reaction rate increases in two ways: not only are collisions more frequent, so $Z$ increases, but the fraction of molecules possessing the activation energy increases as well. The exponential term increases much faster with $T$ than does $Z$:

$$e^{-E_a/RT} = \frac{1}{e^{E_a/RT}}$$

As $T$ increases, the exponent decreases, but because it is in the denominator of the fraction, the entire factor increases.

The activation energy for a reaction can be determined by measuring the rate constant as a function of temperature. Then, if the theory is correct, the calculated $Z$ factor should agree with the observed one. To obtain $E_a$ from rate data, rewrite the expression for $k$ in logarithmic form:

$$k = Ze^{-E_a/RT}$$

$$\ln k = \ln(Ze^{-E_a/RT})$$

$$\ln k = \ln Z + \ln e^{-E_a/RT}$$

$$\ln k = \ln Z - (E_a/RT) \ln e = \ln Z - E_a/RT$$

A plot of ln $k$ vs. $1/T$ gives a straight line of slope $-E_a/R$ and intercept ln $Z$. Strictly speaking, this equation will not give a straight line, because $Z$ changes slowly with $T$. If the temperature range is small, however, the plot is nearly linear, and a good value for $E_a$ can be obtained.

• As the data in Table 20-5 show, the billiard-ball molecular model does not give good values for the pre-exponential factor, $Z$. There really is no good reason to expect such a model to work perfectly; real molecules are not hard spheres. Accordingly, simple collision theory has been modified to account for the fact that molecules must not only have sufficient energy for reaction, but must also be oriented properly. The steric factor, $p$, is the ratio of observed to calculated $Z$ values. The complete expression for the rate constant is then

$$k = pZe^{-E_a/RT}$$

where $Z = Z_{\text{calculated}}$

Because the steric factor, $p$, cannot be predicted, but only measured, the collision theory is not completely satisfactory. Other theories have been developed which address its deficiencies. Collision theory does, however, allow the measurement of activation energies and is quite useful in that respect.

Example 7

At 50.0°C the specific rate for the decomposition of dibromosuccinic acid is $1.08 \times 10^{-4}$ hr$^{-1}$, while at 89.4°C it is $4.54 \times 10^{-3}$ hr$^{-1}$. Calculate the activation energy for this reaction.

Solution: $E_a$ is related to $k$ by

$$k = pZe^{-E_a/RT}$$

Rearranging gives

$$\ln k = \ln pZ - E_a/RT$$

One can assume the pre-exponential factor, $pZ$, to be constant over a short temperature range. Then, at $T_1$ and $T_2$,

$$\ln k_1 = \ln pZ - E_a/RT_1$$

$$\ln k_2 = \ln pZ - E_a/RT_2$$

$$\ln k_2 - \ln k_1 = -E_a/RT_2 + E_a/RT_1$$

$$\ln \frac{k_2}{k_1} = E_a/R\left(\frac{1}{T_1} - \frac{1}{T_2}\right)$$

Substituting the values for $k_1$, $k_2$, $T_1$, and $T_2$ gives

$$\ln (4.54 \times 10^{-3}/1.08 \times 10^{-4}) = E_a/(8.314 \text{ J mol}^{-1} \text{ K}^{-1}) \times \left(\frac{1}{323.1 \text{ K}} - \frac{1}{362.5 \text{ K}}\right)$$

$$(8.314 \text{ J mol}^{-1} \text{ K}^{-1}) \ln(42.04) = E_a(3.10 \times 10^{-3} - 2.76 \times 10^{-3})\text{K}^{-1}$$

$$(8.314)(3.739)/(0.34 \times 10^{-3}) = E_a$$

$$E_a = 9.14 \times 10^4 \text{ J} = 91.4 \text{ kJ}$$

## SECTION 20-7: ACTIVATION ENERGY BARRIERS

The arrangement of atoms whose energy is $E_a$ is called the activated complex, or transition state. This species has characteristics of both reactants and products. The geometry of the transition state is related to the steric factor, $p$. Some activated complexes are depicted in Figures 20-5, 20-8, and 20-3.

Activation energy and enthalpy change are related for a forward and reverse reaction as shown in Figure 20-9:

$$\Delta H = E_a(\text{forward}) - E_a(\text{reverse})$$

Because $\Delta H$ is a difference in activation energies, it is independent of the nature of the transition state or the height of the energy barrier. Thus, if a catalyst is found to lower the activation energy, $\Delta H$ is unaffected. This agrees with the classification of enthalpy as a state function, independent of path.

## SECTION 20-8: CATALYSIS

A catalyst increases reaction rate by lowering $E_a$, the energy barrier. Catalysts have several features in common:

- an alternate reaction mechanism is provided by the catalyst;
- both forward and reverse reactions are catalyzed, so equilibrium is reached more quickly, but $K_{eq}$ and the position of equilibrium are unaffected;
- the catalyst participates in the reaction, but is regenerated at the end.

Section 20-8 in the text includes a nice discussion of surface catalysis, illustrated by Figures 20-12 and 20-13. Note that the term substrate is a general one for a molecule bound to any type of catalyst.

### Terms to Know

activation energy
Arrhenius plot
catalyst
chemical kinetics
collision frequency
collision theory
half-life
mechanism
method of initial rates
molecularity
order
pre-equilibrium step
rack mechanism
rate constant
rate-determining step
rate law
steric factor
substrate

Test Yourself

1. The reaction

$$2NO(g) + 2H_2(g) \longrightarrow N_2(g) + 2H_2O(g)$$

follows the rate law

$$\frac{d[N_2]}{dt} = k[NO]^2[H_2]$$

What is the order of this reaction: a) in NO, b) in $H_2$, and c) overall?

2. Bromine and hydrogen react to form hydrogen bromide, analogous to the reaction between hydrogen and iodine:

$$H_2(g) + Br_2(g) \longrightarrow 2HBr(g)$$

The rate law is a rather complicated expression:

$$\frac{-d[Br_2]}{dt} = \frac{k[H_2][Br_2]^{\frac{1}{2}}}{1 + [HBr]/k[Br_2]}$$

a. What is the order of this reaction in $H_2$, $Br_2$, and HBr?

b. What effect would increasing the concentration of HBr have on the rate?

3. The rate constant for the decomposition of cyclopropane,

$$C_3H_6 \text{ (cyclopropane ring: three CH}_2\text{ groups)} \longrightarrow CH_3\text{-}CH{=}CH_2$$

a first-order process, is $9.2 s^{-1}$ at 1000°C.

a. If cyclopropane is put in a vessel at 1000°C so that its initial pressure is 0.500 atm, what will its partial pressure be after 5 seconds? (Hint: Recall Avogadro's gas law.)

b. What percentage of the cyclopropane originally present has decomposed?

4. Sulfuryl chloride, $SO_2Cl_2$, decomposes to $SO_2$ and $Cl_2$ in a first-order process. The specific rate is $2.2 \times 10^{-5}\ s^{-1}$.

a. What is the half-life of this process?

b. How much time is required for 90% of the original $SO_2Cl_2$ to decompose?

5. The half-life of radium-223 is 11.43 days.

a. What is the rate constant for the decomposition of $^{223}Ra$?

b. How many half-lives would pass before 99% of a sample of $^{223}Ra$ had disintegrated?

6. In 1921, a few years after she discovered radium, Marie Curie was given 1 gram of $^{226}RaCl_2$ for research purposes. The half-life of radium-226 is 1600 years. How many atoms of $^{226}Ra$ from that gram of $^{226}RaCl_2$ remain today?

7. The pollutant nitric oxide reacts with ozone in the atmosphere:

$$O_3(g) + NO(g) \longrightarrow O_2(g) + NO_2(g)$$

The activation energy for this reaction is 10.29 kJ and $\Delta H°$ is -199.6 kJ. Draw an energy profile for this reaction.

8. The rate constant for the reaction in problem 7 is $2.2 \times 10^7$ L $mol^{-1}$ $s^{-1}$ at 25°C. What is the rate constant at 100°C?

9. Nitrosyl chloride decomposes to chlorine and nitric oxide:

$$2NOCl(g) \longrightarrow 2NO + Cl_2$$

a. Write expressions for the relative rates of appearance of NO and $Cl_2$ and the disappearance of NOCl.

b. The rate constants at 350 K and 400 K are $9.3 \times 10^{-6}$ $s^{-1}$ and $6.9 \times 10^{-4}$ $s^{-1}$, respectively. Calculate the activation energy for this process.

10. Triethylamine, $(C_2H_5)_3N$, an organic base, reacts with ethyl iodide in solution to form a quaternary ammonium salt:

$$(C_2H_5)_3N + C_2H_5I \longrightarrow (C_2H_5)_4N^+ + I^-$$

The activation energy for this reaction is 66.9 kJ when the solvent is hexane, $CH_3(CH_2)_4CH_3$. In the solvent acetone, $CH_3-\underset{\underset{CH_3}{|}}{C}=O$, however, the activation energy is only 49.8 kJ. Offer an explanation for this behavior in different solvents.

# 21 The Special Role of Carbon

CHAPTER OVERVIEW AND OBJECTIVES

Carbon compounds in their tremendous variety are the topic of this chapter. It may seem peculiar that a single element can have so much chemistry, but, as you will see, carbon has unique features that allow this. It would seem that the only limit on the carbon compounds that can be synthesized is the ingenuity of chemists.

The chapter was not written with the idea that you should learn all the material in detail, but rather that you survey organic chemistry and biochemistry to gain some appreciation for these topics.

When you finish this chapter you should be able to:

1. List the features of organic compounds that distinguish them from inorganic ones;

2. Compare boron, nitrogen, and silicon with carbon and explain why the chemistry of carbon is so different from that of its neighboring elements;

3. Distinguish alkanes from alkenes and name simple molecules of each type;

4. List some typical reactions of alkanes, alkenes, and aromatic hydrocarbons;

5. Explain what a functional group is and give examples of common functional groups;

6. Relate colors of aromatic compounds to the light they absorb, and explain how acid-base indicators work;

7. List some typical carbohydrates, amino acids, and proteins;

8. Explain how enzymes function as catalysts;

9. Explain how the stepwise metabolism of food supplies energy to living systems.

Answering the Self-Study Questions at the end of the chapter in the text will be very helpful to you. They are keyed to the eleven sections of the chapter as follows:

| Section | Questions |
|---|---|
| 21-1 | 1 - 3 |
| 21-2 | 4 - 15 |

| | |
|---|---|
| 21-3 & 21-4 | 16 - 26 |
| 21-5 | 27 - 42 |
| 21-6 & 21-7 | 43 - 47 |
| 21-8 | 48 - 53 |
| 21-9 | 54 - 59 |
| 21-10 | 60 - 67 |
| 21-11 | 68 - 85 |

## SECTION 21-1: THE SPECIAL TALENTS OF CARBON

The distinctive feature of carbon chemistry is the tremendous variety of compounds it forms. This is possible because of carbon's ability to catenate, or bond to itself in long chains, both straight and branched. The simplest organic compounds, hydrocarbons, contain only carbon and hydrogen. Saturated hydrocarbons contain only single bonds and have the general formula $C_nH_{2n+2}$, unless a ring is present. Carbon also makes multiple bonds with itself and other elements such as nitrogen, oxygen, and sulfur. Compounds containing double or triple bonds are designated as unsaturated. A special class of unsaturated compounds, the aromatics, features extensively delocalized $\pi$ bonding. Aromatic compounds can contain nitrogen as well as carbon and hydrogen. Because electronic transitions in aromatic compounds occur in the visible region of the spectrum, a feature they have in common with transition-metal complexes, they are used as dyes and in systems for storing and transferring light energy.

## SECTION 21-2: THE CHEMISTRY OF THE NEIGHBORS OF CARBON

In this section, the chemistry of boron, nitrogen and silicon is compared to that of carbon. Observed chemical behavior in these four elements reflects both the number of valence electrons and the number of core electrons each possesses. Be sure to study Table 21-1, which summarizes this section.

Boron is electron-deficient; that is, it has three valence electrons but four orbitals. It cleverly makes up for its lack of valence electrons by forming three-center, two-electron bonds, both with itself and hydrogen. Although boron can, in this way, form a variety of compounds, three-center bonds impose geometrical constraints, such that the structures, all portions of the icosahedron, lack flexibility. Moreover, boron cannot form double bonds to itself because of the three-center-bond geometry. Be sure to review the section of Chapter 12 in which bonding in boron compounds is first introduced.

In contrast to boron, nitrogen is able to form multiple bonds to itself and to carbon, but the nitrogen-nitrogen single bond is much weaker than the carbon-carbon single bond, because of repulsion between the lone pairs of electrons on the nitrogen atoms. Thus, long chains of nitrogen atoms are not found. Although the nitrogen-nitrogen single bond is relatively weak, the corresponding triple bond is extremely strong, which provides a driving force for decomposition of these compounds to $N_2$. Nitrogen does, however, bond fairly strongly to carbon, forming a variety of compounds containing both single and multiple carbon-nitrogen bonds.

Silicon, like carbon, has four valence electrons. However, silicon's valence electrons are more shielded from the nucleus than are those of carbon, which serves to weaken the silicon-silicon single bond. Moreover, silicon's size prevents $\pi$ overlap between silicon atoms; multiple silicon-silicon bonds are not observed. Catenation up to six silicon atoms is known, but silanes, or silicon-hydrogen compounds, are extremely reactive, spontaneously decomposing in air to $SiO_2$ and $H_2O$.

A combination of the weak silicon-silicon bond and the extraordinarily strong silicon-oxygen bond provides the driving force for this type of reaction.

The unusual strength of the silicon-oxygen bond arises from its partial double-bond character. $\pi$ overlap between an empty $d$ orbital on Si and a filled $p$ orbital on O results in $p\pi$-$d\pi$ back-bonding. Thus, although chemistry involving the silicon-silicon bond is limited, there exists a wide variety of compounds containing silicon-oxygen bonds. Recall the discussion of the inorganic compounds of silicon in Chapter 13. Si-O tetrahedral units bond together in chains, sheets, and three-dimensional networks to form a huge number of stable compounds. Organic materials containing Si-O units, called silicones, are chemically inert.

In summary, one can say that carbon has a unique combination of properties: size, relative number of valence electrons and orbitals, and a propensity for catenation. These features in combination permit the rich diversity of carbon compounds found both in nature and in the laboratory.

## SECTION 21-3: SATURATED HYDROCARBONS OR ALKANES

Hydrocarbons, or compounds containing only carbon and hydrogen, are classified by bonding type. Alkanes have only single C-C bonds and are referred to as saturated. Their general formula is $C_nH_{2n+2}$ if no rings are present. Structural isomers are possible for compounds containing four or more carbon atoms.

Alkanes are much less reactive than their nitrogen and silicon analogues. They are inert to acids, bases, and most oxidizing agents. The only important reactions of alkanes are combustion, dehydrogenation, and halogenation. Combustion converts alkanes to $CO_2$ and $H_2O$ with the release of heat. Dehydrogenation, or removal of hydrogen atoms, requires very high temperatures and the aid of a catalyst. Carbon-carbon multiple bonds are the products of this type of reaction. Halogenation involves substitution of halogen atoms for hydrogen by reaction with the elements $F_2$, $Cl_2$, or $Br_2$. Halogenated hydrocarbons are useful precursors in the synthesis of other organic compounds.

### Example 1

How many structural isomers are there of formula $C_6H_{14}$?

Solution: The formula indicates that no rings are present. The carbon skeletons of the five isomers are

```
C-C-C-C-C-C        C-C-C-C-C           C
                         |             |
                         C           C-C-C-C
                                       |
                                       C

C-C-C-C            C-C-C-C-C
  | |                  |
  C C                  C
```

### Example 2

Name the compounds in Example 1.

Solution: Two rules are to be followed. First, count the longest carbon chain as the base molecule. Second, number the substituents starting near the first branching point. Thus, we say

hexane $CH_3$-$CH_2$-$CH_2$-$CH_2$-$CH_2$-$CH_3$

| | |
|---|---|
| 2-methylpentane | $CH_3-CH_2-CH_2-\underset{\displaystyle CH_3}{\underset{\vert}{CH}}-CH_3$ |
| 3-methylpentane | $CH_3-CH_2-\underset{\displaystyle CH_3}{\underset{\vert}{CH}}-CH_2-CH_3$ |
| 2,3-dimethylbutane | $CH_3-\underset{\displaystyle CH_3}{\underset{\vert}{CH}}-\underset{\displaystyle CH_3}{\underset{\vert}{CH}}-CH_3$ |
| 2,2-dimethylbutane | $CH_3-\overset{\displaystyle CH_3}{\overset{\vert}{\underset{\displaystyle CH_3}{\underset{\vert}{C}}}}-CH_2-CH_3$ |

Example 3

Name this compound:

$$CH_3 - CH_2 - \overset{\displaystyle H}{\overset{\vert}{\underset{\displaystyle Cl}{\underset{\vert}{C}}}} - \overset{\displaystyle CH_3}{\overset{\vert}{\underset{\displaystyle Cl}{\underset{\vert}{C}}}} - \overset{\displaystyle CH_3}{\overset{\vert}{\underset{\displaystyle \underset{\displaystyle CH_3}{\underset{\vert}{CH_2}}}{\underset{\vert}{C}}}} - CH_2 - \overset{\displaystyle CH_3}{\overset{\vert}{\underset{\displaystyle CH_3}{\underset{\vert}{C}}}} - CH_3$$

Solution: The longest chain is eight C atoms. The first branching point is at the right-hand end of the molecule as written above. Substituents are named in alphabetical order. Thus, one calls the compound 5,6-dichloro-4-ethyl-2,2,4,5-tetramethyloctane.

## SECTION 21-4: UNSATURATED HYDROCARBONS

These compounds feature carbon-carbon multiple bonds. Alkenes, which contain double bonds, are more common than alkynes, which have triple bonds. Three methods of preparations of alkenes are noted in this section. Alkenes display both structural and geometrical isomerism, because the atoms adjacent to a C=C unit are constrained to lie in the same plane with it. Thus, groups can be cis or trans to each other depending on their positions relative to the double bond.

Nomenclature of alkenes is similar to that for alkanes, except that the position of the double bond is given the lowest number possible. Thus, $CH_2=CH-CH_2-CH_2-CH_3$ is 1-pentene, not 4-pentene. The most common reaction of alkenes is addition across the double bond.

Alkenes containing several double bonds can have delocalized $\pi$ bonding if the double bonds alternate with single ones, as in 1,3-pentadiene, $CH_2=CH-CH=CH-CH_3$. Conjugated alkenes behave differently in addition reactions than do alkenes having localized carbon-carbon double bonds. Unsaturated ring compounds having extensively delocalized $\pi$ systems are called aromatic.

Example 4

Predict and name the products of the following reactions:

a. $CH_2=CH-CH_2-CH_2-CH_3 + Br_2 \longrightarrow$

b. $CH_2{=}CH{-}CH_2{-}CH_2{-}CH_3 + H_2 \longrightarrow$

Solution: a. A Br atom adds to each C atom in the double bond, giving

$$\underset{\displaystyle Br}{\underset{|}{CH_2}}{-}\underset{\displaystyle Br}{\underset{|}{CH}}{-}CH_2{-}CH_2{-}CH_3 \qquad \text{1,2-dibromopentane}$$

b. Similarly, an H atom adds to each C atom in the C=C unit, yielding

$$\underset{\displaystyle H}{\underset{|}{CH_2}}{-}\underset{\displaystyle H}{\underset{|}{CH}}{-}CH_2{-}CH_2{-}CH_3 \qquad \text{pentane}$$

Example 5

Which of the following compounds can have geometrical isomers?

a. $Cl_2C{=}CH{-}CH_3$

b. $Cl{-}\underset{\displaystyle CH_3}{\underset{|}{C}} = \underset{\displaystyle Cl}{\underset{|}{CH}}$

c. $CH_3{-}CH_2{-}CH{=}CH{-}CH_3$

Solution: a. There is only one molecule with this formula, because one of the C atoms in the C=C unit is bonded to two groups of the same kind, i.e., Cl.

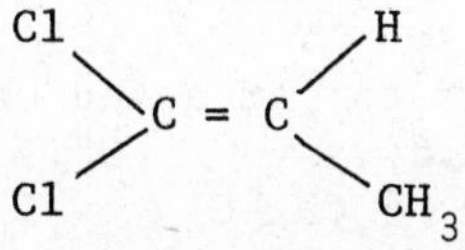

$$\begin{matrix} Cl & & H \\ & C = C & \\ Cl & & CH_3 \end{matrix} \quad \text{same as} \quad \begin{matrix} Cl & & CH_3 \\ & C = C & \\ Cl & & H \end{matrix}$$

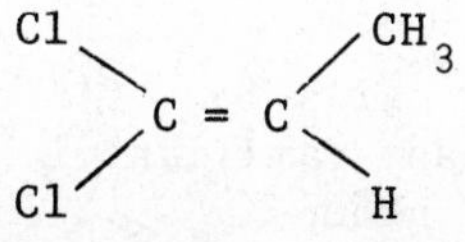

1,1-dichloropropene

b. and c. Both of these compounds have geometrical isomers; different groups are bonded to the C atoms in the C=C unit.

$$\begin{matrix} Cl & & Cl \\ & C = C & \\ H_3C & & H \end{matrix} \qquad \begin{matrix} H_3C & & Cl \\ & C = C & \\ Cl & & H \end{matrix}$$

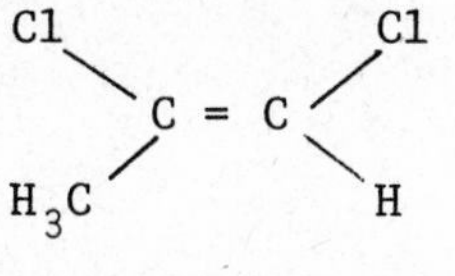

cis-1,2-dichloropropene 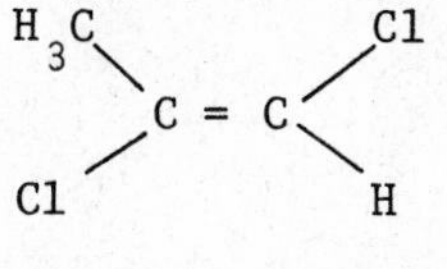 trans-1,2-dichloropropene

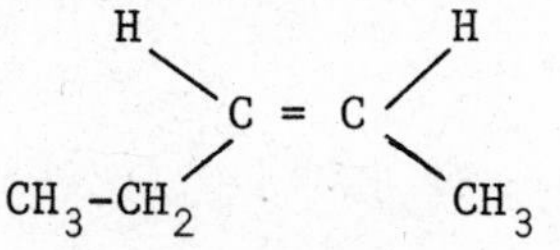

$$\begin{matrix} H & & H \\ & C = C & \\ CH_3{-}CH_2 & & CH_3 \end{matrix} \qquad \begin{matrix} H & & CH_3 \\ & C = C & \\ CH_3{-}CH_2 & & H \end{matrix}$$

cis-2-pentene 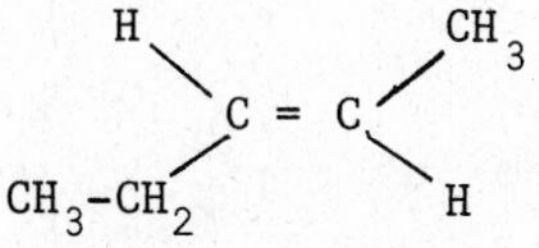 trans-2-pentene

## SECTION 21-5: DERIVATIVES OF HYDROCARBONS: FUNCTIONAL GROUPS

A large number of organic compounds contain a hydrocarbon part, called a radical, attached to a more chemically active set of atoms, called a functional group. For instance, halogenated hydrocarbons contain the halogen functional group, F, Cl or Br, which has replaced hydrogen in a hydrocarbon molecule.

The halogen can be replaced by other functional groups, such as -OH, -SH, or $-NH_2$, leaving the hydrocarbon radical intact. Since the radical is unchanged in these displacement reactions, one can substitute the symbol R- for the radical, whether it is $CH_3-$, $CH_3CH_2-$, $(CH_3)_2CH-$, or something larger. Table 21-3 lists the common functional groups and gives named examples of compounds containing each of them. Be sure to study this table, as well as Table 21-4, which shows various radicals combined with the functional groups and how the resultant molecules are named.

Alcohols, ROH, are good solvents for polar organic molecules. Low-molecular-weight alcohols dissolve inorganic polar molecules and salts as well. Thiols or mercaptans, RSH, are the sulfur analogues of alcohols. Ethers, R-O-R', can be prepared from alcohols. They are less polar than alcohols and have great utility as solvents for organic materials.

Aldehydes and ketones both contain a carbonyl group, $>C=O$. Their general formulas are as follows:

$$R-\overset{O}{\overset{\|}{C}}-H \qquad\qquad R-\overset{O}{\overset{\|}{C}}-R'$$

aldehyde　　　　ketone

Both of these types of compounds can be synthesized by oxidizing appropriate alcohols.

Further oxidation of alcohols leads to formation of carboxylic acids, $RC{\scriptstyle\begin{matrix}\nearrow O\\ \searrow OH\end{matrix}}$. You are already familiar with acetic acid, $CH_3-C{\scriptstyle\begin{matrix}\nearrow O\\ \searrow OH\end{matrix}}$. The carboxyl group, $-C{\scriptstyle\begin{matrix}\nearrow O\\ \searrow OH\end{matrix}}$, characterizes these acids, which are generally weak. When carboxylic acids ionize or when they react with base, the carboxyl group is converted to a carboxylate group, which has two equivalent C-O bonds.

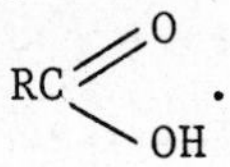

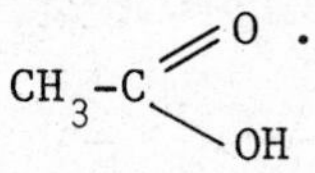

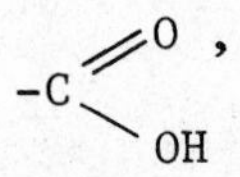

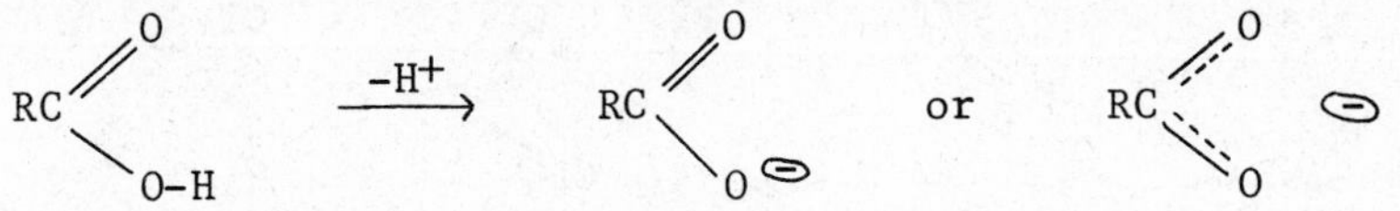

$$RC{\begin{matrix}\nearrow O\\ \searrow O-H\end{matrix}} \xrightarrow{-H^+} RC{\begin{matrix}\nearrow O\\ \searrow O^{-}\end{matrix}} \quad \text{or} \quad RC{\begin{matrix}\nearrow O\\ \searrow O\end{matrix}}^{\ominus}$$

Thus, $CH_3CH_2CH_2C{\scriptstyle\begin{matrix}\nearrow O\\ \searrow OH\end{matrix}}$ is butanoic acid, and $CH_3CH_2CH_2C{\scriptstyle\begin{matrix}\nearrow O\\ \searrow O^-\end{matrix}}$ is butanoate ion.

Esters are derived from the reaction between a carboxylic acid and an alcohol:

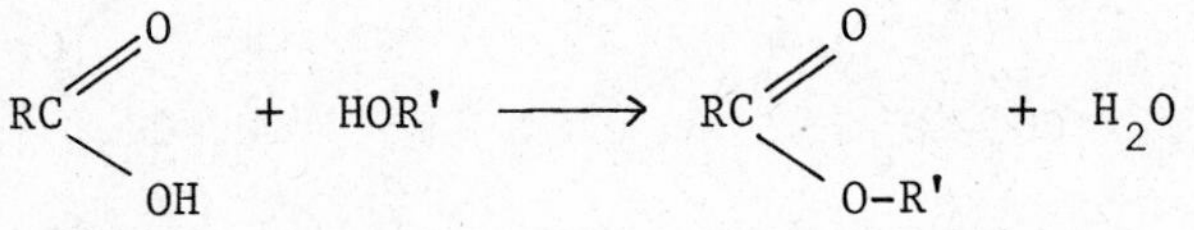

$$RC{\begin{matrix}\nearrow O\\ \searrow OH\end{matrix}} + HOR' \longrightarrow RC{\begin{matrix}\nearrow O\\ \searrow O-R'\end{matrix}} + H_2O$$

acid　　alcohol　　　ester

Thus, butanoic acid plus ethyl alcohol gives the ester ethylbutanoate. Do not confuse the use of "butanoate" in the name of this ester with butanoate ion. Esters are not ionic compounds.

Amines are organic bases related to ammonia. One, two, or three hydrogen atoms on ammonia are replaced by radicals to give primary, secondary, or tertiary amines:

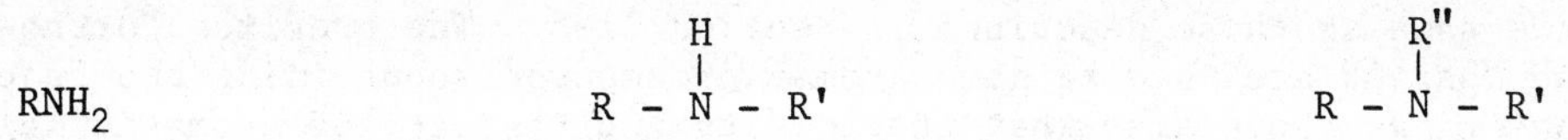

| $RNH_2$ | $R - \underset{}{\overset{H}{\overset{\vert}{N}}} - R'$ | $R - \overset{R''}{\overset{\vert}{N}} - R'$ |
|---|---|---|
| primary | secondary | tertiary |

Amines act as bases in the same way ammonia does; the lone pair of electrons on the nitrogen atom bonds to a proton. The ionized form of an amine is an ammonium ion:

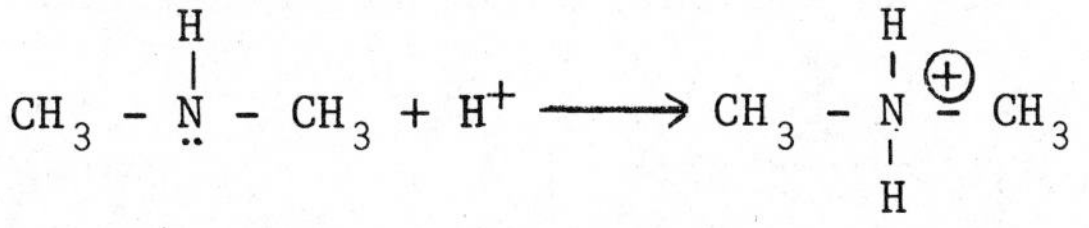

$$CH_3 - \overset{H}{\overset{\vert}{\ddot{N}}} - CH_3 + H^+ \longrightarrow CH_3 - \underset{\underset{H}{\vert}}{\overset{H}{\overset{\vert}{N}}}\overset{\oplus}{-} CH_3$$

dimethylamine dimethylammonium ion

The final class of compounds described in this section are the amino acids. These molecules feature both a primary amine group and a carboxyl group. The carbon atom adjacent to the amine group is asymmetric; thus, amino acids have optical isomers. Amino acids polymerize to give proteins, through formation of peptide bonds. The peptide unit,

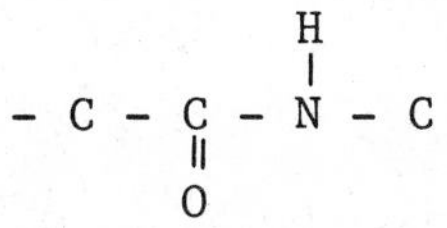

$$- C - \underset{\underset{O}{\Vert}}{C} - \overset{H}{\overset{\vert}{N}} - C$$

is planar, which implies that there is delocalization of the electrons in the C=O bond:

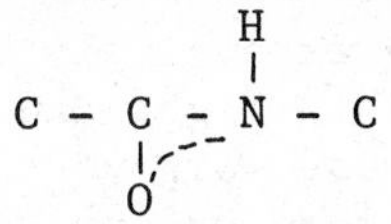

$$C - \underset{\underset{O}{\vert}}{C} \text{-} \overset{H}{\overset{\vert}{N}} - C$$

## SECTION 21-6: AROMATIC COMPOUNDS

The compounds discussed in the preceding sections are aliphatic ones. Aliphatic compounds can be chains or rings, but they are characterized by localized bonding, with delocalized orbitals extending over only three or four atoms. The predominant reaction which unsaturated aliphatic compounds undergo is addition to double or triple bonds. In contrast, aromatic compounds are stable to addition except under extreme conditions. Instead, they undergo substitution reactions, characteristic of extensively delocalized bonding systems. In general, stability of an aromatic compound increases with the number of atoms over which the $\pi$ electrons are delocalized.

Aromatic substitution is called "electrophilic" because one of the reactants is an electrophile, an electron-seeker or Lewis acid. The aromatic ring is electron-rich because it has delocalized $\pi$ electrons. Formation of electrophiles, especially the positively charged ones, often requires assistance from other molecules, such as catalysts. Review the appropriate sections of Chapter 20 which discuss the characteristics of catalysts. Recall that a catalyst cannot change the position of equilibrium, but only assist the system in reaching equilibrium quickly. Organic reactions often yield a mixture of the desired product, other products, and starting material, and do not go to completion.

Note that the functional groups in the aromatic compounds depicted in Figure 21-14 are the same as those described in Section 21-5. The prefixes "ortho-," "meta-," and "para-" are used to name aromatic compounds containing two functional groups on one ring. Note also that the acidity and basicity of aromatic acids and amines is affected by delocalization of electrons from these functional groups into the ring.

Example 6

Show how $AlCl_3$ functions as a catalyst for the substitution reaction

$$C_6H_6 + CH_3CH_2Cl \longrightarrow C_6H_5{-}CH_2CH_3 + HCl$$

Solution: The $AlCl_3$ aids in the formation of the electrophile $CH_3CH_2^+$, called a carbonium ion. The carbonium ion attacks the aromatic ring, displacing $H^+$.

$$AlCl_3 + CH_3CH_2Cl \longrightarrow AlCl_4^- + CH_3CH_2^+$$

$$CH_3CH_2^+ + C_6H_6 \longrightarrow [C_6H_6(H){-}CH_2CH_3]^+ \longrightarrow C_6H_5{-}CH_2CH_3 + H^+$$

$$H^+ + AlCl_4^- \longrightarrow AlCl_3 + HCl$$

SECTION 21-7: AROMATIC COMPOUNDS AND THE ABSORPTION OF LIGHT

The energy levels in compounds having extensively delocalized electrons often lie sufficiently close together that visible light can excite electrons from the ground state into higher levels. Each of these compounds appear as the color that is complementary to the one absorbed. The more extensive the delocalization, the longer the wavelength of light absorbed. Most compounds do not possess this characteristic. The electronic transitions of interest in colored aromatic compounds are the $\pi$-$\pi^*$ type. In transition-metal complexes, they are either charge-transfer or *d*-*d* transitions.

Molecules that are different colors in acid and base can be used as acid-base indicators. The size of the delocalized system changes under acidic and basic conditions, which results in a change in color.

Example 7

The indicator thymol blue changes color in two different pH ranges. In extremely acidic solution, it is red; in moderately acidic solution, yellow; and in basic solution, blue. What colors of light does thymol blue absorb in these three types of solution?

Solution: Colored compounds absorb the complement of their color. Thus, the red form of the indicator absorbs blue-green, the yellow form absorbs indigo, and the blue form absorbs orange light.

Example 8

The indicator methyl orange is an aromatic amine, as well as being a diazo compound. Show how electrons are delocalized in the protonated (ionized) form of the molecule, which is red.

Solution: Protonated methyl orange has the formula

$$\overset{\oplus}{\mathrm{H{-}N}}(CH_3)_2{-}C_6H_4{-}\bar{N}{=}\bar{N}{-}C_6H_4{-}S(=\bar{O})_2{-}\bar{O}|$$

One resonance form, in which the positive charge is delocalized into the $\pi$ system, is

$$\mathrm{H{-}N}(CH_3)_2{=}C_6H_4{=}\overset{\oplus}{N}{-}\overset{-}{N}{-}C_6H_4{-}SO_3$$

## SECTION 21-8: CARBOHYDRATES

Carbohydrates, molecules familiar to everyone, are so named because their empirical formula, $(CH_2O)_n$, appears to contain equal parts of carbon and water. Indeed, one can remove the water with a sufficiently strong dehydrating agent, such as sulfuric acid, and obtain elemental carbon as the other product of the reaction. Your instructor may have performed this reaction between a sugar and sulfuric acid as a lecture demonstration.

The simplest carbohydrates are monosaccharides, meaning "one sugar." Examples are glucose and galactose. Hexoses, such as glucose, contain six carbon atoms. Sucrose, or table sugar, is a disaccharide composed of a glucose molecule bonded to a fructose molecule. Like amino acids, carbohydrates contain asymmetric carbon atoms and thus have optical isomers. Hexose contains five asymmetric carbon atoms and thus has a large number of optical isomers. However, only three of them, glucose, galactose, and mannose, are naturally occurring. Figure 21-15 illustrates these three sugars, as well as α-D-glucose written using three different techniques of illustration. The Fischer projection convention is convenient to use once you get used to it, but it is easier to visualize the shape of a molecule using drawings such as Figure 21-15(b) and (c).

Sugar polymers are called polysaccharides. Two of the most familiar ones, starch and cellulose, are composed of glucose units. The difference between them is the glucoside linkage, illustrated in Figure 21-16. Animals can digest polysaccharides bonded with α-glucoside links, but lack the enzymes to break down the β linkage found in cellulose. Exceptions are termites and ruminants, e.g., cattle, which harbor appropriate microorganisms in their digestive systems. (Be sure to read the footnote which accompanies the discussion of polysaccharides.)

## SECTION 21-9: PROTEINS AND ENZYMES

Amino acids polymerize to make proteins, one of the three structural materials of all organisms. Typically, several hundred amino acids link up through peptide bonds, giving molecules with molecular weights in the thousands. Proteins are divided into two classes based on their shape: globular and fibrous.

The particular sequence of amino acids in a molecule distinguishes one protein from another. The twenty amino acids found in organisms are depicted in Table 21-5. The side groups of the amino acids determine how a protein folds and how it behaves chemically. These side groups are of three types:

- o hydrocarbon-like, thus hydrophobic, or water-avoiding;
- o ionized (charged), thus acidic or basic;
- o polar but uncharged.

In globular proteins, the charged groups are found on the surface, while the hydrophobic groups are folded inside the molecule. The alpha helix is a particularly stable configuration, or folding arrangement, for proteins, and is found in many of them. The helix is held in shape by hydrogen bonding between carbonyl ($>C=O$) and amine (-NH) groups.

Enzymes, which are biochemical catalysts, are proteins. They provide a surface to which the reacting molecule, or substrate, can attach and a low-energy reaction path for the substrate. Moreover, enzymes are highly specific; they can recognize which molecules are substrates and will not bind others. The active sites, or areas of enzymes where catalysis actually occurs, often contain metal ions, which are Lewis acids, to aid bond breaking.

## SECTION 21-10: THE MECHANISM OF ACTION OF AN ENZYME

The peptide hydrolysis, or cleavage by water, reaction discussed in this section is just one of many enzyme-catalyzed reactions which take place in living systems. Trypsin, elastase, and chymotrypsin all catalyze this type of reaction by the mechanism illustrated in Figure 21-18, using the serine group on the enzyme to break the C-N peptide bond. The difference between these enzymes lies in their specificity. Each of them catalyzes peptide hydrolysis at a different position in a protein by being able to recognize particular amino-acid side chains.

Recall that all catalysts have two characteristics: they provide a low-energy reaction path, and they are regenerated at the end of the reaction. Enzymes are particularly efficient because of their high specificity; enzyme and substrate must fit together properly for reaction to occur. Note how often hydrogen bonding and other types of weak interactions aid the catalytic process. Molecular structure of enzymes correlates with reactivity in minute detail.

## SECTION 21-11: ENERGY AND METABOLISM IN LIVING SYSTEMS

Storage of free energy in the body is the purpose of the multistep metabolic process. The efficiency of this storage process in humans is 40% for glucose metabolism. During the conversion of one mole of glucose to $CO_2$ and $H_2O$, 38 moles of adenosine triphosphate, ATP, are synthesized. Hydrolysis of ATP releases free energy when needed:

$$ATP + H_2O \longrightarrow ADP + H_3PO_4 + 30.5\ kJ$$

There are three main steps in glucose metabolism, each composed of several reactions:

1. Glycolysis: glucose cleaved and converted to pyruvic acid and eight ATP molecules synthesized;

2. Citric acid (Krebs) cycle: free energy of pyruvic acid divided into four parts and transferred to NADH and $FADH_2$ molecules; two ATP molecules produced;

3. Respiratory chain: free energy transferred by NADH and $FADH_2$ and stored in twenty-eight molecules of ATP.

Note that enzymes play a large part in the metabolic process. Also note that the vitamins niacin and riboflavin are incorporated into the free-energy carrier molecules $NAD^+$ and FAD.

Organisms depend on photosynthesis for a supply of glucose to metabolize. Sunlight provides the free energy required to produce glucose from water and carbon dioxide. An additional benefit from photosynthesis is the release of oxygen to the atmosphere, which aids in replenishing what is used by organisms and machines. Sunlight is absorbed by the chlorophylls, and its energy is stored in ATP and NADPH. The stored energy is subsequently used to drive the so-called dark reactions in which glucose is synthesized.

## Terms to Know

acid-base indicator
active site
alcohol
aldehyde
aliphatic compound
alkane
alkene
alkyne
amine
amino acid
aromatic compound
asymmetric carbon atom
ATP
boat form
Calvin-Benson cycle
carbohydrate
carboxylic acid
catalyst
cellulose
chair form
chlorination
citric acid cycle
combustion
conjugated system
dark reactions
dehydrogenation
electrophilic groups
enzyme
ester
ether
functional group
geometrical isomers
$\alpha$-glucoside link
$\beta$-glucoside link
glycolysis
halogenation
hexose
hydrocarbon
hydrophobic group
ketone
light reactions

metabolism
micelle
monomer
monosaccharide
optical isomers
paraffin
peptide bond
photosynthesis
$\pi \rightarrow \pi^*$ transition
polymer
polysaccharide
primary amine
protein
protein, globular and fibrous
radical
replacement reaction
respiratory chain
salt
saturated
secondary amine
silane
silicone
starch
steric hindrance
substitution reaction
substrate
substrate specificity
tertiary amine
three-center bond
unsaturated
zwitterion

## Test Yourself

1. Write the structural formulas of all the isomers of $C_4H_8Br_2$ and name them.

2. Indicate the type of hybrid orbitals used by the carbon and nitrogen atoms in the following compounds:

   a. $CH_2F_2$

   b. $CH_3-CN$

   c. $C_2H_2Br_2$

   d. $CF_3-CH_2-\overset{\overset{\displaystyle O}{\|}}{C}-\overset{\overset{\displaystyle H}{|}}{N}-CH_3$

   e. 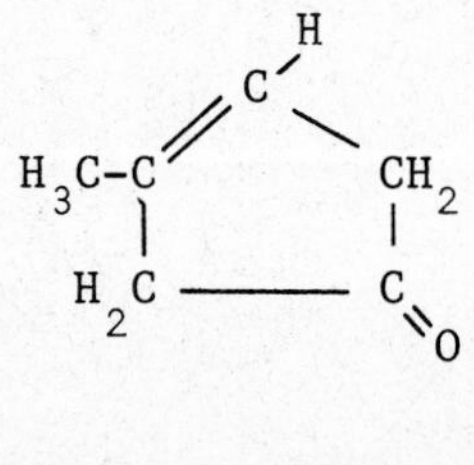
```
          H
         /
        C
      //  \
H3C-C      CH2
    |       |
   H2C ---- C
             \\
              O
```

3. Write the structural formulas of

   a. 1-bromo-3-heptyne

   b. <u>cis</u>-3,4-dibromo-3-hexene

   c. methylheptanoate

   d. 1,3-dimethylcyclopentane

   e. caproic acid

   f. 4-bromo-2-hexanol

4. Draw fifteen isomers of $C_5H_{10}O_2$.

5. Aromatic compounds can be nitrated using a mixture of nitric and sulfuric acids. Suggest a mechanism for this type of reaction:

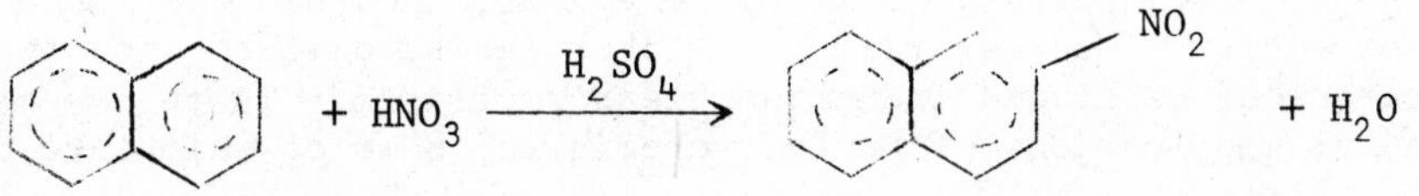

   $$\text{naphthalene} + HNO_3 \xrightarrow{H_2SO_4} \text{2-nitronaphthalene } (NO_2) + H_2O$$

   How does sulfuric acid assist the substitution process?

6. Which compounds might be expected to absorb visible light?

   a. 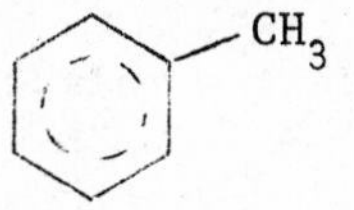 (benzene ring with $CH_3$)

   b. 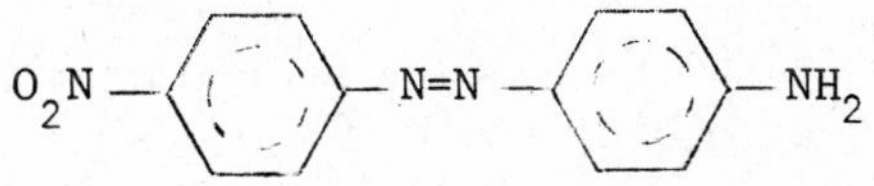 $O_2N$—(benzene ring)—N=N—(benzene ring)—$NH_2$

   c. 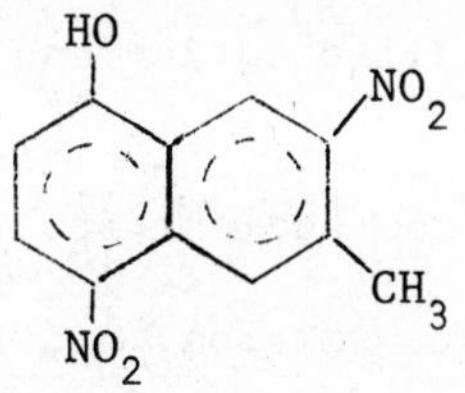 (naphthalene with HO, $NO_2$, $NO_2$, $CH_3$)

   d. 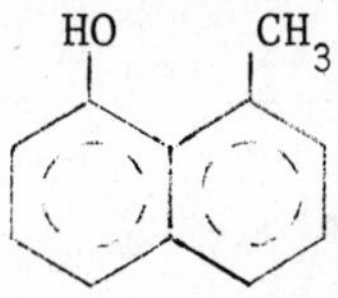 (naphthalene with HO, $CH_3$)

7. Draw a structural formula for a disaccharide made from one α-D-galactose molecule and one α-D-mannose molecule.

8. Would you expect the disaccharide in question 6 to be digestible?

9. Consult Table 21-5 and list five amino acids whose side chains would be expected to be hydrophobic.

10. In what region of a water-soluble globular protein would you expect to find the amino acids you chose for question 8?

11. Consult Table 21-5 and choose five amino acids which could serve to enhance the aqueous solubility of a protein.

# 22 Nuclear Chemistry

## CHAPTER OVERVIEW AND OBJECTIVES

The central focus of the description of chemical processes up to this point has been how the electrons, particularly valence electrons, behave in atoms, molecules, and ions. The only role of the nucleus that has been considered is the way in which it influences electronic energy. In this chapter, reactions of the nucleus itself are considered. These are not ordinary chemical reactions, and they are accompanied by huge quantities of energy. Nuclear transformations can be divided into two broad categories: spontaneous decay and induced nuclear reactions. There are many interesting and practical applications of nuclear chemistry, some of which are discussed at the end of the chapter.

When you finish this chapter you should be able to:

1. Given the symbol for an isotope, determine the number of protons and neutrons it contains;

2. Calculate the binding energy of a nucleus and the energy released by various nuclear processes;

3. List the modes of nuclear decay and predict the products of each;

4. Apply the first-order rate expression, in both differential and integrated forms, to nuclear transformation processes;

5. Explain the relationship between magic numbers and nuclear stability;

6. Describe induced nuclear reactions: bombardment, fission, and fusion;

7. Describe some applications of nuclear chemistry.

## SECTION 22-1: THE NUCLEUS

You are already familiar with the notation and terms used in this section. Two new ideas are those of nuclear shape and binding energy.

Neutron-scattering experiments are used to measure the sizes of nuclei. These measurements indicate that the volume of a nucleus is directly proportional to the number of nucleons, that is, protons and neutrons, that it contains. Or,

$$r = 1.33 \times 10^{-13} A^{1/3} \text{ cm}$$

Nuclei are incredibly tiny and dense, being about 20,000 times smaller than atoms. Most nuclei are spherical, although some are ellipsoidal. Nonspherical nuclei possess an electric quadrupole moment.

Nuclei are held together by binding energy. Think of the mass excess, or difference between the atomic mass and the mass of an equivalent number of individual nucleons, as being converted to energy when a nucleus forms. Mass excess and binding energy are related by $E = mc^2$. In nuclear reactions, unlike ordinary chemical ones, it is the sum of mass and energy that is conserved.

Calculations of the binding energy per nucleon for isotopes heavier than oxygen show that the attractive forces within the nucleus are short-range. That is, the total binding energy is proportional to the mass number, indicating that a given nucleon only interacts with its nearest neighbors. The electron volt, eV, is the most commonly used unit of energy for nuclear processes.

## SECTION 22-2: NUCLEAR DECAY

There are four types of reactions which change the composition of the nucleus. Additionally, nuclei can lose energy by emitting gamma radiation. The first four reactions are:

1. $\beta^-$ emission: equivalent to losing an electron from the nucleus; mass number remains the same, neutrons decrease by one, and protons increase by one:

$$^{A}_{Z}X \rightarrow \beta^- + {}^{A}_{Z+1}X$$

2. Electron capture (EC): orbital electron incorporated within the nucleus; mass number is unchanged, neutrons increase by one, and protons decrease by one:

$$^{A}_{Z}X + \bar{e} \rightarrow {}^{A}_{Z-1}X$$

3. Positron ($\beta^+$) emission: particle has mass of electron but opposite charge; mass number remains unchanged, neutrons increase by one, and protons decrease by one:

$$^{A}_{Z}X \rightarrow \beta^+ + {}^{A}_{Z-1}X$$

4. $\alpha$ emission: equivalent to losing a helium-4 nucleus; mass number decreases by four, neutrons decrease by two, and protons decrease by two:

$$^{A}_{Z}X \rightarrow {}^{4}_{2}\text{He} + {}^{A-4}_{Z-2}X$$

Gamma radiation is emitted by many nuclei, often in conjunction with an alpha particle. Gamma rays are electromagnetic radiation of the same high energy as X rays. The difference between the two is in the mode of production; X rays are given off by a metal that has been bombarded by electrons in a vacuum tube.

The kinetics of nuclear reactions is always first-order for a given process. Review the appropriate sections in Chapter 20, if necessary. The first-order rate law, in its differential and integrated forms, becomes

$$-dn/dt = kn$$

or

$$\ln n_0/n = kt$$

Because any individual nucleus can decay independently of any other one, the number of nuclei present at time zero ($n_0$), and at time $t(n)$ are used in the rate expression. The relative stability of a radioisotope is measured by its half-life ($t_{\frac{1}{2}}$), the time required for half the nuclei originally present in a sample to decay. Recall that half-life is related to the rate constant, $k$, by

$$t_{\frac{1}{2}} = (\ln 2)/k$$

Example 1

What is the energy equivalent of the mass loss due to α emission? Use the reaction ${}^{208}_{84}Po \rightarrow \alpha + {}^{204}_{82}Pb$ for reference.

Solution: In this reaction, a polonium-208 nucleus decays to a lead-204 nucleus, a helium-4 nucleus, and two electrons. The mass loss is the difference in mass between reactants and products. The energy equivalent of this mass loss is found from Einstein's relationship.

$$\text{mass loss} = \text{mass } {}^{208}Po - \text{mass } {}^{204}Pb - \text{mass } {}^{4}He - 2 \text{ mass } \bar{e}$$

$$\text{mass loss} = (207.9813 - 203.973 - 4.00260 - 0.001098) \text{ amu}$$
$$= 0.0046 \text{ amu}$$

$$E = mc^2$$

$$E = (0.0046 \text{ amu/atom})(1.66057 \times 10^{-27} \text{ kg/amu})(2.998 \times 10^{8} \text{ m/s})^2$$

$$E = (6.9 \times 10^{-13} \text{ J/atom})(1 \text{ eV}/1.60219 \times 10^{-19} \text{ J})$$
$$= 4.3 \text{ MeV/atom}$$

Example 2

Strontium-80 decays by electron capture, with a half-life of 1.7 hours. What mass of ${}^{80}Sr$ would remain after a 1.0-g sample had decayed for 10.0 hours?

Solution: All radioactive-decay processes follow first-order kinetics. This problem requires the use of the integrated rate law:

$$\ln n_0/n = kt$$

The ratio of masses, $m_0/m$, can be substituted for the atom ratio, $n_0/n$, since converting one to the other involves multiplying the numerator and denominator by atomic weight and dividing by Avogadro's number. We need the rate constant, $k$, but are given the half-life.

$$t_{\frac{1}{2}} = (\ln 2)/k$$

$$k = 0.693/1.7 \text{ hr} = 0.408 \text{ hr}^{-1}$$

$$\ln m_0/m = kt = \ln m_0 - \ln m$$

$$\ln (1.0) - (0.408 \text{ hr}^{-1})(10.0 \text{ hr}) = \ln m$$

$$\ln m = 0 - 4.08$$

$$m = 0.017 \text{ g}$$

Less than 2% of the original sample remains after 10.0 hours.

## SECTION 22-3: STABILITY SERIES

Study Figure 22-4 and Table 22-2 and note the following:

1. Most stable isotopes contain more neutrons than protons; neutrons reduce the charge density of their nuclei;

2. Many stable isotopes have even numbers of neutrons and protons;

3. Radioactive isotopes decay so as to achieve stability: $\beta^-$ emission reduces the number of neutrons, $\beta^+$ emission and EC reduce the number of protons, while $\alpha$ decay, which reduces both protons and neutrons, is observed in isotopes beyond mercury, element 80;

4. Magic numbers of protons and neutrons provide a rough indicator of nuclear stability.

The shell theory of nuclear structure incorporates several features of modern atomic theory, but it is not as extensively developed. Nuclear quantum shells of protons and neutrons occur at the magic numbers of 2, 8, 20, 28, 50, 82, and 126, analogous to electronic shells, which close at the noble gases. Just as the noble gases undergo very few chemical reactions, isotopes having magic numbers of protons or neutrons tend to be stable to radioactive decay. The last element having stable isotopes is bismuth, number 83, although several other heavy elements have isotopes with extremely long half-lives. Be sure to study Figure 22-5, which shows the decay paths of $^{235}U$ and $^{238}U$. Each decays, through many steps, to lead.

Example 3

All isotopes of the noble gas radon are radioactive. Radon-223 decays by beta emission to a product which emits both an alpha and a beta particle. Write the reaction scheme which describes these early steps in the $^{223}Rn$ decay chain.

Solution: Beta emission converts a neutron to a proton, so *Z* increases by one and *A* is unchanged. Alpha decay reduces *A* by four and *Z* by two.

$$^{223}_{86}Rn \rightarrow \beta^- + {}^{223}_{87}Fr \begin{cases} \nearrow \beta^- + {}^{223}_{88}Ra \\ \searrow \alpha + {}^{219}_{85}At \end{cases}$$

Radon decays to francium, an alkali metal, which decays to radium, an alkaline-earth metal, and astatine, a halogen. These isotopes eventually decay to lead.

## SECTION 22-4: NUCLEAR REACTIONS

Three types of reactions are discussed in this section: bombardment, fission, and fusion. Transmutation of an element can be effected by bombarding one nucleus with another, providing there is sufficient kinetic energy to overcome the coulombic repulsion of the two nuclei. Neutron bombardment is easier to accomplish, because neutrons are uncharged. All the elements beyond uranium must be synthesized by bombardment reactions. The yields of these reactions, which take place in accelerators, are small, sometimes only a few atoms.

According to the shell theory of nuclear structure, an island of nuclear stability should exist around element 114. The isotope of element 114 of mass number 298 would have a magic number of both protons and neutrons, and thus should be very stable. If element 114 is synthesized, then it might be possible to prepare a series of elements having occupied 5 *g* orbitals, the hypotransition metals.

Fission is a reaction in which neutron bombardment splits a large nucleus into smaller ones. This is the type of reaction which occurs in nuclear reactors and atomic bombs. Uranium-235 can be split into two nuclei and three neutrons upon bombardment with one neutron. If enough $^{235}U$ nuclei, the critical mass, are present in a sample, the reaction can proceed rapidly by a chain mechanism, causing an explosion. Controlling this chain reaction requires that some of the neutrons be absorbed; for example, by cadmium. Uranium-235 can be concentrated in a sample by converting naturally occurring uranium to $UF_6(g)$, then separating $^{235}UF_6(g)$ from $^{238}UF_6(g)$ by differential effusion.

A nuclear-power plant produces electricity by using the heat produced by controlled $^{235}U$ fission to boil water. The steam drives a turbine, which generates electrical current, just as in fossil-fuel-fired power plants. At the present time, nuclear energy cannot be directly converted to electrical energy.

Fusion of small nuclei releases large amounts of energy without generating the radioactive products of fission reactions. However, the energy required to initiate a large-scale fusion reaction is attained in very hot plasmas, or ionized gases, which are extremely difficult to contain. Lasers can be used to generate a plasma. The magnetic bottle technique for plasma containment holds promise, but it will be many years before fusion becomes commercially available as a source of power.

## SECTION 22-5: APPLICATIONS OF NUCLEAR CHEMISTRY AND ISOTOPES

The analytical techniques discussed in this section take advantage of the fact that isotopes, whether radioactive or not, allow one to follow the course of individual atoms in a chemical reaction. Five types of applications are described:

1. Isotopic labeling: substitution of a particular isotope for certain atoms in a molecule, which aids in elucidation of reaction mechanism;

2. Radiometric analysis: quantitative analysis by measuring radioactivity, rather than by isolation and weighing of the substance of interest;

3. Isotope dilution: quantitative analysis for systems in which isolation is difficult, by mixing a known quantity of radioactively labeled compound with the sample to be analyzed;

4. Radiocarbon dating: method of determining ages of carbon-containing materials derived from living organisms by measuring radioactivity of $^{14}C$ in sample; counting tree rings is one way to check accuracy;

5. Other dating methods: similar to radiocarbon dating, but primarily used for

nonorganic materials; several methods, K/Ar, Rb/Sr, $^{40}Ar/^{39}Ar$, $^{238}U/^{206}Pb$, provide independent checks.

Example 4

All iostopes of technetium, element 43, are radioactive. $^{99m}Tc$, an excited state of $^{99}Tc$, is used in various medical procedures. How may disintegrations per minute would take place in the body of a patient who was given 1.0 μg of $^{99m}Tc$?

Solution: The question asks for the rate of disintegration, $-dn/dt$. The rate of a reaction is calculated using the rate law in differential form. For a first-order process, it is $-dn/dt = kn$. The rate constant, $k$, is obtained from the half-life. The number of atoms present is calculated from the mass of the isotope, 1.0 μg.

$$t_{\frac{1}{2}} = (\ln 2)/k = 0.693/k$$

$$6.0 \text{ hr} = 0.693/k$$

$$k = 0.115 \text{ hr}^{-1}$$

$$n = \frac{(1.0\ \mu\text{g})(10^{-6}\ \text{g}/\mu\text{g})(6.02 \times 10^{23}\ \text{atoms/mol})}{98.9\ \text{g/mol}}$$

$$n = 6.09 \times 10^{15} \text{ atoms}$$

$$\text{rate} = -dn/dt = (0.115 \text{ hr}^{-1})(6.09 \times 10^{15} \text{ atoms})$$

$$-dn/dt = 7.0 \times 10^{14} \text{ atoms/hr} = 1.2 \times 10^{13} \text{ atoms/min}$$

Note: $^{99m}Tc$ decays to ground-state $^{99}Tc$, which has a half-life of $2.12 \times 10^5$ yr, and thus does very little, if any, harm to the patient.

Terms to Know

alpha particle
artificial elements
beta particle
binding energy
critical mass
electric quadrupole moment
electron capture
fission
fusion
gamma radiation
half-life
hypotransition metals
isotope dilution
isotopic tagging
magic numbers
neutron bombardment
nucleons
positron
radioactive isotope
radiocarbon dating
radioisotope dating

radiometric analysis
specific activity
stable isotope

## Test Yourself

1. Technetium-99m ($^{99m}Tc$), used in the diagnosis of heart disease, decays by gamma emission. One $\gamma$ is given off, of energy 142.7 keV. What are its frequency and wavelength?

2. Calculate the size of a $^{99}Tc$ nucleus, and compare it to the size of a $^{12}C$ nucleus.

3. Platinum-191 decays by electron capture with a 3.0-day half-life.

   a. What is the product of the decay process?

   b. How many $^{191}Pt$ atoms remain after a 25-mg sample has decayed for two weeks?

4. Complete the following decay path, in which polonium-207 is transformed into lead:

$$^{207}_{84}Po \longrightarrow \beta^+ + \_\_\_\_\_\_ \xrightarrow{EC} \_\_\_\_\_\_$$

5. Complete the multistep decay scheme for the transformation of polonium-215 into lead:

$$^{215}_{84}Po \longrightarrow \alpha + \_\_\_\_ \longrightarrow \beta^- + \_\_\_\_ \nearrow \alpha + \_\_\_\_ \longrightarrow \beta^- + {}^{207}_{82}Pb$$

$$\searrow \beta^- + \_\_\_\_ \longrightarrow \alpha + {}^{207}_{82}Pb$$

6. Tellurium-123, a Group VIA element, decays by electron capture.

   a. Write an equation which describes the decay process.

   b. Calculate the energy released during this spontaneous transmutation.

7. The most abundant stable isotope of indium, a metal in Group IIIA, is $^{115}In$. By what modes would you expect $^{124}In$, $^{121}In$, and $^{109}In$ to decay?

8. The only stable isotope of scandium, the lightest transition metal, is $^{45}Sc$. Predict by which modes the isotopes $^{40}Sc$, $^{41}Sc$, and $^{50}Sc$ would decay.

9. A sample of conglomerate rock containing shells of marine animals has a $^{14}C$ disintegration rate of 8.6 c/m·g of C. How old are the shells in this rock?

10. The solvent ethyl acetate is an organic ester, a compound synthesized from an alcohol and a carboxylic acid:

$$\underset{\text{acetic acid}}{CH_3\text{-}\overset{O}{\overset{\|}{C}}\text{-}O\text{-}H} + \underset{\text{ethyl alcohol}}{H\text{-}O\text{-}CH_2\text{-}CH_3} \longrightarrow \underset{\text{ethyl acetate}}{CH_3\text{-}\overset{O}{\overset{\|}{C}}\text{-}O\text{-}CH_2\text{-}CH_3} + H_2O$$

Suggest a way in which isotopes could be used to determine whether the O-H or the O-C bond in ethanol is broken in this reaction.

11. A 2.00-mL sample containing a small amount of $Hg^{2+}$ is treated with $H_2S$, 100% labeled with $^{35}S$. The half-life of $^{35}S$ is 88 days. The HgS which precipitates is collected and washed free of excess $H_2S$. If the activity of 1.00 millimole of $^{35}S$ is $3.29 \times 10^{15}$ counts/min and the activity of the HgS is $5.64 \times 10^{9}$ counts/min, how many millimoles of $Hg^{2+}$ were present in the sample? What was the molarity of $Hg^{2+}$?

12. Radon-224, the heaviest known noble gas, decays through a series of steps to lead-208, which is stable. Trace the decay of $^{224}Rn$ by completing the scheme which follows.

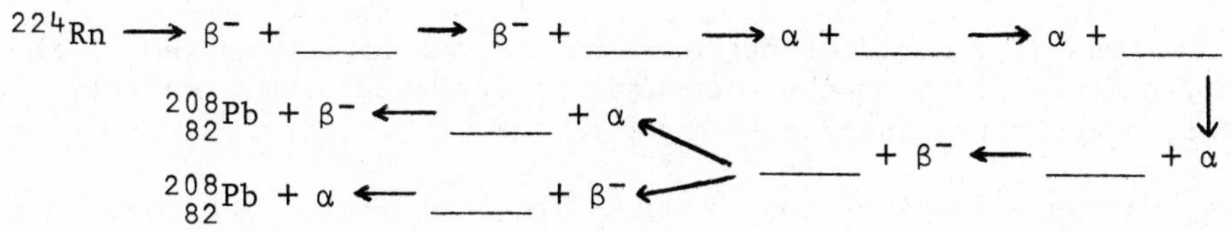

$^{224}Rn \longrightarrow \beta^- +$ _____ $\longrightarrow \beta^- +$ _____ $\longrightarrow \alpha +$ _____ $\longrightarrow \alpha +$ _____ $\downarrow$

$^{208}_{82}Pb + \beta^- \longleftarrow$ _____ $+ \alpha \nwarrow$

_____ $+ \beta^- \longleftarrow$ _____ $+ \alpha$

$^{208}_{82}Pb + \alpha \longleftarrow$ _____ $+ \beta^- \swarrow$

13. Potassium-argon dating can be used to determine the age of certain rocks.

a. Write an equation describing the decay of $^{40}K$ to $^{40}Ar$.

b. The half-life of $^{40}K$ is $1.28 \times 10^{9}$ years. A rock sample is found to contain 2.5 times as much $^{40}Ar$ as $^{40}K$ by weight. How old is the rock?

c. What assumptions did you make when calculating the age of the sample in part b?

# Appendix: Solutions

CHAPTER 1

1. a. $^{58}Co^{2+}$ has a mass number of 58 and an atomic number of 27. Because it has a charge of +2, it has two fewer electrons than protons. The number of protons is the same as the atomic number. The number of neutrons is obtained by subtracting the atomic number from the mass number. There are 27 protons, 31 neutrons, and 25 electrons in $^{58}Co^{2+}$.

   b. $^{79}Se^{2-}$ has a mass number of 79, an atomic number of 34, and a charge of -2. Therefore, it has two more electrons than protons. Subtract the atomic number from the mass number to obtain the number of neutrons. There are 34 protons, 45 neutrons, and 36 electrons in $^{79}Se^{2-}$.

2. The mass excess is the difference between the sum of the masses of the protons, neutrons, and electrons in the atom and the observed atomic weight. There are 7 protons, 8 neutrons, and 7 electrons in $^{15}_{7}N$.

$$\text{mass excess} = (\text{mass protons} + \text{mass electrons} + \text{mass neutrons}) - \text{atomic weight}$$

$$\text{mass excess} = [7p(1.00728\ \text{amu}/p) + 7\bar{e}(0.00055\ \text{amu}/\bar{e}) + 8n(1.00867\ \text{amu}/n)] - 15.00011\ \text{amu}$$

$$= [7.05096 + 0.00385 + 8.06936 - 15.00011]\ \text{amu}$$

$$= 0.12406\ \text{amu}$$

3. The natural atomic weight is a weighted average of the weights of the isotopes. It is calculated by multiplying the percent abundance of an isotope by the weight of the isotope and then adding the results.

$$0.00337 \times 35.96755\ \text{amu} = 0.13560\ \text{amu}$$

$$0.00063 \times 37.96272\ \text{amu} = 0.02392\ \text{amu}$$

$$0.9960 \times 39.948\ \text{amu} = \underline{39.788\ \text{amu}}$$

$$39.948\ \text{amu}$$

4. The natural atomic weight is calculated by multiplying the abundance of an isotope by the weight of the isotope and then adding the results. In this problem, the two percent abundances are to be calculated. Because the sum of the two abundances must be unity, we can express one abundance as $x$ and the other as $1 - x$.

$$(\text{abundance})(V - 50) + (\text{abundance})(V - 51) = \text{natural atomic weight}$$

$$(x)(49.9472) + (1 - x)(50.9440) = 50.942$$

$$49.9472x + 50.9440 - 50.9440x = 50.942$$

$$0.9968x = 0.0020$$

$$x = 0.0020$$

$$1 - x = 0.9980$$

5. a. The formula for silver dichromate is $Ag_2Cr_2O_7$. The formula weight is obtained by multiplying the atomic weight of each atom in the molecule by the number of times it appears in the formula and then adding the results.

$$2 \times 107.87 = 215.74$$

$$2 \times 51.99 = 103.98$$

$$7 \times 16.00 = \underline{112.00}$$

$$431.72 \text{ amu}$$

b. $Ni_3(PO_4)_2$ is the formula for nickel (II) phosphate. Be sure to include each atom in the phosphate group twice when calculating the formula weight.

$$3 \times 58.71 = 176.13$$

$$2 \times 30.97 = 61.94$$

$$8 \times 16.00 = \underline{128.00}$$

$$366.07 \text{ amu}$$

c. The formula for calcium chlorite is $Ca(ClO_2)_2$. Don't forget that there are two chlorites in the formula.

$$1 \times 40.08 = 40.08$$

$$2 \times 35.45 = 70.90$$

$$4 \times 16.00 = \underline{64.00}$$

$$174.98 \text{ amu}$$

d. $Al_2(S_2O_3)_3$ is the formula for aluminum thiosulfate. The formula weight is calculated as follows:

$$2 \times 26.98 = 53.96$$

$$6 \times 32.06 = 192.36$$

$$9 \times 16.00 = \underline{144.00}$$

$$390.32 \text{ amu}$$

6. The number of heartbeats per minute is given. We must calculate the number of years required to count a mole of heartbeats. A mole consists of $6.02 \times 10^{23}$ heartbeats.

$$6.02 \times 10^{23} \text{ heartbeats} \times \frac{1 \text{ minute}}{72 \text{ heartbeats}} \times \frac{1 \text{ hour}}{60 \text{ min}} \times \frac{1 \text{ day}}{24 \text{ hours}} \times \frac{1 \text{ year}}{365 \text{ days}}$$

$$= 1.59 \times 10^{16} \text{ years}$$

7. We are given the number of moles of silver dichromate ($Ag_2Cr_2O_7$). To calculate the mass, multiply the number of moles by the molecular weight.

$$0.125 \text{ mol } Ag_2Cr_2O_7 \times \frac{421.72 \text{ g}}{1 \text{ mol } Ag_2Cr_2O_7} = 54.0 \text{ g}$$

8. The number of chromium atoms can be calculated by multiplying the number of moles of silver dichromate by the number of moles of chromium per mole of silver dichromate. Then multiply by Avogadro's number, the number of atoms per mole.

$$0.125 \text{ mol } Ag_2Cr_2O_7 \times \frac{2 \text{ mol Cr}}{1 \text{ mol } Ag_2Cr_2O_7} \times \frac{6.02 \times 10^{23} \text{ atoms}}{1 \text{ mol}}$$

$$= 1.51 \times 10^{23} \text{ chromium atoms}$$

9. We are given the mass of calcium chlorite, and we must calculate the number of moles. To do this, divide by the molecular weight of calcium chlorite, calculated in problem 5.

$$25.00 \text{ g } Ca(ClO_2)_2 \times \frac{1 \text{ mol } Ca(ClO_2)_2}{174.98 \text{ g}}$$

$$= 0.1429 \text{ mol calcium chlorite}$$

## CHAPTER 2

1. a. First, calculate the molecular weight of calcium phosphate.

$$3 \times 40.08 = 120.24$$

$$2 \times 30.97 = 61.94$$

$$8 \times 16.00 = \underline{128.00}$$

$$310.18 \text{ g mol}^{-1}$$

Next, divide the mass of the sample by the molecular weight.

$$10.0 \text{ g } Ca_3(PO_4)_2 \times \frac{1 \text{ mol } Ca_3(PO_4)_2}{310.18 \text{ g}} = 0.0322 \text{ mol}$$

b. There are 8 oxygen atoms per mole of $Ca_3(PO_4)_2$; therefore, the number of moles of O is eight times the number of moles of $Ca_3(PO_4)_2$.

$$0.0322 \text{ mol } Ca_3(PO_4)_2 \times \frac{8 \text{ mol O}}{1 \text{ mol } Ca_3(PO_4)_2} = 0.258 \text{ mol O}$$

c. First, calculate the number of moles of phosphorus by multiplying the number of moles of calcium phosphate by two. Then, multiply the result by Avogadro's number to determine the number of P atoms.

$$0.0322 \text{ mol } Ca_3(PO_4)_2 \times \frac{2 \text{ mol P}}{1 \text{ mol } Ca_3(PO_4)_2} \times \frac{6.02 \times 10^{23} \text{ atoms}}{1 \text{ mol}}$$

$$= 3.88 \times 10^{22} \text{ P atoms}$$

d. Determine the number of moles of calcium, and then multiply the result by the molecular weight of calcium.

$$0.0322 \text{ mol } Ca_3(PO_4)_2 \times \frac{3 \text{ mol Ca}}{1 \text{ mol } Ca_3(PO_4)_2} \times \frac{40.08 \text{ g}}{1 \text{ mol Ca}} = 3.87 \text{ g Ca}$$

e. Multiply the number of moles of $Ca_3(PO_4)_2$ by Avogadro's number to calculate the number of molecules.

$$0.0322 \text{ mol } Ca_3(PO_4)_2 \times \frac{6.02 \times 10^{23} \text{ molecules}}{1 \text{ mol}}$$

$$= 1.94 \times 10^{22} \; Ca_3(PO_4)_2 \text{ "molecules," i.e. formula units}$$

2. First balance the atoms that appear in only one reactant and one product.

$$Ca_3(PO_4)_2 + SiO_2 + C \xrightarrow{\Delta} P_4 + CaSiO_3 + CO$$

Start by balancing the P atoms.

$$2Ca_3(PO_4)_2 + SiO_2 + C \xrightarrow{\Delta} P_4 + CaSiO_3 + CO$$

Next, balance the Ca atoms.

$$2Ca_3(PO_4)_2 + SiO_2 + C \xrightarrow{\Delta} P_4 + 6CaSiO_3 + CO$$

Now, balance the Si atoms.

$$2Ca_3(PO_4)_2 + 6SiO_2 + C \xrightarrow{\Delta} P_4 + 6CaSiO_3 + CO$$

Finally, balance the C and O atoms.

$$2Ca_3(PO_4)_2 + 6SiO_2 + 10C \xrightarrow{\Delta} P_4 + 6CaSiO_3 + CO$$

Double-check to be sure the reaction is properly balanced.

| | Reactants | Products |
|---|---|---|
| C atoms: | $2 \times 3 = 6$ | $6 \times 1 = 6$ |
| P atoms: | $4 \times 1 = 4$ | $4 \times 1 = 4$ |
| O atoms: | $(8 \times 2) + (6 \times 2) = 28$ | $(6 \times 3) + (10 \times 1) = 28$ |
| Si atoms: | $6 \times 1 = 6$ | $6 \times 1 = 6$ |
| C atoms: | $10 \times 1 = 10$ | $10 \times 1 = 10$ |

3. The equation for this process is as follows:

$$Zn(s) + H^+(aq) \longrightarrow H_2(g) + Zn^{2+}(aq)$$

For a chemical equation to be balanced, both the atoms and the charge must be balanced. A coefficient of 2 for $H^+(aq)$ will accomplish this.

$$Zn(s) + 2H^+(aq) \longrightarrow H_2(g) + Zn^{2+}(aq)$$

4. We are given the balanced chemical equation and the mass of $O_2$ that is to be produced. We are asked to calculate the mass of $KMnO_4$ that is required. To do this, first convert the mass of $O_2$ to moles. Next, use the balanced equation to determine the relative amount of $KMnO_4$ necessary. Finally, convert the moles of potassium permanganate to grams.

$$5H_2O + 2KMnO_4 + 3H_2SO_4 \longrightarrow 5O_2 + 2MnSO_4 + K_2SO_4 + 8H_2O$$

$$64.0 \text{ g } O_2 \times \frac{1 \text{ mol } O_2}{32.0 \text{ g}} \times \frac{2 \text{ mol } KMnO_4}{5 \text{ mol } O_2} \times \frac{158.04 \text{ g}}{1 \text{ mol } KMnO_4} = 126 \text{ g } KMnO_4$$

5. We are given the mass of each reactant and asked to calculate the mass of product that can be formed. To do this, first calculate the number of moles of each reactant.

$$10.0 \times 10^3 \text{ g } C_3H_6 \times \frac{1 \text{ mol } C_3H_6}{42.09 \text{ g}} = 238 \text{ mol } C_3H_6$$

$$10.0 \times 10^3 \text{ g NO} \times \frac{1 \text{ mol NO}}{30.01 \text{ g}} = 333 \text{ mol NO}$$

To determine which reagent is limiting, divide the number of moles of each substance by its numerical coefficient in the balanced chemical equation.

$$4C_3H_6 + 6NO \longrightarrow 4C_3H_3N + 6H_2O + N_2$$

$$\frac{238 \text{ mol } C_3H_6}{4} = 59.5 \qquad \frac{333 \text{ mol NO}}{6} = 55.5$$

From this calculation, we see that NO is the limiting reagent (even though there is a larger number of moles of NO present). Since NO is the limiting reagent, the amount of product formed is proportional to the amount of NO that is present.

$$333 \text{ mol NO} \quad \frac{4 \text{ mol } C_3H_3N}{6 \text{ mol NO}} \times \frac{53.07 \text{ g}}{1 \text{ mol } C_3H_3N} \times \frac{1 \text{ kg}}{1000 \text{ g}} = 11.8 \text{ kg } C_3H_3N$$

Be sure to express the answer in the proper units.

6. a. Given: $KCN(aq) + Fe(NO_3)_2(aq) \longrightarrow K_4[Fe(CN)_6](aq) + K^+(aq) + NO_3^-(aq)$
Balance C first, because it only appears once on each side.

$$6KCN(aq) + Fe(NO_3)_2(aq) \longrightarrow K_4[Fe(CN)_6](aq) + K^+(aq) + NO_3^-(aq)$$

Coefficients of 2 in front of $K^+(aq)$ and $NO_3^-(aq)$ will balance both the atoms and the charge. Fe is also balanced.

$$6KCN(aq) + Fe(NO_3)_2(aq) \longrightarrow K_4[Fe(CN)_6](aq) + 2K^+(aq) + 2NO_3^-(aq)$$

b. We are given the mass of potassium cyanide that is to react. We must calculate the volume of 0.100 M $Fe(NO_3)_2$ that is required. To do this, we must first change KCN from grams to moles. Then, use the balanced equation to determine the number of moles of $Fe(NO_3)_2$ that are necessary. Finally, use the concentration of the solution to calculate the necessary volume.

$$5.50 \text{ g KCN} \times \frac{1 \text{ mol KCN}}{65.12 \text{ g}} \times \frac{1 \text{ mol } Fe(NO_3)_2}{6 \text{ mol KCN}} = 0.0141 \text{ mol } Fe(NO_3)_2$$

$$0.0141 \text{ mol } Fe(NO_3)_2 \times \frac{1 \text{ L}}{0.100 \text{ mol } Fe(NO_3)_2} = 0.141 \text{ L of } 0.100 \text{ M } Fe(NO_3)_2$$

7. a. To determine the equivalent weight of the acid, calculate the number of millimoles of base that were necessary for neutralization. In this case, the number of millimoles of base is equal to the number of milliequivalents. Then, divide the mass of the acid by the number of milliequivalents.

$$24.73 \text{ mL KOH} \times \frac{0.1011 \text{ mmol}}{\text{mL}} = 2.5 \text{ mmol KOH}$$

$$\frac{225.2 \text{ mg acid}}{2.5 \text{ meq}} = 90.1 \text{ mg/meq}$$

b. If the acid contains one acidic proton, the molecular weight is equal to the equivalent weight: 90.1 g $mol^{-1}$.

8. We are given the following information:

$$HgO(s) \longrightarrow Hg(l) + \tfrac{1}{2}O_2\ (g) \qquad \Delta H° = 90.8 \text{ kJ}$$

We are asked to calculate the number of kJ of heat required to decompose 10.0 g of HgO. First, calculate the number of moles of HgO. Then, multiply by the value of ΔH°, which is given in kJ per mole.

$$10.0 \text{ g HgO} \times \frac{1 \text{ mol HgO}}{216.59 \text{ g}} \times \frac{90.8 \text{ kJ}}{1 \text{ mol HgO}} = 4.19 \text{ kJ}$$

9. To calculate the enthalpy change for the process $CO(g) + 2H_2(g) \longrightarrow CH_3OH(l)$, we must add the given reactions in a way that will produce the desired reaction. This process involves reversing some of the reactions. When a reaction is reversed, the sign of ΔH changes. Finally, add all of the ΔH's to calculate the enthalpy change. (Use only the reactions that are necessary.)

| | ΔH(kJ) |
|---|---|
| $CO(g) + \cancel{H_2}(g) \longrightarrow \cancel{H_2O}(g) + \cancel{C}(gr)$ | -130 |
| $\cancel{C} + 2H_2 + \cancel{\tfrac{1}{2}O_2} \longrightarrow CH_3OH(l)$ | -239 |
| $\cancel{H_2O}(g) \longrightarrow \cancel{H_2} + \cancel{\tfrac{1}{2}O_2}$ | +286 |
| $CO(g) + 2H_2(g) \longrightarrow CH_3OH(l)$ | -83 kJ |

## CHAPTER 3

1. We are given a sample of gas at constant $T$ and $n$. We are asked to find the change in pressure that will produce a 25% decrease in volume (i.e., $V_2 = 0.75\ V_1$). Boyle's law tells us that $PV$ = constant, or $P_1V_1 = P_2V_2$.

$$P_1V_1 = P_2(0.75)V_1$$

Because $PV$ = constant, if $V$ decreases, $P$ must increase.

$$P_1V_1/0.75V_1 = P_2$$

$$1.3P_1 = P_2$$

For a 25% decrease in volume, the final pressure must be 1.3 times the initial pressure.

2. Charles' law gives the relationship between temperature and volume: $V$ = constant × $T$. From this relationship we can see that if the temperature is increased, the volume must also increase. If the potato is not pricked with a fork, it will explode, because the water within vaporizes and expands.

3. We are given the initial volume and temperature of a hydrogen-gas thermometer. We are asked to calculate the temperature that corresponds to a volume of 655.0 mL. Because volume is directly proportional to temperature, we can make a ratio: $V_1/T_1 = V_2/T_2$. Substitute the given data ($V_1, T_1, V_2$) and solve for $T_2$.

$$T_2 = \frac{V_2 T_1}{T_1} = \frac{(0.655\ \text{L})(100°\text{C})}{(1\ \text{L})} = 65.5°\text{C}$$

4. a. The balanced equation for the synthesis of ammonia from hydrogen and nitrogen is

$$N_2(g) + 3H_2(g) \longrightarrow 2NH_3(g)$$

b. If the temperature and pressure remain constant, the volume is proportional to the number of moles. Divide each volume by the corresponding stoichiometric coefficient to determine which reagent is limiting.

$$75\ \text{L}\ H_2/3 = 25$$

$$28\ \text{L}\ N_2/1 = 28$$

$H_2$ is the limiting reagent. Therefore, 2 × 25 = 50 L of $NH_3$ will be produced.

c. Avogadro's law, $V \propto n$ at constant temperature and pressure, was used to solve this problem.

5. We are given the mass and volume of a gas at STP (273 K, 1 atm), and we are asked to calculate its molecular weight. First, use the ideal gas law to calculate the number of moles.

$$PV = nRT$$

$$n = \frac{PV}{RT} = \frac{(1\ \text{atm})(2.80\ \text{L})}{(0.08205\ \text{L}\cdot\text{atm/mol}\cdot\text{K})(273\ \text{K})}$$

$$n = 0.125\ \text{moles}$$

Divide the mass of the sample by the number of moles to determine the molecular weight.

$$\frac{5.75\ \text{g}}{0.125\ \text{mol}} = 46.0\ \text{g mol}^{-1}$$

6. a. We are given the temperature and pressure at which a sample containing $HCO_3^-$ reacts. We are also given the balanced equation for the reaction. We are asked to calculate the number of moles of $CO_2$ produced. To do this, use the ideal gas law and solve for $n$. First, convert the units of pressure from torr to atm, and convert the temperature from Celsius

to Kelvin.

$$756.8 \text{ torr} \times \frac{1 \text{ atm}}{760 \text{ torr}} = 0.996 \text{ atm}$$

$$23°\text{C} + 273 = 298 \text{ K}$$

$$PV = nRT$$

$$n = \frac{PV}{RT} = \frac{(0.996 \text{ atm})(0.04163 \text{ L})}{(0.08205 \text{ L·atm/mol·K})(298 \text{ K})}$$

$$n = 0.00170 \text{ mol } CO_2$$

b. To determine the mass percent of $HCO_3^-$ in the sample, first convert the moles of $HCO_3^-$ (which is equal to the moles of $CO_2$) to grams.

$$0.00170 \text{ mol } HCO_3^- \times \frac{61.02 \text{ g}}{1 \text{ mol } HCO_3^-} = 0.1037 \text{ g } HCO_3^-$$

Because the stoichiometric ratio of $CO_2$:$HCO_3^-$ is 1:1, we can calculate the mass percent of $HCO_3^-$ directly. Proceed by dividing the mass of $HCO_3^-$ by the mass of the sample.

$$\frac{0.1037 \text{ g } HCO_3^-}{0.2742 \text{ g sample}} = 0.3782 = 37.82\% \text{ } HCO_3^-$$

7. We are given the time required for a quantity of argon to effuse. We are also given the time required for an unknown gas (at the same temperature and pressure) to effuse.

a. To determine the molecular weight of the unknown, we must derive a relationship between time necessary for effusion and molecular weight. We are given the relationship $v_{rms} = \sqrt{3RT/M}$. We also know that velocity is inversely proportional to time.

$$1/\text{time} = \sqrt{3RT/M}$$

The temperature remains constant throughout; therefore, we can make a ratio and solve for the molecular weight of the unknown.

$$\frac{\text{time}_{\text{Argon}}}{\text{time}_{\text{unknown}}} = \sqrt{\frac{\text{MW}_{\text{Argon}}}{\text{MW}_{\text{unknown}}}}$$

$$\frac{(\text{time}_{\text{Argon}})^2}{(\text{time}_{\text{unknown}})^2} = \frac{\text{MW}_{\text{Argon}}}{\text{MW}_{\text{unknown}}}$$

$$\frac{(60 \text{ min})^2}{(19 \text{ min})^2} = \frac{39.95 \text{ g mol}^{-1}}{\text{MW}_{\text{unknown}}}$$

$$\text{MW}_{\text{unknown}} = \frac{(39.95)(19 \text{ min})^2}{(60 \text{ min})^2}$$

$$\text{MW}_{\text{unknown}} = 4.01 \text{ g mol}^{-1}$$

b. If the unknown is an element, the molecular weight indicates that it is helium.

## CHAPTER 4

1. a. $K_{eq} = [O_2]^{\frac{1}{2}}$

 b. The yield of the reaction would increase if $O_2$ were removed as it was produced. Stressing the system in this way would cause more HgO to decompose. A second way to increase the yield of the reaction is to raise the temperature.

2. a. $$K_{eq} = \frac{[H_2O]^2[SO_2]^2}{[O_2]^3[H_2S]^2}$$

 b. $$K_{eq} = \frac{[SO_3]^2}{[O_2]^3}$$

 c. $$K_{eq} = \frac{1}{[O_2]}$$

 d. $$K_{eq} = \frac{[O_2]^{3/2}[H_2S]}{[SO_2][H_2O]}$$

3. Derive the relationship between $K_c$ and $K_p$ using the ideal gas law.

$$P = \frac{nRT}{V} \text{ and } \frac{n}{V} = \text{concentration}$$

$$P = (\frac{n}{V})RT = c\ RT \qquad c = p/RT$$

 a. $$K_p = \frac{(P_{H_2O})^2(P_{SO_2})^2}{(P_{O_2})^3(P_{H_2S})^2} \qquad K_c = \frac{(P_{H_2O}/RT)^2(P_{SO_2}/RT)^2}{(P_{O_2}/RT)^3(P_{H_2S}/RT)^2} = K_p(RT)$$

 b. $$K_p = \frac{(P_{SO_2})^2}{(P_{O_2})^3} \qquad K_c = \frac{(P_{SO_2}/RT)^2}{(P_{O_2}/RT)^3} = K_p(RT)$$

 c. $$K_p = \frac{1}{(P_{O_2})} \qquad K_c = \frac{1}{(P_{O_2}/RT)} = K_p(RT)$$

 d. $$K_p = \frac{(P_{O_2})^{3/2}(P_{H_2S})}{(P_{SO_2})(P_{H_2O})} \qquad K_c = \frac{(P_{O_2}/RT)^{3/2}(P_{H_2S}/RT)}{(P_{SO_2}/RT)(P_{H_2O}/RT)} = K_p/\sqrt{RT}$$

4. First, write the expressions for the two equilibrium constants:

$$K_{eq} - a = [SO_2]^2[H_2O]^2/[O_2]^3[H_2S]^2$$

$K_{eq} - d = [O_2]^{3/2}[H_2S]/[SO_2][H_2O]$

By inspection, we can see that $K_{eq} - d$ is the square root of the reciprocal of $K_{eq} - a$.

5. A large value for $K$ indicates that the reaction has gone nearly to completion.

   a. $K$ for this process has a very small value. Therefore, the reaction will not go to completion.

   b. This reaction has a large $K$. It will go nearly to completion.

   c. The equilibrium lies to the right because $K > 1$, but it will not approach completion.

   d. This reaction will not approach completion ($K < 1$).

6. a. We are given the balanced chemical equation, $K_p$, and the partial pressures of two of the three gases. Solve the $K_p$ expression for the partial pressure of phosgene, $COCl_2$.

$$K_p = P_{COCl_2}/P_{Cl_2}P_{CO}$$

$$P_{COCl_2} = K_pP_{Cl_2}P_{CO}$$

$$= (71.3)(0.493 \text{ atm})(0.263 \text{ atm})$$

$$= 9.25 \text{ atm}$$

   b. Set up a chart to determine the equilibrium pressure of each gas.

$$P_{COCl_2} = \frac{(1.00 \text{ mol})(0.08205 \text{ L·atm/mol·K})(673 \text{ K})}{(10.0) \text{ L}} = 5.52 \text{ atm}$$

| Pressure (atm) | CO | $Cl_2$ | $COCl_2$ |
|---|---|---|---|
| start | 0 | 0 | 5.52 |
| change | $+X$ | $+X$ | $-X$ |
| equilibrium | $X$ | $X$ | $5.52 - X$ |

Substitute these values into the expression for $K_p$.

$$K_p = P_{COCl_2}/P_{Cl_2}P_{CO} = (5.52 - X)/(X)(X) = 71.3$$

$$5.52 - X = 71.3X^2$$

$$71.3X^2 + X - 5.52 = 0$$

Solve for $X$ using the quadratic formula.

$$X = \frac{b \pm \sqrt{b^2 - 4ac}}{2a} = \frac{-1 \pm \sqrt{1 - 4(71.3)(-5.52)}}{2(71.3)}$$

$$X = 0.27, -0.29$$

The negative value can be disregarded because it is not physically real. $p_{CO} = p_{Cl_2} = X = 0.27$ atm. $p_{COCl_2} = 5.52 - X = 5.25$ atm. Use the ideal gas law to calculate the number of moles of CO, $Cl_2$, and $COCl_2$.

$$n_{CO} = \frac{p_{CO}V}{RT} = \frac{(0.27 \text{ atm})(10.0 \text{ L})}{(0.08205 \text{ L·atm/mol·K})(673 \text{ K})} = 0.0489 \text{ mol CO}$$

$$n_{Cl_2} = n_{CO} = 0.0489 \text{ mol } Cl_2$$

$$n_{COCl_2} = \frac{p_{COCl_2}}{RT} = \frac{(5.25 \text{ atm})(10.0 \text{ L})}{(0.08205 \text{ L·atm/mol·K})(673 \text{ K})} = 0.951 \text{ mol } COCl_2$$

c. Calculate the starting pressure of each gas. Then set up a chart to determine the equilibrium pressure of each gas.

$$p_{CO} = \frac{nRT}{V} = \frac{(0.100 \text{ mol})(0.08205 \text{ L·atm/mol·K})(673 \text{ K})}{(5.0 \text{ L})} = 1.1 \text{ atm}$$

$$p_{Cl_2} = \frac{nRT}{V} = \frac{(0.200 \text{ mol})(0.08205 \text{ L·atm/mol·K})(673 \text{ K})}{(5.0 \text{ L})} = 2.2 \text{ atm}$$

| Pressure (atm) | CO | $Cl_2$ | $COCl_2$ |
|---|---|---|---|
| start | 1.1 | 2.2 | 0 |
| hange | $-X$ | $-X$ | $+X$ |
| equilibrium | $1.1 - X$ | $2.2 - X$ | $X$ |

Now, substitute these values into the $K_p$ expression.

$$K_p = \frac{p_{COCl_2}}{p_{CO}p_{Cl_2}} = 71.3 = \frac{X}{(1.1 - X)(2.2 - X)}$$

$$71.3(1.1 - X)(2.2 - X) = X$$

$$71.3(2.42 - 3.3X + X^2) = X$$

$$172.5 - 235.3X + X^2 = X$$

$$X^2 - 234.3X + 172.5 = 0$$

$$X = \frac{b \pm \sqrt{b^2 - 4ac}}{2a} = \frac{234.3 \pm \sqrt{(-234.3)^2 - 4(1)(172.5)}}{2(1)}$$

$$X = 233, 0.75.$$

Disregard the ridiculously large answer.

$$p_{COCl_2} = X = 0.75 \text{ atm at equilibrium.}$$

7. a. From the information given, we can see that as the temperature increases, $K_p$ decreases. Therefore, the reaction is exothermic. Supplying more heat favors the reactants.

   b. Because chlorine is one of the reactants, removing it will cause the equilibrium to shift to the left.

   c. Decreasing the volume of the reaction vessel will increase the pressure, causing the equilibrium to shift to the right.

   d. A catalyst will enable the reaction to reach equilibrium more quickly. It will not affect the position of the equilibrium.

## CHAPTER 5

1. The larger the value of $K_a$, the stronger the acid. In addition, the stronger the acid, the weaker the conjugate base. We are given the acid and its $K_a$. We are asked to arrange the acids in order of decreasing strength of the conjugate base. To do this, list the acids according to increasing $K_a$ values (decreasing base strength).

| | |
|---|---|
| o-boric acid | $K_a = 7.3 \times 10^{-10}$ |
| cacodylic acid | $K_a = 6.4 \times 10^{-7}$ |
| 3,6-dinitrophenol | $K_a = 7.1 \times 10^{-6}$ |
| n-caproic acid | $K_a = 1.43 \times 10^{-5}$ |
| benzosulfonic acid | $K_a = 2 \times 10^{-1}$ |

2. It is better to add $K_2SO_4$ to the lead (II) solution because the second proton in $H_2SO_4$ is not nearly as easily removed as the first. Therefore, there would be less free $SO_4^{2-}$ in solution.

3. We are given the pH and concentration of a solution of uric acid. We are asked to calculate the $K_a$. To do this, we must first convert the pH to $[H^+]$ and then substitute this value into the $K_a$ expression.

$$pH = -\log[H^+]$$

$$2.44 = -\log[H^+]$$

$$0.0036 = [H^+] = [C_5H_3N_4O_3^-]$$

$$K_a = \frac{[H^+][C_5H_3N_4O_3^-]}{[C_5H_4N_4O_3]} = \frac{(0.0036)(0.0036)}{(0.100)}$$

$$K_a = 1.3 \times 10^{-4}$$

4. We are given the $pK_b$ and the concentration of a solution of imidazol. We are asked to calculate the pH of the solution. First, convert the $pK_b$ to the $K_b$. Then, solve the $K_b$ expression for $[OH^-]$.

$$pK_b = -\log K_b$$

$7.05 = -\log K_b$

$8.9 \times 10^{-8} = K_b$

$K_b = \dfrac{[\text{imidazolium}^+][\text{OH}^-]}{[\text{imidazol}]}$ Let $X = [\text{OH}^-] = [\text{imidazolium}^+]$

$8.9 \times 10^{-8} = \dfrac{X^2}{0.015}$

$X = 3.6 \times 10^{-5} = [\text{OH}^-]$

Convert $[OH^-]$ to pOH and use the expression pH + pOH = 14 to calculate the pH.

$\text{pOH} = -\log(3.6 \times 10^{-5})$

$\text{pOH} = 4.44$

$\text{pH} + \text{pOH} = 14$

$\text{pH} = 14 - 4.44$

$\text{pH} = 9.56$

5. We are given the $K_b$ and concentration of a solution of hydroxylammonium chloride. We are asked to calculate the pH. First, write the chemical equation for the dissociation of hydroxylammonium ion.

$HONH_3^+ \rightleftharpoons H^+ + HONH_2$

$$K = \frac{[H^+][HONH_2]}{[HONH_3^+]}$$

The solution is acidic. The equilibrium constant for this reaction is calculated from $K_w$ and $K_b$:

$K = K_w/K_b = 1.00 \times 10^{-14}/(1.1 \times 10^{-8}) = 0.91 \times 10^{-6}$

Let $x = [H^+] = [HONH_2]$

$\dfrac{x^2}{0.18 - x} = 0.91 \times 10^{-6} \simeq \dfrac{x^2}{0.18}$

$x^2 = 0.16 \times 10^{-6}$

$x = 0.40 \times 10^{-3} = 4.0 \times 10^{-4}\ \text{M} = [H^+]$

$\text{pH} = -\log(4.0 \times 10^{-4}) = 3.40$

6. We are given the volume and concentration of a lactic acid solution. We are also given the pH of the buffer. We are asked to calculate the mass of KOH that must be added to produce this buffer. First, use the pH to determine $[H^+]$. Then, use the $K_a$ expression to determine the concentration of lactate ion that is necessary.

$\text{pH} = -\log[H^+]$

$3.70 = -\log[H^+]$

$2.0 \times 10^{-4}\ M = [H^+]$

$$K_a = \frac{[lac^-][H^+]}{[lactic\ acid]}$$

$$\frac{K_a\ [lactic\ acid]}{[H^+]} = [lac^-] = \frac{(1.37 \times 10^{-4})(0.115\ M)}{(2.0 \times 10^{-4}\ M)}$$

$[lac^-] = 0.0788\ M$

Lactate ion is present as potassium lactate, the potassium salt. Use the volume of the solution (6.00 L) and the calculated concentration of lactate ion to determine the number of moles of lactate that are necessary. The number of moles of lactate is equal to the number of moles of KOH that must be added. Multiply by the molecular weight of KOH to determine the mass that must be added.

$$\frac{0.0788\ mol\ lac^-}{L} \times 6.00\ L \times \frac{1\ mol\ KOH}{1\ mol\ lac^-} \times \frac{56.1\ g\ KOH}{1\ mol} = 26.5\ g\ KOH$$

7. We are given the $K_{sp}$ for lead (II) chloride at 25°C and 95°C. We are asked to calculate the volume of hot water that is necessary to dissolve 25.0 mg $PbCl_2$. First, calculate the solubility of $PbCl_2$ in water at 95°C.

$K_{sp} = [Pb^{2+}][Cl^-]^2 = 6 \times 10^{-3}$

Let $X$ be the solubility of $PbCl_2$. The $K_{sp}$ expression now becomes:

$K_{sp} = (X)(2X)^2 = 6 \times 10^{-3}$

$4X^3 = 6 \times 10^{-3}$

$X = 0.114\ mol\ L^{-1}$

Now convert 25.0 mg $PbCl_2$ to moles:

$$25.0\ mg\ PbCl_2 \times \frac{1\ g}{1000\ mg} \times \frac{1\ mol}{278.09\ g} = 8.99 \times 10^{-5}\ mol\ PbCl_2$$

Use the solubility (calculated above) to determine the volume of water that must be added.

$$8.99 \times 10^{-5}\ mol\ PbCl_2 \times \frac{1\ L}{0.114\ mol} = 7.89 \times 10^{-4}\ L\ hot\ H_2O = 0.789\ mL\ hot\ H_2O$$

8. a. Given $K_{a_1}$, $K_{a_2}$, and $K_{a_3}$, we are asked to calculate the pH of a 0.15 M citric acid solution. First, consider only the first dissociation.

$$K_{a_1} = \frac{[H^+][H_2Cit^-]}{[H_3Cit]}$$

$$K_{a_1} = 8.4 \times 10^{-4} = \frac{x^2}{0.15 - x} \text{ where } x = [H^+] = [H_2Cit^-]$$

Neglecting $x$ in the denominator, we have $x = 0.011$ M. This is the concentration of $H^+$ and $H_2Cit^-$.

Now consider the second dissociation.

$$K_{a_2} = \frac{[H^+][HCit^{2-}]}{[H_2Cit^-]}$$

Hydrogen ion is present from the first dissociation.

$$K_{a_2} = 1.8 \times 10^{-5} = \frac{y(0.011 + y)}{0.011 - y} \quad \text{where } y = [HCit^{2-}]$$

Neglecting $y$ in the numerator and denominator we have

$$y = 1.8 \times 10^{-5} = [HCit^{2-}]$$

$$[H^+] = 0.011 + 1.8 \times 10^{-5} \simeq 0.011 \text{ M}$$

Finally, consider the third dissociation.

$$K_{a_3} = \frac{[H^+][Cit^{3-}]}{[HCit^{2-}]} = 5.0 \times 10^{-7}$$

Very little hydrogen ion is produced in this step.

$$K_{a_3} = 5.0 \times 10^{-7} = \frac{z(0.011 + z)}{1.8 \times 10^{-5} - z} \quad \text{where } z = [Cit^{3-}]$$

Neglecting $z$ in the numerator and denominator we have

$$5.0 \times 10^{-7} = \frac{0.011z}{1.8 \times 10^{-5}}$$

$$z = \frac{(5.0 \times 10^{-7})(1.8 \times 10^{-5})}{1.1 \times 10^{-2}} = 8.2 \times 10^{-10} = [Cit^{3-}]$$

Finally, we have $[H^+] = (0.011 + 1.8 \times 10^{-5} + 8.2 \times 10^{-10})$ M $= 0.011$ M

$$\text{pH} = -\log[H^+] = 1.96$$

b. We are asked to calculate the following ratios at pH 6.0: $[H_3Cit]/[H_2Cit^-]$, $[H_2Cit^-]/[HCit^{2-}]$ and $[HCit^{2-}]/[Cit^{3-}]$. These ratios can be obtained from the equilibrium-constant expressions for $K_{a_1}$, $K_{a_2}$, and $K_{a_3}$. At pH 6.0, $[H^+] = 1.0 \times 10^{-6}$.

$$K_{a_1} = 8.4 \times 10^{-4} = \frac{[H^+][H_2Cit^-]}{[H_3Cit]}$$

$$[H_3Cit]/[H_2Cit^-] = \frac{1.0 \times 10^{-6}}{8.4 \times 10^{-4}} = 1.2 \times 10^{-3}$$

$$K_{a_2} = 1.8 \times 10^{-5} = \frac{[H^+][HCit^{2-}]}{[H_2Cit^-]}$$

$$[H_2Cit^-]/[HCit^{2-}] = \frac{1.0 \times 10^{-6}}{1.8 \times 10^{-5}} = 0.056$$

or $[HCit^{2-}]/[H_2Cit^-] = 18$

$$K_{a_3} = 5.0 \times 10^{-7} = \frac{[H^+][Cit^{3-}]}{[HCit^{2-}]}$$

$$[HCit^{2-}]/[Cit^{3-}] = \frac{1.0 \times 10^{-6}}{5.0 \times 10^{-7}} = 2.0$$

The predominant species at this pH is $HCit^{2-}$.

## CHAPTER 6

1. a. To predict the boiling point of astatine, look for a trend in the boiling points of the other halogens.

| F | Cl | Br | I | At | |
|---|---|---|---|---|---|
| -188.14 | -34.6 | 58.78 | 184.35 | ? | boiling point (°C) |

Using this information, and taking into account the large difference in atomic weights of I and At, a boiling point of around 350°C is predicted. The actual boiling point is 337°C.

b. The formula of a sodium salt of a halide is NaX. Therefore, the formula of sodium astatide is NaAt.

c. The oxyacids of halogens have the formulae $HXO_n$, where $n = 1,2,3,4$. The oxyacids of astatine have the formulae HAtO, $HAtO_2$, $HAtO_3$, and $HAtO_4$.

2. a. The alkaline earth metals are in the second column of the periodic table (Group IIA). They include Be, Mg, Ca, Sr, Ba, and Ra.

b. The second transition series includes elements 39-48: Y, Zr, Nb, Mo, Tc, Ru, Rb, Pd, Ag, and Cd.

c. The semimetals, or metalloids, include B, Si, Ge, As, and Te.

d. The actinides include elements 90-103: Th, Pa, U, Np, Pu, Am, Cm, Bk, Cf, Es, Fm, Md, No, and Lr.

3. Metallic character increases from the top to the bottom of a column. Therefore, in order of increasing metallic character, we have: N, P, As, Sb, Bi.

4. a. The reaction of $SO_2$ with $H_2O$ will produce an acidic solution.

$$SO_2 + H_2O \longrightarrow H^+ + HSO_3^-$$

b. The strongly basic solution will result from the reaction of $Cs_2O$ with water.

$$Cs_2O + H_2O \longrightarrow 2Cs^+ + 2OH^-$$

c. Hydrolysis of $P_4O_6$, the oxide of a nonmetal, should produce phosphorus acid, $H_3PO_3$.

$$P_4O_6 + 6H_2O \longrightarrow 4H_3PO_3$$

d. Barium, an alkaline earth metal, should form an ionic compound which reacts with water to produce a base.

$$BaO + H_2O \longrightarrow Ba^{2+}(aq) + 2OH^-(aq)$$

5. The reactions of gallium oxide, $Ga_2O_3$, in acidic and basic solutions are as follows:

$$Ga_2O_3(s) + 6H^+(aq) \longrightarrow 2Ga^{3+}(aq) + 3H_2O(l)$$

$$Ga_2O_3(s) + 2OH^-(aq) + 3H_2O \longrightarrow 2Ga(OH)_4^-$$

6. $Na_2S_2O_3$: Na, an alkali metal, has an oxidation number of +1. O has an oxidation number of -2. The oxidation number of S is positive:

$$-(3 \text{ O atmos} \times \frac{-2}{\text{O atom}}) + (2\text{Na atoms} \times \frac{+1}{\text{Na atom}}) = \frac{4}{2} = +2$$

$CH_3CN$: In $CH_3CN$, H has an oxidation number of +1, N has an oxidation number of -3, and C has an oxidation number of 0.

$Na_3AlF_6$: F, a halogen, has an oxidation number of -1. Na has an oxidation number of +1. This leaves an oxidation number of +3 for Al.

$BiO(NO_3)$: As a unit, $NO_3$ has a charge of -1 (-2/O atom × 3 atoms + +5/N atom × 1 N atom). The additional O atom has an oxidation number of -2, leaving Bi with an oxidation number of +3.

$OPCl_3$: As usual, O has an oxidation number of -2 and Cl has an oxidation number of -1. Therefore, the oxidation number of P is +5.

$Ag_3AsO_4$: The oxidation number of O is -2, and the oxidation number of Ag is +1. The oxidation number of As is -(3Ag atoms × +1/Ag atom + 4 O atoms × -2/O atom) = +5.

$S_2F_{10}$: F, a halogen, has an oxidation number of -1. The oxidation number of S is +5.

$SO_2Cl_2$: O has an oxidation number of -2 and Cl has an oxidation number of -1. S has an oxidation number of +6.

$Na_2SnO_2$: +1 is the oxidation number of Na and -2 is the oxidation number of O. Sn has an oxidation number of +2.

7. a. Oxidation: Balance the charge by adding electrons:

$$2Br^- \longrightarrow Br_2 + 2\bar{e}$$

Reduction: Balance the oxygen by adding water.

$$SO_4^{2-} \longrightarrow SO_2 + 2H_2O$$

Balance H by adding $H^+$.

$$SO_4^{2-} + 4H^+ \longrightarrow SO_2 + 2H_2O$$

Balance charge by adding electrons.

$$SO_4^{2-} + 2\bar{e} + 4H^+ \longrightarrow SO_2 + 2H_2O$$

Add the two half-reactions to get the final balanced equation.

$$2Br^- \longrightarrow Br_2 + 2\bar{e}$$

$$SO_4^{2-} + 2\bar{e} + 2H^+ \longrightarrow SO_2 + 2H_2O$$

$$2Br^- + SO_4^{2-} + 4H^+ \longrightarrow Br_2 + SO_2 + 2H_2O$$

In this reaction, bromine is oxidized and sulfur is reduced. $SO_4^{2-}$ is the oxidizing agent, and $Br^-$ is the reducing agent.

b. Sn is being oxidized. Its oxidation number increases from 0 to +4. The oxidation number of H goes from +1 (in $OH^-$) to 0 (in $H_2$). It is reduced. Balance the $4\bar{e}$ from the change of oxidation state of Sn with $4OH^-$. Balance the H atoms by adding $2H_2O$ to the reactants and including a coefficient of 4 in front of $H_2$. Finally, O will be balanced if a coefficient of 2 is placed in front of Sn and $SnO_3^{2-}$.

$$2Sn + 4OH^- + 2H_2O \longrightarrow 2SnO_3^{2-} + 4H_2$$

In this example, Sn is the reducing agent and $OH^-$ is the oxidizing agent.

c. Oxidation: Balance H by adding $H^+$.

$$H_2S \longrightarrow S + 2H^+$$

Balance charge by adding electrons.

$$H_2S \longrightarrow S + 2H^+ + 2\bar{e}$$

Reduction: Balance O by adding $H_2O$.

$$SO_4^{2-} \longrightarrow SO_2 + 2H_2O$$

Balance H by adding $H^+$.

$$SO_4^{2-} + 4H^+ \longrightarrow SO_2 + 2H_2O$$

Balance charge by adding electrons.

$$SO_4^{2-} + 4H^+ + 2\bar{e} \longrightarrow SO_2 + 2H_2O$$

Add the two half-reactions to get the final balanced equation.

$$H_2S \longrightarrow S + 2H^+ + 2\bar{e}$$

$$SO_4^{2-} + 4H^+ + 2\bar{e} \longrightarrow SO_2 + 2H_2O$$

$$H_2S + SO_4^{2-} + 2H^+ \longrightarrow S + SO_2 + 2H_2O$$

d. Oxidation: First, balance the hydroxide ions.

$$Zn + 4OH^- \longrightarrow [Zn(OH)_4]^{2-}$$

Now, balance the charge.

$$Zn + 4OH^- \longrightarrow [Zn(OH)_4]^{2-} + 2\bar{e}$$

Reduction: Balance O with $OH^-$; then balance H with $H_2O$.

$$NO_3^- + 6H_2O \longrightarrow NH_3 + 9OH^-$$

Balance charge by adding electrons.

$$NO_3^- + 6H_2O + 8\bar{e} \longrightarrow NH_3 + 9OH^-$$

Multiply the first half-reaction by 4 so the electrons will cancel. Then add the two half-reactions. The balanced equation is:

$$4Zn + NO_3^- + 6H_2O + 7OH^- \longrightarrow NH_3 + 4[Zn(OH)_4]^{2-}$$

Zn is oxidized and N is reduced. Zn is the reducing agent and $NO_3^-$ is the oxidizing agent.

e. Oxidation: Balance O with water.

$$2H_2O \longrightarrow O_2$$

Balance H with $H^+$.

$$2H_2O \longrightarrow O_2 + 4H^+$$

Balance charge with electrons.

$$2H_2O \longrightarrow O_2 + 4H^+ + 4\bar{e}$$

Reduction: Balance O with water.

$$NO_3^- \longrightarrow NO_2 + H_2O$$

Balance H with $H^+$.

$$NO_3^- + 2H^+ \longrightarrow NO_2 + H_2O$$

Balance charge with electrons.

$$NO_3^- + 2H^+ + \bar{e} \longrightarrow NO_2 + H_2O$$

Multiply the reduction half-reaction by 4 so the electrons will cancel. Then add the two half-reactions.

$$2H_2O \longrightarrow O_2 + 4H^+ + 4\bar{e}$$

$$4NO_3^- + 8H^+ + 4\bar{e} \longrightarrow 4NO_2 + 4H_2O$$

---

O was oxidized and N was reduced. $NO_3^-$ was the oxidizing agent, and $H_2O$ was the reducing agent.

f. The oxidation number of Mn changes from +7 to +4. This represents a gain of 3 electrons. The oxidation number of Se changes from -2 to 0, which represents a loss of 2 electrons. Balance the electrons by placing a coefficient of 3 in front of $Se^{2-}$ and Se and a coefficient of 2 in front of $MnO_4^-$ and $MnO_2$.

$$2MnO_4^- + 3Se^{2-} \longrightarrow 2MnO_2 + 3Se$$

Balance the O atoms and charge by adding $OH^-$ to the right side of the equation. Finally, balance H by adding $H_2O$ to the left side. The balanced equation is

$$2MnO_4^- + 3Se^{2-} + 4H_2O \longrightarrow 2MnO_2 + 3Se + 8OH^-$$

Se is oxidized and Mn is reduced. $MnO_4^-$ is the oxidizing agent. $Se^{2-}$ is the reducing agent.

8. The oxidation state of Se increases by 2 units, while that of Mn decreases by 3 units. The normality of $MnO_4^-$ is

$$\frac{0.025 \text{ mol } MnO_4^-}{1 \text{ L}} \times \frac{3 \text{ equivalents}}{1 \text{ mol } MnO_4^-} = 0.075 \text{ N}$$

9. a. Use the oxidation number method to balance the equation. First, balance the atoms that undergo a change in oxidation state (i.e., Cu and S). Next, balance the species that do not change oxidation state. Balance the O atoms with $OH^-$. Finally, balance the H atoms with $H_2O$. The balanced equation is

$$[Cu(NH_3)_4]^{2+} + 2S_2O_4^{2-} + 4OH^- \longrightarrow 4SO_3^{2-} + Cu + 4NH_3 + 4H_2O$$

b. Two moles of $Na_2S_2O_4$ are necessary for each mole of $[Cu(NH_3)_4]^{2+}$. Therefore, the equivalent weight of $Na_2S_2O_4$ is one-half the molecular weight.

$$\frac{174.10 \text{ g}}{1 \text{ mol } Na_2S_2O_4} \times \frac{1 \text{ mol } Na_2S_2O_4}{2 \text{ equiv}} = 87.05 \text{ g/equiv}$$

c. $$1.00 \text{ g Cu} \times \frac{1 \text{ mol}}{63.55 \text{ g}} \times \frac{2 \text{ mol } S_2O_4^{2-}}{1 \text{ mol Cu}} \times \frac{174.10 \text{ g } Na_2S_2O_4}{1 \text{ mol}} = 5.48 \text{ g } Na_2S_2O_4$$

## CHAPTER 7

1. Rutherford disproved Thomson's model of the atom. This model described the atom as having its mass and positive charge spread uniformly throughout the atom with negative charges embedded in this structure. Rutherford and Geiger disproved this model by measuring the scattering of a beam of α particles. Marsden, who carried out the experiment, observed some α particles being scattered backward. This back-scattering would be expected if all of the mass and positive charge were concentrated at the center of the atom (i.e., the nucleus).

2. a. $E = h\nu = \dfrac{hc}{\lambda}$

$$E = \frac{(6.626 \times 10^{-34}\ \text{J}\cdot\text{sec})(3.00 \times 10^{10}\ \text{cm/sec})}{(0.50\ \text{cm})} = 3.98 \times 10^{-23}\ \text{J}$$

$$E = h\nu$$

$$\nu = \frac{E}{h} = \frac{3.98 \times 10^{-23}\ \text{J}}{6.626 \times 10^{-34}\ \text{J}\cdot\text{sec}} = 6.01 \times 10^{10}\ \text{sec}^{-1}$$

$$\overline{\nu} = \frac{1}{\lambda} = \frac{1}{0.5\ \text{cm}} = 2.0\ \text{cm}^{-1}$$

b. Energy is inversely proportional to wavelength; therefore, a 0.10 cm microwave will have higher energy. Frequency and wave number are also inversely proportional to wavelength. These will also be higher than the frequency and wave number of a 0.50 cm microwave.

3. We are given the velocity of the electron and the work function of selenium. We are asked to calculate the wavelength of light that is necessary to eject the electron. Use the relationship

$$E_{light} = \text{work function} + \text{kinetic energy of } \bar{e}$$

Because $E = h\nu = hc/\lambda$, we can solve for $\lambda$, the wavelength of the light. Convert $eV$ to Joules.

$$E_{light} = \text{work function} + \tfrac{1}{2}mv^2$$

$$E = \left(\frac{4.63\ eV}{\bar{e}} \times \frac{1.602 \times 10^{-19}\ \text{J}}{eV}\right) + \tfrac{1}{2}(9.1095 \times 10^{-31}\ \text{kg})(5.25 \times 10^{5}\ \text{m/s})^2$$

$$E = 7.40 \times 10^{-19}\ \text{J} + 1.26 \times 10^{-19}\ \text{J}$$

$$E_{light} = 8.66 \times 10^{-19}\ \text{J}$$

$$E = \frac{hc}{\lambda}$$

$$\lambda = \frac{hc}{E} = \frac{(6.626 \times 10^{-34}\ \text{J}\cdot\text{s})(3.00 \times 10^{8}\ \text{m/s})}{(8.66 \times 10^{-19}\ \text{J})}$$

$$\lambda = 2.30 \times 10^{-7}\ \text{m} = 230\ \text{nm}$$

4. The energy calculated in problem 3 is for a single photon. The energy per mole is obtained by multiplying the result by Avogadro's number:

$$\frac{1.26 \times 10^{-19}\ \text{J}}{\text{photon}} \times \frac{6.02 \times 10^{23}\ \text{photons}}{1\ \text{mol photons}} = 7.59 \times 10^{4}\ \text{J mol}^{-1}\ \text{photons}$$

5. Use the Rydberg equation to calculate the wavelength of radiation necessary to raise the excited electron from the fourth to the seventh Bohr orbit.

$$\overline{\nu} = R_H\ (1/n_1^2 - 1/n_2^2)$$

$\bar{\nu} = (109{,}678 \text{ cm}^{-1})(1/4^2 - 1/7^2)$

$\bar{\nu} = 4.62 \times 10^3 \text{ cm}^{-1}$

$\lambda = 2.17 \times 10^{-4}$ cm

6. We are told that $n_f = 5$ in the Pfund series and asked to calculate the longest possible wavelength for a spectral line. To do this, let $n_i = 6$; then use the Rydberg equation to calculate the wavelength. The longest wavelength has the lowest frequency.

$\bar{\nu} = 109{,}678 \text{ cm}^{-1} (1/5^2 - 1/6^2)$

$\bar{\nu} = 1340 \text{ cm}^{-1}$

$\lambda = 7.46 \times 10^{-4}$ cm

7. We are given the ionization energy of hydrogen in its ground state and asked to calculate the ionization energy of an excited $Li^{2+}$ ion. This is the third ionization energy, $IE_3$.

$IE_3 = (3)^2 \text{ K}$

$IE_3 = (3)^2(1312 \text{ kJ mol}^{-1})$

$IE_3 = 1.18 \times 10^4 \text{ kJ mol}^{-1}$

8. It was hypothesized that all matter has particle-like and wave-like properties. In fact, deBroglie hypothesized that with every particle there is an associated wave. Other experiments on electron beams showed that electron beams were diffracted in exactly in same way as X-ray beams. This led to the belief in the wave and particle descriptions of matter.

9. We are given Superman's velocity and his mass. We are asked to calculate his wavelength. First, change miles, hours, and pounds to meters, seconds, and kilograms.

$$\frac{560 \text{ mi}}{\text{hr}} \times \frac{5280 \text{ ft}}{\text{mi}} \times \frac{12 \text{ in}}{\text{ft}} \times \frac{2.54 \text{ cm}}{\text{in}} \times \frac{1 \text{ m}}{100 \text{ cm}} \times \frac{1 \text{ hr}}{3600 \text{ s}} = 250 \text{ m/s}$$

$$195 \text{ lbs} \times \frac{2.2 \text{ kg}}{1 \text{ lb}} = 429 \text{ kg}$$

Calculate his wavelength using the relationship $\lambda = h/mv$.

$$\lambda = \frac{h}{mv} = \frac{(6.636 \times 10^{-34} \text{ J·sec})}{(429 \text{ kg})(250 \text{ m/s})}$$

$\lambda = 6.18 \times 10^{-39}$ m

10. We are given the uncertainty in Superman's speed and asked to calculate the uncertainty in his position. Use the Heisenberg uncertainty principle. Be sure to convert mi/hr to m/s.

$[\Delta x][\Delta(mv_x)] \geq h/4\pi$

$\Delta x \geq h/4\pi[\Delta(mv_x)]$

$$\Delta x = \frac{6.62 \times 10^{-34}\ \text{J}\cdot\text{sec}}{4\pi(429\ \text{kg})(4.5\ \text{m/s})} = 1.17 \times 10^{-35}\ \text{m}$$

Use the mass of a neutron and the uncertainty of Superman's velocity to calculate the uncertainty in the position of the neutron.

$$\Delta x = \frac{h/4\pi}{\Delta(mv)} = \frac{(6.626 \times 10^{-34}\ \text{J}\cdot\text{s})/4\pi}{(1.675 \times 10^{-27}\ \text{kg})(4.5\ \text{m/s})} = 7.00 \times 10^{-9}\ \text{m}$$

11. An orbital is an electron-probability cloud, or wave function. This is not to be confused with the electron in orbit around the nucleus (Bohr model).

12. There are four nodes in a $5d$ orbital, two nodal planes and two nodal surfaces within each lobe.

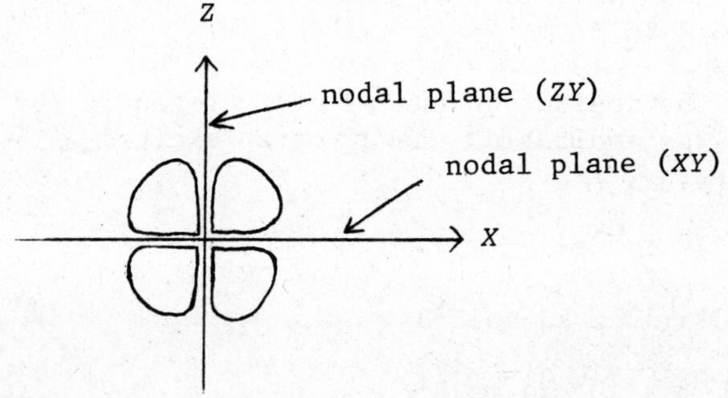


13. Set (*d*) cannot exist because $|m| > l$. The allowed values of $m$ are $-l$. . . 0 . . . $+l$. Set (*b*) cannot exist because $l = n$. The allowed values of $l$ are 0, 1, . . . $n$-1. All the other sets of quantum numbers are allowed.

14. a. $n = 2$, $l = 1$, $m = -1$. These quantum numbers represent a $2p$ orbital.

 c. $n = 5$, $l = 4$, $m = 4$. These quantum numbers represent a $5g$ orbital.

 e. $n = 3$, $l = 2$, $m = 0$. These quantum numbers represent a $3d$ orbital.

## CHAPTER 8

1. a. Bi: [Xe] $4f^{14}5d^{10}6s^26p^3$

 b. $Au^+$: [Xe] $4f^{14}5d^{10}$

 c. $P^{3-}$: [Ne] $3s^2$

 d. $Tc^{2+}$: [Kr] $4d^5$

 e. $At^-$: [Xe] $4f^{14}5d^{10}6s^26p^6$

 f. Fr: [Rn] $7s^1$

 g. Rn: [Xe] $4f^{14}5d^{10}6s^26p^6$

 h. Ce: [Xe] $6s^24f^2$

2. The electronic configuration of Tl is $[Xe]4f^{14}5d^{10}6s^{2}6p^{1}$ and that of Hg is $[Xe]4f^{14}5d^{10}6s^{2}$. The 6*p* electron in Tl is not held as tightly as the 6*s* electrons in Hg because the 6*s* orbital penetrates to the nucleus, while the 6*p* orbital has a node at the nucleus. Therefore, the ionization potential of Tl is less than that of Hg, even though Tl has a higher nuclear charge.

3. As a general trend, ionization potential increases across the periodic table. The ionization energy of fluorine is unusually high compared with the other halogens because it is a relatively small atom and the electrons feel a stronger nuclear charge. Therefore, they are more difficult to remove. Because fluorine is small relative to the other halogens, it experiences stronger electron-electron repulsions when an electron is added. For this reason, its electron affinity is low.

4. a. Cs and I are on opposite sides of the periodic table. It is likely that CsI will be ionic. The electronegativity difference is 2.7 - 0.7 = 2.0. $(Cs^{+}I^{-})$

   b. The electronegativity difference between Sr and O is 2.4. An ionic bond is indicated. $(Sr^{+2}O^{-2})$

   c. There will be a polar covalent bond in HgCl. The electronegativity difference is 1.2. $(Hg^{\delta+}Cl^{\delta-})$

   d. P-H will form a covalent bond. The difference in electronegativity is 0.01.

   e. Ag-S will form a polar covalent bond. The electronegativity difference is 0.7. $(Ag^{\delta+}S^{\delta-})$

   f. NO will form a polar covalent bond. The difference in electronegativity is 0.4. $(N^{\delta+}O^{\delta-})$

5. In acidic solution, the reaction of stannous oxide is

$$SnO + H_2O + 2OH^- \longrightarrow Sn(OH)_4^{2-}$$

In basic solution, we have

$$SnO + H_2O + 2OH^- \longrightarrow Sn(OH)_4^{2-}$$

6. a. $Cu(s) + H_2SO_4(aq) \longrightarrow$ no reaction unless oxygen $(O_2)$ present.

   b. $Cu(s) + 4HNO_3(conc.) \longrightarrow 2NO_2(g) + Cu(NO_3)_2(aq) + 2H_2O(l)$

   c. $3Cu(s) + 8HNO_3(dilute) \longrightarrow 2NO(g) + 3Cu(NO_3)_2(aq) + 4H_2O(l)$

7. There is an increase in atomic number of 32 when going from element 77 to element 109. Therefore, a significant increase in relative size would be expected if the actinides did not intervene. An actinide contraction is predicted for elements 104-112, similar to the observed lanthanide contraction.

8. $2Eu + 3H_2O \longrightarrow Eu_2O_3 + 3H_2(g)$

The actinides also react with water to form oxides.

9. a. If the solution is green, the light it absorbs is purple. The wavelength of this light is about 520 nm.

b. $Pr^{3+}$: [Xe] $6s^2$

CHAPTER 9

1. a. 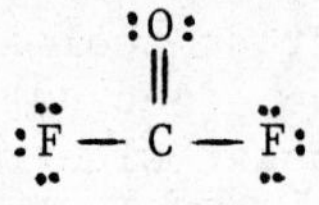 :F̤ — C(=O:) — F̤:

b. [:C̤l — As(— C̤l:)(— C̤l:) — C̤l:]$^+$

c. Ö = N̈ - B̤̈r:

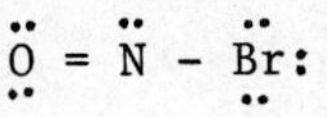

d. 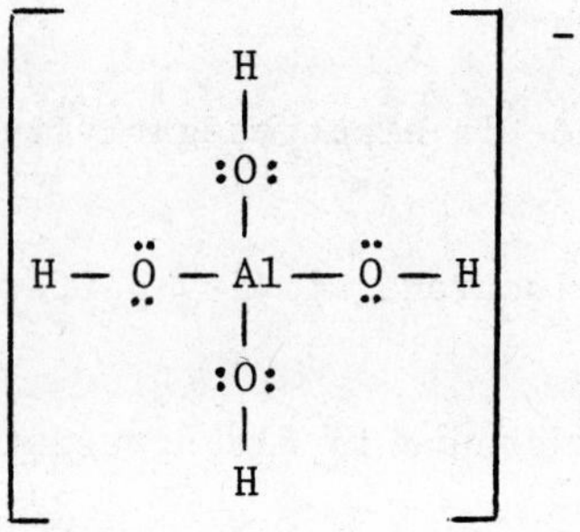 [H — Ö — Al(— :O: — H)(— :O: — H) — Ö — H]$^-$

e. 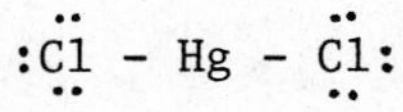 :C̤̈l - Hg - C̤̈l:

f. 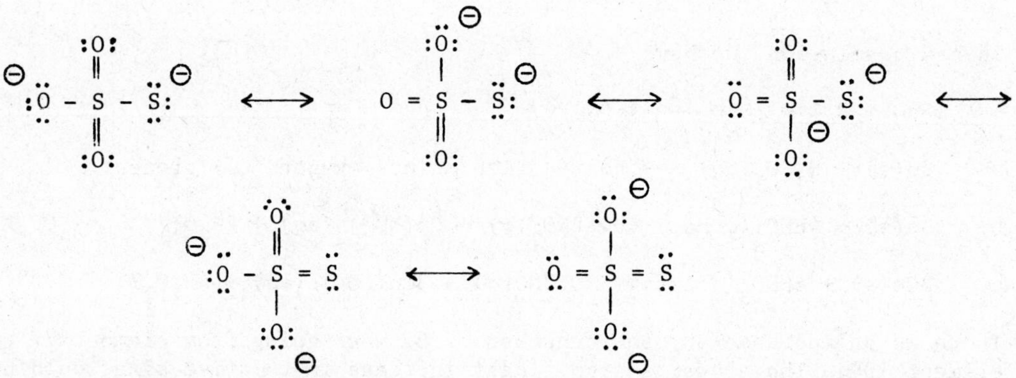 ⊖:Ö - S(=O:)(=O:) - S̤̈:⊖ ⟷ O = S(— :Ö:⊖)(=O:) - S̤̈:⊖ ⟷ Ö = S(=O:)(— :Ö:⊖) - S̤̈:⊖ ⟷

⊖:Ö - S(=O)(— :Ö:⊖) = S̤ ⟷ Ö = S(— :Ö:⊖)(— :Ö:⊖) = S̤

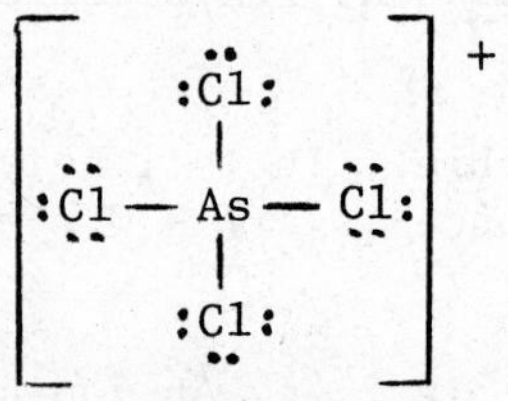

g. 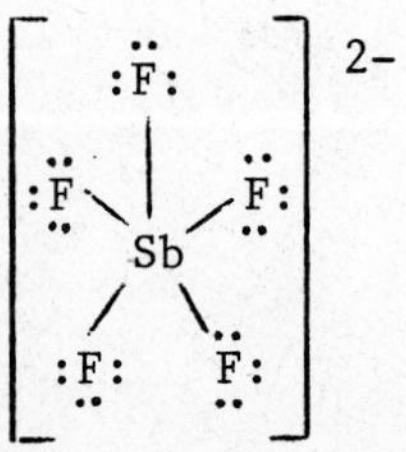 [Sb(:F̤:)$_5$]$^{2-}$

h. :S̈e = C = S̈e:

i. Lewis structure of $TeCl_4$: Te bonded to four :C̈l: atoms

j. :F̈ - K̈r - F̈: (three lone pairs on Kr)

k. :S̈ = P(—F̈:)₃ (P double-bonded to S and single-bonded to three F)

2. $[:\ddot{I} - \ddot{I} - \ddot{I}:]^-$ formal charges 0, −1, 0 ⟷ formal charges −2, +1, 0 ⟷ formal charges 0, +1, −2

3. $XeOF_2$: :O: double-bonded to Xe, Xe bonded to two :F̈:, lone pairs on Xe

$XeOF_4$: O double-bonded to Xe, Xe bonded to four :F̈:

$[XeO_6]^{4-}$ resonance structures (Xe with two double-bonded O and four single-bonded :Ö:) ⟷ ⟷ etc.

The xenon-oxygen bond length is expected to be shorter in $XeOF_2$ and $XeOF_4$ than in $XeO_6^{4-}$. Because of the delocalization of the negative charge in $XeO_6^{4-}$, all the xenon-oxygen bonds are equivalent and intermediate in length between a double and a single bond.

4. $H - \ddot{O} - As(=O)(-\ddot{O}-H) - \ddot{O} - H$    $H - \ddot{O} - As(=O)(-\ddot{O}-H) - \ddot{O}:^{\ominus}$    $H - \ddot{O} - As(=O)(-O:^{\ominus}) - \ddot{O}^{\ominus}$

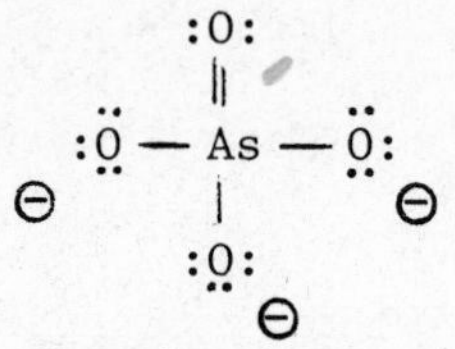

$$
\begin{array}{c}
:\ddot{O}: \\
\| \\
{}^{\ominus}:\ddot{\underset{..}{O}}-\mathrm{As}-\ddot{\underset{..}{O}}:{}^{\ominus} \\
| \\
:\underset{..}{O}:{}^{\ominus}
\end{array}
$$

and other resonance forms

The bond between arsenic and oxygen not attached to hydrogen is shortest in arsenic acid and becomes increasingly longer as arsenic acid is ionized.

5. $HONH_2$ Lewis base

$BF_2Cl$ Lewis acid

$OH^-$ Lewis base

$H_3O^+$ Lewis acid-base addition compound

$CH_3OH$ Lewis base

$Ni^{2+}$ Lewis acid

$BeF_4^{2-}$ Lewis acid-base addition compound

$CHBr_3$ neither

$F_3BNC(CH_3)_3$ Lewis acid-base addition compound

CO Lewis base

$Ag(CN)_2^-$ Lewis acid-base addition compound

$I^-$ Lewis base

$Al(OH)_3$ Lewis acid

$H_2O$ Lewis acid or Lewis base

$NH_4^+$ Lewis acid-base addition compound

$CO_2$ Lewis acid

$H^+$ Lewis acid

6. a. $Sb_2S_3(s) + 3S^{2-} \longrightarrow 2SbS_3^{3-}$

Lewis acid (Sb₂S₃), Lewis base (S²⁻)

b. 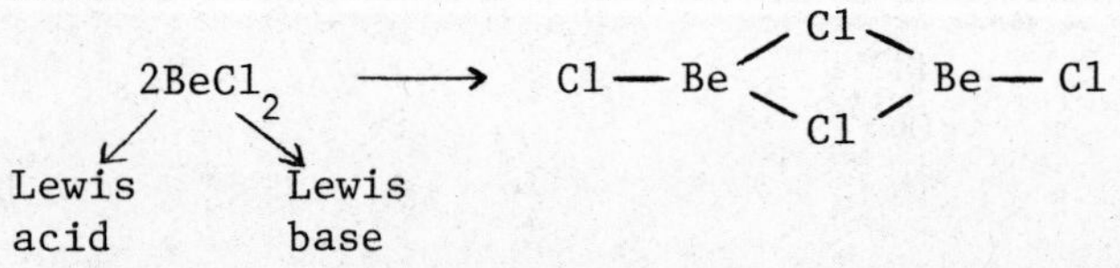 $2BeCl_2 \longrightarrow Cl-Be\langle^{Cl}_{Cl}\rangle Be-Cl$

$2BeCl_2$: Lewis acid, Lewis base

7. $Ge(OH)_4$: acid (weak)

   $Ca(OH)_2$: base

   $O_2BrOH$: acid

   $Ga(OH)_3$: ampholyte

   KOH: base

8. a. $HBrO_4$ is the stronger acid because acidity increases with increasing number of oxygen atoms that do not have hydrogen atoms attached.

   b. The stronger acid is $HNO_2$ because it has one more oxygen atom that is not bound to a hydrogen atom.

   c. $HIO_2$ is the stronger acid because the formal charge on I, the central atom, is greater.

   d. $HNO_3$ is expected to be stronger because there is a formal charge of +1 on the nitrogen atom.

9. a. The Lewis structure for HCN is:

   H – C ≡ N̈

   The steric number is 2. The geometry is linear.

   b. The Lewis structure is:

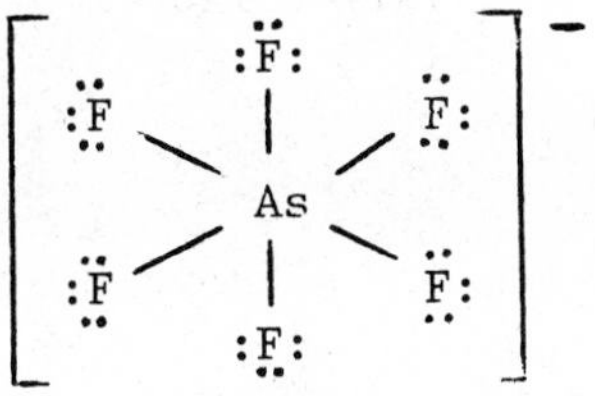

   [$AsF_6$]⁻ : As bonded to six F atoms, each F with three lone pairs (:F̤̈:)

   The steric number is 6. The geometry is octahedral.

   c. The Lewis structure of $ICl_3$ is:

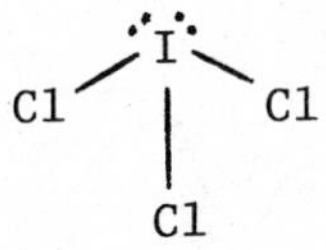

   I (two lone pairs) bonded to three Cl atoms

   The steric number is 5 because there are 3 atoms bound to I and there are 2 lone pairs. The electron pairs are arranged in a trigonal bipyramidal arrangement around I, with the 2 lone pairs occupying equatorial positions. The resulting geometry is T-shaped.

   d. The Lewis structure for $BeF_2$ is:

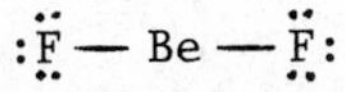

   :F̤̈— Be —F̤̈:

   The steric number is 2. The geometry is linear.

e. The Lewis structure for $SOCl_2$ is:

```
      O
      ‖
Cl \  S  / Cl
      ..
```

The steric number is 4 (3 atoms bound and 1 lone pair). The geometry will be trigonal pyramidal.

f. The Lewis structure for ClHC = $CCl_2$ is:

```
 :Cl:          :Cl:
     \   α     /
  β   C  =  C
     /         \
   H            :Cl:
```

There are 2 double-bonded carbon atoms, each with 2 substituents. The geometry is planar. Angle α will be larger than angle β due to electrostatic repulsions.

g. The Lewis structure for $BF_2Cl$ is:

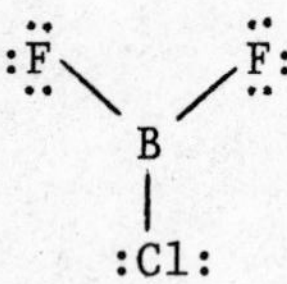


Boron has a steric number of 3. The geometry is trigonal planar.

h. The Lewis structure of $BrF_5$ is:

```
          :F:
   :F:     |     :F:
       \   |   /
:F: ——— Br ——— :F:
```

The steric number is 6. There are 5 F atoms attached to Br and 1 lone pair. The expected geometry is square pyramidal.

i. The Lewis structure of $PBr_4^+$ is:

```
     :Br:     :Br:
         \   /
:Br: ———  P  ——— :Br:
          ⊕
```

The steric number is 4. The expected geometry is tetrahedral.

j. The Lewis structure of $XeOF_2$ is:

```
           O
           ‖
:F: ——— :Xe: ——— :F:
```

The steric number is 5. There are 2 lone pairs and 3 atoms bound to Xe. The expected geometry is T-shaped (trigonal bipyramidal, with 2 lone pairs occupying equatorial positions).

k. The Lewis structure of $CH_3NH_2$ is:

```
      H
      |    ..  / H
  H — C — N
      |        \ H
      H
```

The steric number is 4. There are 4 substituents bound to carbon, and 3 atoms bound to nitrogen plus 1 lone pair. The expected geometry is tetrahedral about both C and N.

CHAPTER 10

1. a. $SO_2 + Cl_2 \longrightarrow SO_2Cl_2$

The equation is already balanced. It is an oxidation-reduction reaction. Sulfur is oxidized, and chlorine is reduced.

b. $2AgF(aq) + Ni(NO_3)_2(aq) \longrightarrow NiF_2(s) + 2AgNO_3(aq)$

This is a metathesis reaction. Fluoride and nitrate ions are exchanged between nickel and silver.

c. $CO_2 + Ba(OH)_2 \longrightarrow BaCO_3 + H_2O$

The equation is balanced as is. It is an acid-base reaction.

d. $Cl_2O_7 + H_2O \longrightarrow 2HClO_4$

This is an acid-base reaction. Specifically, it is the reaction of an anhydride and water.

e. $2NaNO_3 \longrightarrow 2NaNO_2 + O_2$

Nitrogen is reduced from +5 to +3. Oxygen is oxidized from -2 to 0. Therefore, this is an oxidation-reduction reaction.

f. $H_2SO_4(aq) + CaF_2(aq) \longrightarrow 2HF(aq) + CaSO_4(s)$

This is a metathesis reaction. Fluoride and sulfate ions are exchanged between hydrogen and calcium.

2. Based on solubility rules for ionic compounds, the following compounds are soluble in water: $CuSO_4$, $Rb_2CO_3$, $NH_4I$, $NiC_2H_3O_2$, $Pb(ClO_3)_2$.

3. a. This is an elimination reaction. Hydrogen is eliminated as hydrogen gas; the tin then reacts to form $Na_2SnO_2$.

b. Both displacement and elimination occur. $SO_3^{2-}$ is replaced by $SO_4^{2-}$ to form $Na_2SO_4$. Also $2H^+$ (from $H_2SO_4$) forms water and $SO_2$.

c. This is an addition reaction. $PCl_3$ and $O_2$ react to form $OPCl_3$.

d. Displacement occurs in this reaction. $Br_2$ and $H_2O$ react to form HBr and HOBr.

e. This is an elimination reaction. $(NH_4)_2Cr_2O_7$ decomposes to form $N_2$, $Cr_2O_3$, and $H_2O$.

4. a. $N_2O_3 + H_2O \longrightarrow 2HNO_2$

b. $NaHSO_3 + H_2O \longrightarrow H_2SO_3 + Na^+ + OH^-$

c. $HF + BF_3 \longrightarrow BF_4^- + H^+$

d. $2HCl + BaCO_3 \longrightarrow BaCl_2 + H_2CO_3$ ($H_2CO_3$ is actually $CO_2 + H_2O$)

e. $C_2H_3O^- + H_3PO_4 \longrightarrow C_2H_3OH + H_2PO_4^-$

5. a. The following pairs will form precipitates:

$K_2CO_3$ and $MnSO_4$ will form $MnCO_3$

$AgNO_3$ and $NH_4Cl$ will form AgCl

$NiCl_2$ and $Pb(C_2H_3O_2)_2$ will form $PbCl_2$

b. The following pairs will form homogeneous solutions:

$AgNO_3$ and $Pb(C_2H_3O_2)_2$

$NH_4Cl$ and $K_2CO_3$

$MnSO_4$ and $NiCl_2$

6. a. $Na_2CO_3(aq) + NiSO_4(aq) + 2AgC_2H_3O_2 \longrightarrow$

$NiCO_3(s) + Ag_2SO_4(s) + Ag_2CO_3(s) + 2NaC_2H_3O_2(aq)$

b. $Zn(s) + H_2SO_4(aq) \longrightarrow ZnSO_4(aq) + {}_2(g)$

c. $F_2(g) + 2KI(aq)$ —— $2KF(aq) + I_2(s)$

d. $Al(OH)_3(s) + OH^-(aq) \longrightarrow Al(OH)_4^-$

e. $2Al(s) + 3Cu^{2+}(aq) \longrightarrow 2Al^{3+}(aq) + 3Cu(s)$

## CHAPTER 11

1. The bond length in $O_2$ is shorter than the bond length in $C_2$ because O has a greater nuclear charge. Both $C_2$ and $O_2$ have a bond order of 2. Subtle distinctions can be made when the electronic structures are examined more closely.

2. The bond in $O_2$ is weaker than the bond in $C_2$ because there are more lone electron pairs on the oxygen molecule. This makes the molecule "fall apart" more easily, because of repulsion between the lone pairs. Also, $O_2$ has two unpaired electrons in antibonding orbitals.

3. a. PN has 10 valence electrons, 2 antibonding and 8 bonding. (BO = $\frac{1}{2}(8 - 2) = 3$) SN has 11 valence electrons, 8 bonding and 3 antibonding. (BO = $\frac{1}{2}(8 - 3) = 2\frac{1}{2}$)

   b. The general trend is that bond order is inversely proportional to bond length. Therefore, SN has a longer bond length than PN.

   c. PN has no unpaired electrons and is, therefore, diamagnetic. SN has 1 unpaired electron. It is paramagnetic.

   d. The relative bond energy is directly proportional to the bond order. Therefore, we would predict PN to have a higher bond energy than SN.

4. In order of decreasing bond length: CS, $CO^+$, CO, $CO^-$.

5. $CO^-$ is paramagnetic. It has 11 valence electrons and 1 unpaired electron.

   $Se_2$ is paramagnetic. It has 2 unpaired electrons.

   SCl is paramagnetic. It has 13 valence electrons and 1 unpaired electron.

6. SnO has a shorter bond length and a higher bond energy. SnS has a longer bond length and a lower bond energy. The SnO bond has greater ionic character because O is more electronegative than S.

7. LiF: $\%\text{ ionic character} = \dfrac{6.33\text{ D}}{1.5639\text{Å}(4.80\text{ D/Å})} = 84.3\%$

   LiH: $\%\text{ ionic character} = \dfrac{5.88\text{ D}}{1.5953\text{Å}(4.80\text{ D/Å})} = 76.8\%$

   These values are consistent with the electronegativity differences between Li and F (3.0) and Li and H (1.2), although consideration of electronegativity alone would predict greater covalency for LiH.

8. LiF: $\%\text{ ionic character} = \dfrac{6.33\text{ D}}{1.5639\text{Å}(4.80\text{ D/Å})} = 84.3\%$

   LiCl: $\%\text{ ionic character} = \dfrac{7.13\text{ D}}{2.018\text{Å}(4.80\text{ D/Å})} = 73.6\%$

   LiBr: $\%\text{ ionic character} = \dfrac{7.27\text{ D}}{2.1704\text{Å}(4.89\text{ D/Å})} = 69.8\%$

   LiI: $\%\text{ ionic character} = \dfrac{7.43\text{ D}}{2.3919\text{Å}(4.80\text{ D/Å})} = 64.7\%$

   The percent ionic character decreases with decreasing electronegativity. The dipole moment increases with decreasing electronegativity. The electronegativity decreases from the top to the bottom of the column.

9. SrO is expected to be more ionic and to have a larger dipole moment than SrS because O is more electronegative than S.

CHAPTER 12

1. The structure of $BF_4^-$ is tetrahedral. The hybridization of boron's valence orbitals is $sp^3$.

2. The Lewis structure of $CSe_2$ is $\ddot{S}\dot{e}=C=\ddot{S}\dot{e}$. The molecular orbital theory suggests that the Se-C double bonds are due to localized π orbitals. The carbon atom is $sp^2$ hybridized. The geometry is linear.

3. 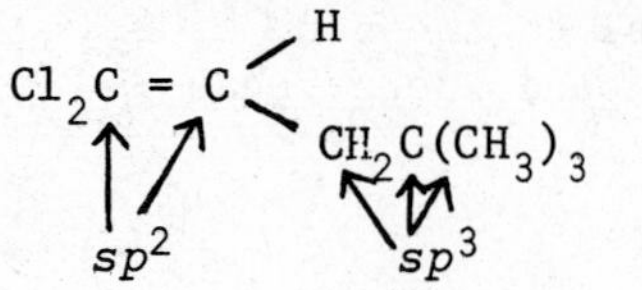 $Cl_2C = C(H)CH_2C(CH_3)_3$

($Cl_2C$ and $=C$ carbons: $sp^2$; $CH_2$ and $C(CH_3)_3$ carbons: $sp^3$)

4. a. Lewis structure:

$$\left[\begin{array}{c} :\ddot{O}: \\ | \\ \ddot{O}=P-\ddot{O}: \\ | \\ :\ddot{O}: \end{array}\right]^{3-}$$

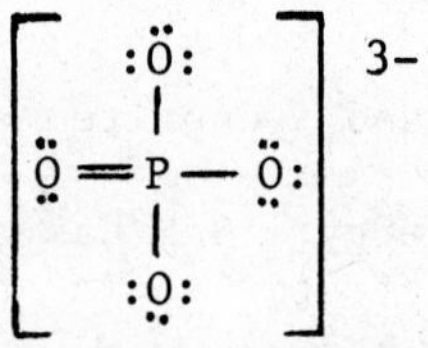

and resonance forms

b. Molecular orbital structure: The geometry of $PO_4^{3-}$ is tetrahedral. The P-O bonds are all of equal length. The delocalization of the π orbitals accounts for this observation.

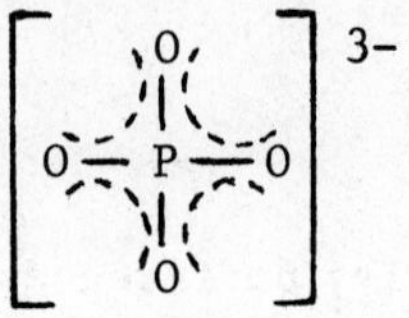

$$\left[\begin{array}{c} O \\ \vdots | \\ O \overset{..}{=} P \overset{..}{=} O \\ \vdots | \\ O \end{array}\right]^{3-}$$

5. 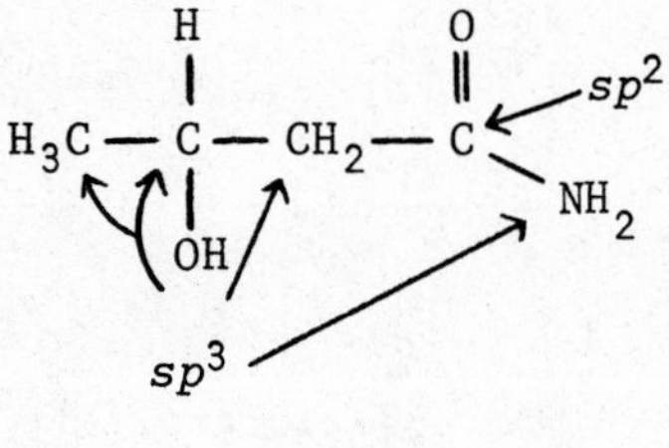 $H_3C-CH(OH)-CH_2-C(=O)NH_2$

(carbonyl C: $sp^2$; $H_3C$, CH(OH) carbon, OH oxygen, and $NH_2$: $sp^3$)

6. a. $SO_2$ will be bent. The Lewis structure is:

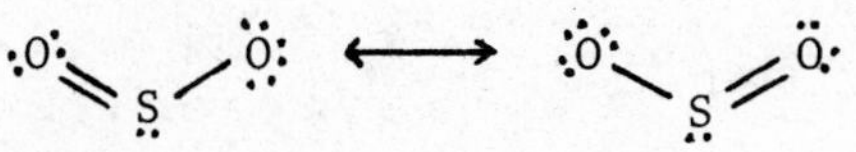

$$\dot{O}=S-\ddot{O}: \longleftrightarrow :\ddot{O}-S=\dot{O}$$

One Lewis structure of $SO_3$ is:

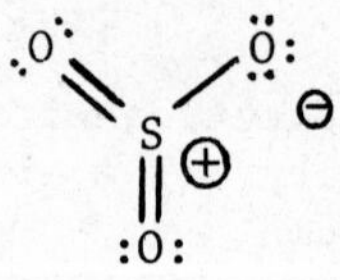

$$O=S^{\oplus}(=O)-O^{\ominus}$$

It is trigonal planar. There are other resonance forms.

One Lewis structure of $SO_3^{2-}$ is:

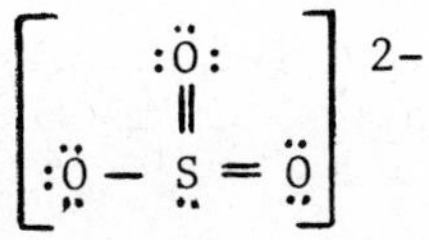

$\left[\ \ddot{O} - S = \ddot{O}\ \text{with}\ :\ddot{O}: \text{double-bonded above S}\ \right]^{2-}$ It is pyramidal. There are other resonance forms.

One Lewis structure of $SO_4^{2-}$ is:

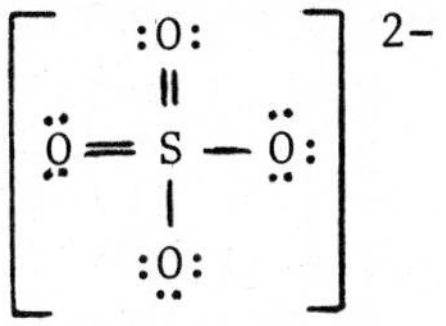

$\left[\ \ddot{O} = S - \ddot{O}:\ \text{with}\ :O: \text{double-bonded above S and}\ :O: \text{single-bonded below S}\ \right]^{2-}$ It is tetrahedral. There are other resonance forms.

b. $SO_2$ is polar and $SO_3$ is nonpolar.

c. In all of these there is delocalization of the $\pi$ electrons. The sulfur atom in $SO_3$ is $sp^2$ hybridized. In $SO_2$, the sulfur atom is $sp^2$ hybridized. The $SO_4^{2-}$ ion has tetrahedral geometry, and the sulfur is $sp^3$ hybridized. In general, when resonance Lewis structures can be written, the molecule can be described by delocalized molecular orbitals.

7. There are 5 $\pi$ bonds. They are circled.

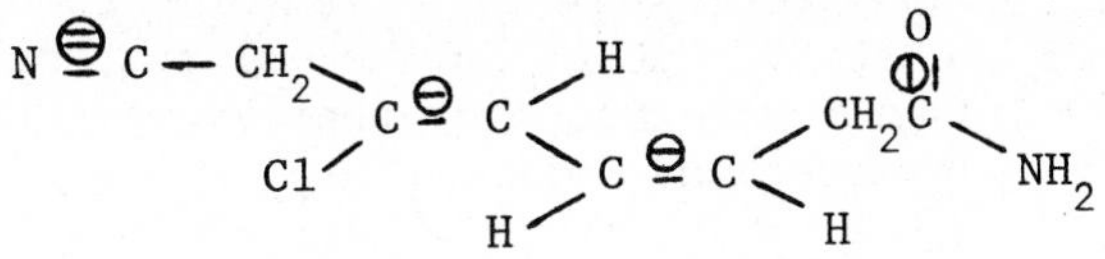

N≡C—CH₂—C(Cl)=CH—CH=CH—CH₂—C(=O)—NH₂

8. The following molecules are polar: $ClF_3$, $PF_3$, $CCl_2Br_2$

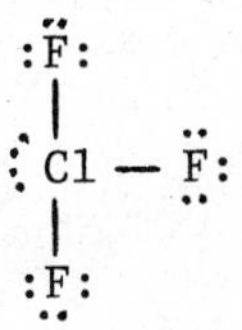

T-shaped ($ClF_3$) trigonal pyramidal ($PF_3$)

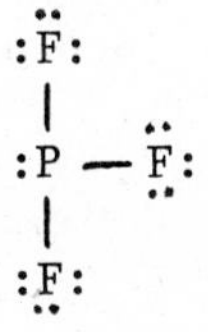

$CCl_2Br_2$ is a distorted tetrahedron.

9. Rotational energy transitions occur in the far infrared to the microwave regions of the electromagnetic spectrum.

10. Electronic energy transitions are observed in the visible and ultraviolet regions of the electromagnetic spectrum.

11. Both vibrational and rotational modes are excited simultaneously in infrared spectra. This is the reason for the broader bands. Only rotational transitions occur in microwave spectra.

12. The stretching frequency of a nitrile should be higher than that of an imine because the C ≡ N bond is shorter and stronger than the C = N bond.

## CHAPTER 13

1. In both hexagonal close packing and cubic close packing each atom has twelve nearest neighbors. Therefore, two metals that crystallize in different geometrical arrangements can have the same number of nearest neighbors.

2. a. $K_2SO_4$ is an ionic solid. The forces binding it together are strong electrostatic interactions. $SO_3$ is a molecular solid. It is bound by weaker interactions (i.e., dipole-dipole).

   b. $K_2SO_4$ has a high melting point. This is due to the strong ionic bonding. $SO_3$ has a low melting point because the intermolecular attractions in a molecular solid are weak.

   c. $K_2SO_4$ is hard; $SO_3$ is soft.

3. Ra, Ag, Ca, and Pt are good conductors because they are all metals. In diamond, all of the electrons are used for sigma bonding. None are free to conduct electricity. Rn is a noble gas and I is a halogen. Neither are good conductors; they form molecular solids.

4. Phosphorus exists in tetrahedral units bound loosely together. There are four phosphorus atoms per tetrahedron. There is no atom in the center of the tetrahedron. This accounts for its softness and insulating properties. Bismuth crystallizes in a metallic structure with a low coordination number. It has strong metallic properties such as hardness and electrical conductivity.

5. Sulfur has the valence electronic configuration $3s^2 3p^4$. It forms two electron-pair bonds per atom because there are two vacancies in the valence shell. An $S_8$ molecule exists as a ring. Solid sulfur is held together by weak London forces between the $S_8$ rings. It is a molecular solid.

6. The sea-of-electrons model describes the metallic crystal as a series of positive charges surrounded by a "sea" of electrons that are free to move throughout the crystal. The band model considers the entire metallic crystal to be a giant molecule. The atomic orbitals interact to form a set of delocalized orbitals that extend throughout the entire crystal.

7.

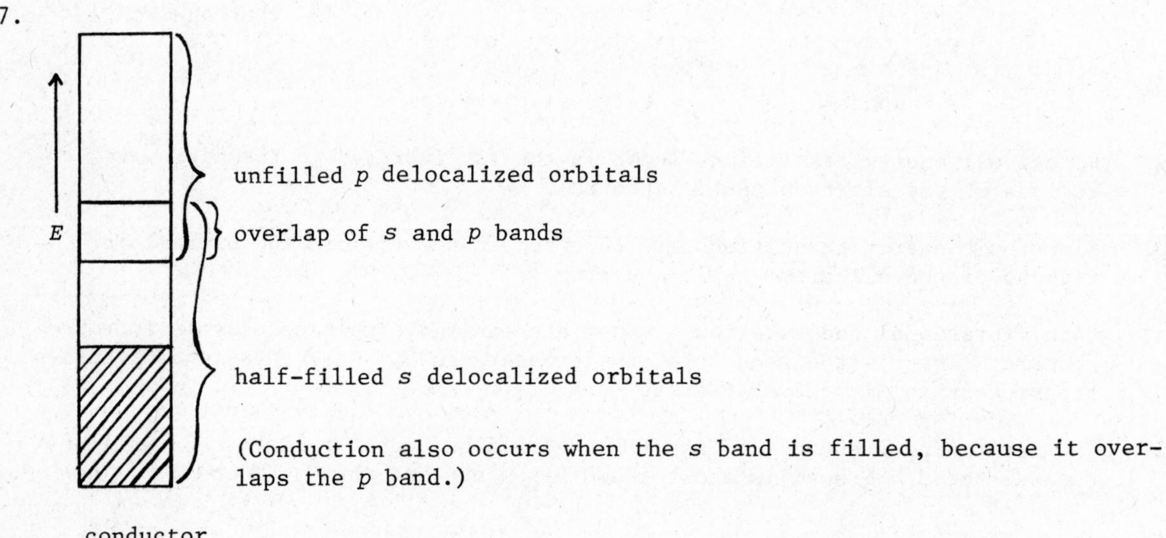

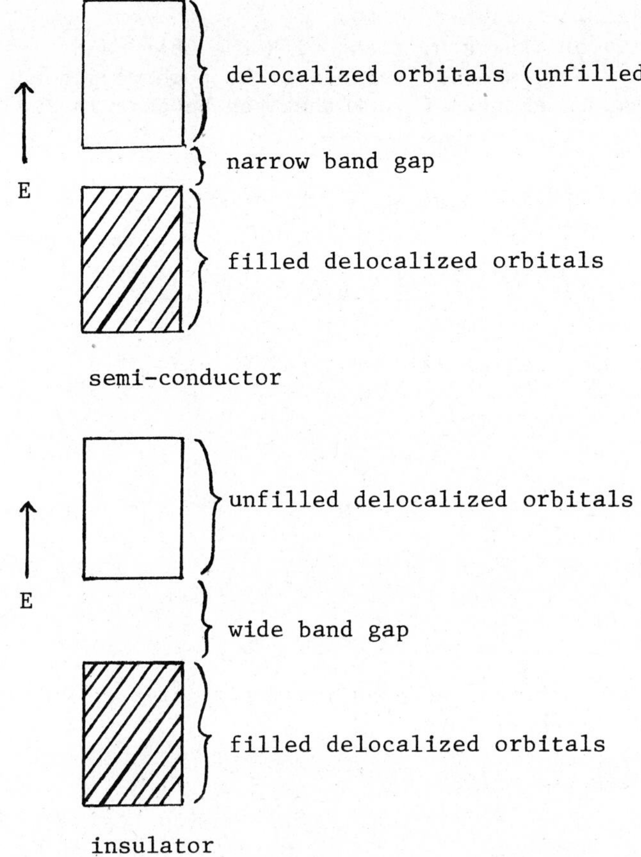


8. A trace amount of arsenic in a semi-conductor will enhance conductivity by narrowing the band gap. Arsenic has one more valence electron than silicon and germanium.

9. Ethyl methyl ether is somewhat polar, but 2-propanol is much more polar. The hydrogen bonding that occurs in 2-propanol accounts for the higher boiling point because the network of hydrogen bonds must also be broken.

10. Both mica and talc have sheet structures. In mica, one fourth of the $Si^{4+}$ ions are replaced by $Al^{3+}$ ions. Electrostatically, the presence of $Al^{3+}$ holds the silicate sheets together much more strongly. Talc does not have any $Al^{3+}$ ions in its structure. The sheets are held together by weak van der Waals forces. These weak forces allow the layers to slide past one another, which gives talc its slippery feeling. Mica is hard because the sheets are fixed into position and do not slide.

11. Quartz is a three-dimensional silicate network. All four oxygen atoms in $SiO_4^{4-}$ are shared with four other $Si^{4+}$ ions. Quartz has the empirical formula $(SiO_2)_n$. In quartz all of the tetrahedral structures have $Si^{4+}$ (no other ions). Glass is a non-crystalline aggregate of silicate chains. The structure is somewhat disordered. Glass is actually a very viscous liquid, not a true solid.

12. Al is a good conductor. It has a melting point of 660.37°C and a hardness of 2 - 2.9. Si is a semi-conductor. It has a melting point of 1410°C and a hardness of 7.0. The bonding in Al is metallic. Si forms a non-metallic network.

## CHAPTER 14

1. We are given the mass and efficiency of a person, along with the units and necessary conversions for power. We are asked to calculate the power expended by the person's muscles and the maximum amount of work that can be done in one second.

$$\text{Power} = 60 \text{ kg} \times 0.45 \times \frac{0.3 \text{ hp}}{\text{kg}} \times \frac{746 \text{ W}}{1 \text{ hp}} = 6.04 \times 10^3 \text{ W}$$

$$\text{Maximum work per second} = 6.04 \times 10^3 \text{ W} \times \frac{1 \text{ J/s}}{\text{W}} = 6.04 \times 10^3 \text{ J/s}$$

2. We are given the external pressure and the initial and final volumes of a gas that is expanding isothermally. We are asked to calculate $w$, $q$, and $\Delta E$ for this process.

$$w = P_{ext}\Delta V$$

$$= (1.0 \text{ atm})(20.0 \text{ L} - 5.0 \text{ L})$$

$$= 15.0 \text{ L}\cdot\text{atm} \times \frac{101.3 \text{ J}}{\text{L}\cdot\text{atm}} = 1520 \text{ J}$$

$\Delta E = 0$ because this process is isothermal and the internal energy of an ideal gas depends only on temperature.

Since $\Delta E = q - w$, $q = w$. In this case, $q = 1520$ J.

3. At constant pressure

$$\Delta H = q_p = \Delta E + \Delta(PV)$$

Where $q_p$ represents the heat of a specified constant pressure path for the gas. For an ideal gas, $\Delta(PV) = \Delta(nRT) = nR\Delta T$. Since $\Delta T = 0$, $\Delta(PV) = 0$ and $\Delta H = 0$.

4. We are given the standard heat of formation of silver phosphate and asked to write the corresponding chemical equation. The equation represents the synthesis of one mole of silver phosphate from elemental silver, phosphorus, and oxygen gas.

$$2Ag(s) + \tfrac{1}{4}P_4(s) + 2O_2(g) \longrightarrow Ag_3PO_4(s)$$

5. Because rhombic sulfur is the standard state, the standard heat of formation is, by definition, zero. Since monoclinic sulfur and S($g$) are not standard state, their standard heats of formation will be nonzero.

6. We are given a reaction and asked to calculate the standard enthalpy change at 25°C.

$$N_2O_5(s) + H_2O(l) \longrightarrow 2H^+(aq) + 2NO_3^-(aq)$$

$$\Delta H° = \Sigma\Delta H_f° \text{ (products)} - \Sigma\Delta H_f° \text{ (reactants)}$$

$$\Delta H° = [(0.0 + (-206.57) - (-41.8) + (-285.84)] \text{ kJ mol}^{-1}$$

$\Delta H° = [-206.57 - (-327.64)]$ kJ mol$^{-1}$

$\Delta H° = 121.1$ kJ mol$^{-1}$

7. We are asked to calculate $\Delta H$ for the process

$$BaCl_2 \cdot 2H_2O(s) \longrightarrow BaCl_2(s) + 2H_2O(g)$$

$\Delta H° = \Sigma\Delta H_f°$ (products) $- \Sigma\Delta H_f°$ (reactants)

$\Delta H° = [2(-241.83) + (-1461.7) - (-538.36)]$ kJ

$\Delta H° = (-483.66 - 1461.7 + 538.36)$ kJ $= -1407.0$ kJ

1407.0 kJ of heat are required.

8. We are given the initial and final volumes and pressures of an ideal gas that is isothermally compressed. We are asked to calculate $\Delta H$. Since the process is isothermal, $\Delta E = 0$.

$\Delta H = \Delta(PV)$

$= [(.50 \text{ L})(1.0 \text{ atm}) - (10.0 \text{ L})(0.05 \text{ atm})]$

$= 0$

9. We are given the heat capacity of aluminum and asked to calculate the amount of heat that is necessary to raise the temperature of 2.0 kg of aluminum by 75°C. This process takes place at constant pressure. Use the following expression and solve for $q_p$.

$C_p = q_p/\Delta T$

$q_p = C_p\Delta T = (20.7 \text{ J mol}^{-1} \text{ K}^{-1})(75 \text{ K}) = 1552 \text{ J mol}^{-1}$

Now, convert 2.0 kg of aluminum to moles to determine the amount of heat that is required.

$$2.0 \text{ kg Al} \times \frac{1000 \text{ g}}{1 \text{ kg}} \times \frac{1 \text{ mol Al}}{26.98 \text{ g}} \times \frac{1552 \text{ J}}{1 \text{ mol Al}} = 1.15 \times 10^5 \text{ J} = 115 \text{ kJ}$$

10. The formation of urea from gaseous atoms is represented by

$$C(g) + O(g) + 4H(g) + 2N(g) \longrightarrow CH_4N_2O$$

Sum the bond energies: $\Delta H° = 728 + 4(391) + 2(242) = 2776$ kJ

$C(gr) \longrightarrow C(g)$ $\Delta H° = 718.38$ kJ

$\frac{1}{2}O_2(g) \longrightarrow O(g)$ $\Delta H° = 247.52$ kJ

$2H_2(g) \longrightarrow 4H(g)$ $\Delta H° = 4(217.95) = 871.80$ kJ

$N_2(g) \longrightarrow 2N(g)$ $\Delta H° = 2(472.65) = 945.30$ kJ

Using Hess' law, we can combine this information to calculate the heat of formation of urea.

$\Delta H° = (2776 - 718.38 - 247.52 - 871.80 - 945.30)$ kJ

$\Delta H° = -7.00$ kJ

The structure of urea is not adequately represented by $H_2N\text{-}\overset{\overset{O}{\|}}{C}\text{-}NH_2$ alone; include also $H_2\overset{\oplus}{N}{=}\overset{O^{\ominus}}{\overset{|}{C}}\text{-}NH_2$, etc.

11. The standard enthalpy of sublimation of $I_2$ can be calculated as follows:

$I_2(s) \longrightarrow I_2(g) \qquad H°_{sub} = ?$

$\Delta H°_{sub} = \Delta H°_{I_2(g)} - \Delta H°_{I_2(s)}$

$= (62.241 \text{ kJ mol}^{-1}) - (0.0 \text{ kJ mol}^{-1})$

$\Delta H°_{sub} = 62.241 \text{ kJ mol}^{-1}$

$1.0 \text{ kg } I_2 \times \frac{1000 \text{ g}}{\text{kg}} \times \frac{1 \text{ mol } I_2}{253.8 \text{ g}} \times \frac{62.241 \text{ kJ}}{1 \text{ mol } I_2} = 245 \text{ kJ of heat}$

## CHAPTER 15

1. a. $\Delta S$ is negative. There are more gas molecules, and therefore more randomness, in the products.

   b. $\Delta S$ is positive because there is more disorder associated with the products than with the reactants.

   c. $\Delta S$ is negative. There are 7 gaseous molecules in the reactants and only two in the products. There is less disorder associated with a liquid than with a gas.

   d. $\Delta S$ is positive. In this reaction a solid and a liquid react to form a gas.

   e. $\Delta S$ is positive. There are two gaseous molecules in both the reactants and the products, but the product is chemically more complex.

2. a. $I_2(s)$ has less entropy than $I_2(aq)$ because dissolving a solid in water increases its entropy.

   b. Kr(*g*) has the lower entropy because its mass is less than that of Rn(*g*).

   c. $NH_4Br(s)$ has the lower entropy because the solid has less entropy than the aqueous solution.

   d. $Cl_2(aq)$ has the lower entropy because entropy decreases when a gas is dissolved.

3. a. $\Delta S° = \Sigma S°(\text{products}) - \Sigma S°(\text{reactants})$

   $= [(289.2) - (197.91 + 222.95)] \text{ J K}^{-1} \text{ mol}^{-1}$

   $= -134.7 \text{ J K}^{-1} \text{ mol}^{-1}$

b. $\Delta S° = \Sigma S°(\text{products}) - \Sigma S°(\text{reactants})$

$= [(4)(210.62) + (6)(188.72) - 4(192.5) - 5(205.03)]\ \text{J K}^{-1}\ \text{mol}^{-1}$

$= (1974.80 - 1795.15)\ \text{J K}^{-1}\ \text{mol}^{-1}$

$= 179.6\ \text{J K}^{-1}\ \text{mol}^{-1}$

c. $\Delta S° = \Sigma S°(\text{products}) - \Sigma S°(\text{reactants})$

$= [2(191.49) + 6(69.94) - 4(192.5) + 3(205.03)]\ \text{J K}^{-1}\ \text{mol}^{-1}$

$= (802.62 - 1385.09)\ \text{J K}^{-1}\ \text{mol}^{-1}$

$= -582.5\ \text{J K}^{-1}\ \text{mol}^{-1}$

d. $\Delta S° = \Sigma S°(\text{products}) - \Sigma S°(\text{reactants})$

$= [2(259) - (117 + 152.3)]\ \text{J K}^{-1}\ \text{mol}^{-1}$

$= (518 - 269.30)\ \text{J K}^{-1}\ \text{mol}^{-1}$

$= 249\ \text{J K}^{-1}\ \text{mol}^{-1}$

e. $\Delta S° = \Sigma S°(\text{products}) - \Sigma S°(\text{reactants})$

$= [2(259) - (260.58 + 245.35)]\ \text{J K}^{-1}\ \text{mol}^{-1}$

$= (518 - 505.93)\ \text{J K}^{-1}\ \text{mol}^{-1}$

$= 12\ \text{J K}^{-1}\ \text{mol}^{-1}$

4. The chemical equation for this process is:

$NH_4NO_3(s) \longrightarrow NH_4NO_3(aq)$

The driving force is the increase in entropy associated with dissolving a solid to form an aqueous solution.

5. For the reaction

$2Al(s) + Fe_2O_3(s) \longrightarrow Al_2O_3(s) + 2Fe(s)$

The standard free energy change is calculated as follows:

$\Delta G° = \Sigma\Delta G°(\text{products}) - \Sigma\Delta G°(\text{reactants})$

$= [(0 - 1576.4) - (0 - 741.0)]\ \text{kJ mol}^{-1}$

$= -835.4\ \text{kJ mol}^{-1}$

$S° = \Sigma S°(\text{products}) - \Sigma S°(\text{reactants})$

$= \{[(2)(27.2) + 50.986] - [(2)(28.32) + 90.0]\}\ \text{J K}^{-1}\ \text{mol}^{-1}$

$= [105.39 - 146.64]\ \text{J K}^{-1}\ \text{mol}^{-1} = -41.25\ \text{J K}^{-1}\ \text{mol}^{-1}$

A large negative $\Delta H°$ provides the driving force for the reaction, since $\Delta S°$ is negative.

6. We are given the heat of vaporization and the boiling point of Freon-22, and the heat of fusion and the melting point of ice. We are asked to calculate the number of grams of Freon-22 that must vaporize in order to freeze one pint of water at 0°C.

First, convert the given mass of water to moles. Then calculate the amount of energy that is necessary to freeze this mass of water.

$$1.0 \text{ pound } H_2O \times \frac{2.2 \text{ kg}}{1 \text{ lb}} \times \frac{1000 \text{ g}}{1 \text{ kg}} \times \frac{1 \text{ mol } H_2O}{18 \text{ g}} \times \frac{6.01 \text{ kJ}}{1 \text{ mol } H_2O} = 734.56 \text{ kJ}$$

$$734.56 \text{ kJ} = \frac{1 \text{ mol Freon-22}}{18.79 \text{ kJ}} \times \frac{85.46 \text{ g}}{1 \text{ mol Freon-22}} = 3340 \text{ g Freon-22 vaporized}$$

7. We are given a reaction and asked to calculate $\Delta H°$, $\Delta S°$, $\Delta G°$ and $K_{eq}$ for the process:

$$S(s) + 6H^+(aq) + 6NO_3^-(aq) \longrightarrow H^+(aq) + HSO_4^-(aq) + 6NO_2(g) + 2H_2O(l)$$

$$\Delta H° = \Sigma H_f°(\text{products}) - \Sigma H_f°(\text{reactants})$$

$$= [(0) + (-885.9) + 6(33.85) + 2(-285.84) - (0) + (610) + 6(-206.57)] \text{ kJ mol}^{-1}$$

$$= (-1254.48 - 1239.42) \text{ kJ mol}^{-1}$$

$$\Delta H° = -15.1 \text{ kJ mol}^{-1}$$

$$\Delta S° = \Sigma S°(\text{products}) - \Sigma S°(\text{reactants})$$

$$= [(0) + 126.8) + 6(240.5) + 2(69.94)] - [(0) + (31.9) + 6(146)]$$

$$= (1709.68 - 907.90) \text{ J K}^{-1} \text{ mol}^{-1}$$

$$\Delta S° = 801.8 \text{ J mol}^{-1} \text{ K}^{-1}$$

$$\Delta G° = \Delta H° - T\Delta S°$$

$$= (-15.06 \text{ kJ mol}^{-1}) - (298 \text{ K})(0.8018 \text{ kJ mol}^{-1} \text{ K}^{-1})$$

$$= -254.0 \text{ kJ mol}^{-1}$$

$$\Delta G° = -2.303\ RT \log K_{eq}$$

$$\log K_{eq} = [\frac{\Delta G°}{-2.303\ RT}]$$

$$K_{eq} = \text{antilog } [\frac{\Delta G°}{-2.303\ RT}]$$

$$= \text{antilog } [\frac{-254{,}000 \text{ J mol}^{-1}}{(-2.303)(8.314)(298)}]$$

$$K_{eq} = \text{antilog } (44.52)$$

$K_{eq} = 3.28 \times 10^{44}$

Since $\Delta H°$ is negative, the reaction is exothermic. The yield can be increased by lowering the temperature.

8. a. For a free isothermal expansion into a vacuum:

$w = 0$ because the gas is expanding into a vacuum: $P_{ext} = 0$.

$\Delta E = 0$ because the expansion is isothermal.

$q = 0$ because $\Delta E = 0$, $w = 0$.

$\Delta H = E + \Delta(PV) = 0$ because the $\Delta T$ is 0: $\Delta(PV) = \Delta(nRT)$

$\Delta S = q_{rev}/T > 0$ (the gas is expanding)

$\Delta G = \Delta H - T\Delta S < 0$

b. For an isothermal expansion of an ideal gas against an external pressure of 1.0 atm:

$$w = P_{ext}\Delta V = (1 \text{ atm})(5.0 \text{ L} - 1.0 \text{ L}) \times \frac{101.3 \text{ J}}{\text{L}\cdot\text{atm}}$$

$= 405.2$ J

$\Delta E = 0$ because the expansion is isothermal

$q = \Delta E + w = 405.2$ J

$\Delta H = \Delta E + \Delta(PV) = 0$

$\Delta S = q_{rev}/T > 0$ Because the expansion is not reversible, $q_{rev} > q$ and $\Delta S > 405.2$ J/298 K

$\Delta G = \Delta H - T\Delta S$ $\Delta G \neq 0$ because the process is not at equilibrium

$\Delta G < 0$ because $T\Delta S > \Delta H$

c. For a reversible isothermal expansion of an ideal gas:

$w = 3.99$ kJ (given)

$\Delta E = 0$ because the expansion is isothermal

$q = \Delta E + w = 3.99$ kJ

$\Delta H = \Delta E + \Delta(PV) = 0$

$$\Delta S = q_{rev}/T = \frac{3.99 \text{ kJ}}{298 \text{ K}} = 1.34 \times 10^{-2} \text{ kJ/K} \qquad (q = q_{rev})$$

Because the process is reversible, the entropy of the universe decreases by an equivalent amount. $\Delta S$ has the same value for all three paths, since the initial and final states are the same.

$$\Delta G = \Delta H - T\Delta S = \Delta H - q_{rev}$$

$$\Delta G = 0 - 3.99 \text{ kJ} = -3.99 \text{ kJ}$$ $\Delta G \neq 0$ because pressure is not constant.

9. a. We are given a reaction and its corresponding $\Delta G°$. We are asked to calculate the equilibrium constant at 298 K.

$$\Delta G° = -2.303\ RT \log K_{eq}$$

$$\log K_{eq} = \frac{\Delta G°}{-2.303\ RT}$$

$$K_{eq} = \text{antilog}\left[\frac{\Delta G°}{-2.303\ RT}\right]$$

$$= \text{antilog}\left(\frac{-210.5 \times 10^3}{-2.303(8.314)(298)}\right)$$

$$= \text{antilog}\ (36.89)$$

$$K_{eq} = 7.80 \times 10^{36}$$

b. We are given the pressure of each gas and asked to calculate the free energy of the mixture.

$$K_{eq} = \frac{P_{COCl_2}}{P_{CO}P_{Cl_2}} = \frac{(0.30)}{(0.25)(0.15)} = 8.0$$

$$\Delta G° = -2.303\ RT \log K_{eq}$$

$$= -2.303\ RT \log (8)$$

$$= -5153 \text{ J}$$

$$\Delta G° = -5.2 \text{ kJ}$$

10. No, it is not possible to cool your kitchen on a hot day by opening the refrigerator door, because the refrigerator must pump heat into the room in order to cool its interior (i.e., do work). To cool the kitchen, the refrigerator would have to exhaust heat outdoors, like an air conditioner does.

## CHAPTER 16

1. The reaction of interest is:

$$SO_2(g) + NO_2(g) \rightleftharpoons SO_3(g) + NO(g)$$

The equilibrium constant can be derived using the equilibrium constants of the following equations.

$$2SO_3(g) \rightleftharpoons O_2(g) + 2SO_2(g) \qquad K_{eq} = \frac{P_{O_2}(P_{SO_2})^2}{(P_{SO_3})^2}$$

$$NO(g) + \tfrac{1}{2}O_2(g) \rightleftharpoons NO_2(g) \qquad K_{eq} = \frac{P_{NO_2}}{P_{NO}(P_{O_2})^{\frac{1}{2}}}$$

The reaction of interest is obtained by dividing the coefficients of the first equation by two and reversing it. This corresponds to taking the square root of the reciprocal of $K_{eq}$. Similarly, the second equation must be reversed and we must take the reciprocal of $K_{eq}$. After performing these manipulations on the $K_{eq}$'s, multiply them together to obtain the desired $K_{eq}$.

$$\left(\frac{(P_{SO_3})^2}{P_{O_2}(P_{SO_2})^2}\right)^{\frac{1}{2}} \left(\frac{P_{NO}(P_{O_2})^{\frac{1}{2}}}{P_{NO_2}}\right) = \frac{P_{SO_3}P_{NO}}{P_{SO_2}P_{NO_2}}$$

2. First, set up a chart with starting, change, and equilibrium pressures.

| Pressure: | NO | Cl | NOCl |
|---|---|---|---|
| start | 0 | 0 | 1.0 |
| change | $+X$ | $+\frac{1}{2}X$ | $-X$ |
| equilibrium | $X$ | $\frac{1}{2}X$ | $1.0 - X$ |

Set up the equilibrium constant expression

$$K_{eq} = 5.20 = \frac{(P_{NOCl})^2}{(P_{NO})^2 P_{Cl_2}} = \frac{(1.0 - X)^2}{X^2(\frac{1}{2}X)}$$

Assume that $X$ is small compared to 1.00. Solve for $X$.

$$5.20 = \frac{(1.0)^2}{\frac{1}{2}X^3}$$

$$\tfrac{1}{2}X^3 = 1/52.0$$

$$X = 0.34$$

The approximation was not a good one because 0.34 is not negligible compared with one. Therefore, we must use the method of successive approximations. To do this substitute the value of 0.34 and solve for $X$.

$$5.20 = \frac{(1.00 - 0.34)^2}{\frac{1}{2}X^3}$$

$$\tfrac{1}{2}X^3 = \frac{(1.00 - 0.34)^2}{5.20}$$

$$X = 0.26$$

This is still not a good approximation, so we must repeat the process.

$$52.0 = \frac{(1.00 - 0.26)^2}{\frac{1}{2}X^3}$$

$$\tfrac{1}{2}X^3 = \frac{(1.00 - 0.26)}{52.0}$$

$$X = 0.28$$

Since 0.26 and 0.28 are very close, we can stop here. Use $X = 0.26$ to calculate the partial pressures of the gases at equilibrium.

$$p_{NOCl} = 1.0 - X = 0.74 \text{ atm}$$

$$p_{NO} = X = 0.26 \text{ atm}$$

$$p_{O} = \tfrac{1}{2}X = 0.13 \text{ atm}$$

3. Assume the reaction goes nearly to completion. Set up a chart with starting, completion, change, and equilibrium pressures. Let $x$ equal the partial pressure of NOCl.

| Pressure: | NO | $Cl_2$ | NOCl |
|---|---|---|---|
| start | 0.5 | 0.5 | 0 |
| completion | 0 | 0.25 | 0.5 |
| change | $+x$ | $+\tfrac{1}{2}x$ | $-x$ |
| equilibrium | $x$ | $0.25 + \tfrac{1}{2}x$ | $0.5 - x$ |

Substitute these values into the equilibrium constant expression.

$$K_{eq} = 52.0 = \frac{p^2_{NOCl}}{p^2_{NO}p_{Cl_2}} = \frac{(0.5 - x)^2}{x^2(0.25 + .5x)}$$

Assume that $x$ is small compared to 0.5 and solve for $x$.

$$52.0 = \frac{(0.5)^2}{0.25x^2 + .5x}$$

$$13x^2 + 26x - 0.25 = 0$$

$$x = \frac{-26 \pm\sqrt{26^2 - 4(13)(-0.25)}}{2(13)}$$

$$x = 0.01, -2.01$$

The negative value can be disregarded.

$$p_{NOCl} = 0.5 - x = 0.49 \text{ atm}$$

$$p_{NO} = x = 0.01 \text{ atm}$$

$$p_{Cl_2} = 0.25 + 0.5x = 0.255 \text{ atm}$$

4. The percent dissociation is the amount of gas present initially minus that present at equilibrium, divided by the amount that was present initially.

$$\% \text{ dissociation} = \frac{0.26 \text{ atm}}{1.00 \text{ atm}} = 0.26 = 26\%$$

5. a. Increasing the pressure of the system will favor the product, which has fewer gaseous molecules than the reactants.

   b. Raising $T$ will favor the reactants because the process is exothermic.

   c. Adding a catalyst will have no effect on the equilibrium.

   d. Removing some $Cl_2$ will cause the reaction to go in the reverse direction.

6. We are given a reaction and asked to calculate $\Delta G°$ and $K_{eq}$. The reaction is:

$$2NO(g) + Cl_2(g) \rightleftharpoons 2NOCl(g)$$

To calculate $\Delta G°$, we need to know $\Delta H°$ and $\Delta S°$:

$$\Delta H° = \Sigma\Delta H_f°(\text{products}) - \Sigma\Delta H_f°(\text{reactants})$$

$$= 2(52.59) - [2(90.374) + 0.0]$$

$$= (105.18 - 180.75) \text{ kJ mol}^{-1}$$

$$\Delta H° = -75.57 \text{ kJ mol}^{-1}$$

$$\Delta S° = \Sigma S°(\text{products}) - \Sigma S°(\text{reactants})$$

$$= (2)(263) - (2(210.62) + 222.95)$$

$$= (526 - 644.19) \text{ J mol}^{-1} \text{ K}^{-1}$$

$$\Delta S° = -118.19 \text{ J mol}^{-1} \text{ K}^{-1}$$

$$\Delta G° = \Delta H° - T\Delta S°$$

$$= (-75.57 \times 10^3 \text{ J mol}^{-1}) - (298 \text{ K})(-118.19 \text{ J mol}^{-1} \text{ K}^{-1})$$

$$= -40{,}350 \text{ J mol}^{-1}$$

$$= 40.35 \text{ kJ mol}^{-1}$$

$$\Delta G° = -2.303\, RT \log K_{eq}$$

$$K_{eq} = \text{antilog } \left(\frac{\Delta G°}{-2.303\, RT}\right)$$

$$K_{eq} = \text{antilog } \left[\frac{-40{,}350}{(-2.303)(8.314)(298)}\right]$$

$$K_{eq} = 1.18 \times 10^7$$

7. Enthalpy provides the driving force for the reaction. It is an exothermic reaction. If the temperature is high enough, there is a point when the reaction will no longer be spontaneous. At this point $\Delta G$ will be zero. At equilibrium, $\Delta G = 0$. When $\Delta G = 0$, $\Delta H = T\Delta S$ and $T = \Delta H/\Delta S$

$$\frac{\Delta H}{\Delta S} = \frac{-75{,}570 \text{ J mol}^{-1}}{-118.19 \text{ J mol}^{-1} \text{ K}^{-1}} = 639 \text{ K}$$

If the temperature goes above 639 K, the reaction will not be spontaneous.

8. In all three examples we are asked to calculate the equilibrium constant at 25°C. To do this, first calculate $\Delta H°$ and $\Delta S°$; then calculate $\Delta G°$; finally, calculate $K_{eq}$.

a. $\Delta H° = \Sigma\Delta H_f°\text{(products)} - \Sigma\Delta H_f°\text{(reactants)}$

$= (-348.0 - 110.523) - (0 - 393.513)$

$= -65.01 \text{ kJ mol}^{-1}$

$\Delta S° = \Sigma S°\text{(products)} - \Sigma S°\text{(reactants)}$

$= (43.9 + 197.91) - (41.6 + 213.64)$

$= -13.43 \text{ J mol}^{-1} \text{ K}^{-1}$

$\Delta G° = \Delta H° - T\Delta S°$

$= (-65.01 \times 10^3 \text{ J mol}^{-1}) - (298 \text{ K})(-13.43 \text{ J mol}^{-1} \text{ K}^{-1})$

$= -61{,}000 \text{ J mol}^{-1}$

$K_{eq} = \text{antilog } \left(\frac{\Delta G°}{-2.303\ RT}\right)$

$= \text{antilog } \left[\frac{-61{,}000}{(-2.303)(8.314)(298)}\right]$

$= \text{antilog } 10.69$

$= 4.91 \times 10^{10}$

b. $\Delta H° = \Sigma\Delta H_f°\text{(products)} - \Sigma\Delta H_f°\text{(reactants)}$

$= [4(33.85) + 6(-241.83)] - [4(-46.19) + 7(0.0)]$

$= (-1316 + 184.76) \text{ kJ mol}^{-1}$

$= -1131 \text{ kJ mol}^{-1}$

$\Delta S° = \Sigma S°\text{(products)} - \Sigma S°\text{(reactants)}$

$= [4(240.5) + 6(188.72)] - [4(192.5) + 7(205.03)]$

$= (2094 - 2205) \text{ J mol}^{-1} \text{ K}^{-1}$

$= -111.0 \text{ J mol}^{-1} \text{ K}^{-1}$

$\Delta G° = \Delta H° - T\Delta S°$

$= -1131 \times 10^3 - (298)(-111.0)$

$= -1.097 \times 10^6 \text{ J mol}^{-1}$

$K_{eq} = \text{antilog } (\frac{\Delta G°}{(-2.303)\ RT})$

$= \text{antilog } [\frac{-1.097 \times 10^6}{(-2.303)(8.314)(298)}]$

$= \text{antilog } (192.26)$

$= 1.80 \times 10^{192}$

c. $\Delta H° = \Sigma\Delta H_f°(\text{products}) - \Sigma\Delta H_f°(\text{reactants})$

$= (-333.2 - 241.83) - [2(-46.19) - 393.513]$

$= (-575.03 + 485.89) \text{ kJ mol}^{-1}$

$= -89.14 \text{ kJ mol}^{-1}$

$\Delta S° = \Sigma S°(\text{products}) - \Sigma S°(\text{reactants})$

$= (104.6 + 188.72) - (192.5 + 213.64)$

$= (293.32 - 406.14) \text{ J/K·mol}$

$= -112.82 \text{ J/K·mol}$

$\Delta G° = \Delta H° - T\Delta S°$

$= (-89.14 \times 10^3) - (298)(-112.82)$

$= -55{,}520 \text{ J}$

$K_{eq} = \text{antilog } (\frac{\Delta G°}{-2.303\ RT})$

$= \text{antilog } [\frac{-55{,}520}{(-2.303)(8.314)(298)}]$

$= \text{antilog } (9.73)$

$= 5.37 \times 10^9$

9. a. $\Delta G° = \Delta H° - T\Delta S°$

$= (-89.14 \times 10^3) - (373)(-112.82)$

$= -4.71 \times 10^4 \text{ J}$

$= \text{antilog } (\frac{\Delta G°}{-2.303\ RT})$

$= \text{antilog } [\frac{-4.71 \times 10^4}{-2.303(8.314)(373)}]$

$= \text{antilog } 6.59$

$= 3.93 \times 10^6$ Compare with $K_{eq} = 5.37 \times 10^9$ at 25° C.

b. Since the reaction is exothermic, the yield can be increased by decreasing the temperature. It can also be increased by increasing the pressure or by removing $H_2O(g)$ as the reaction progresses.

CHAPTER 17

1. We are asked to calculate $\Delta H°$, $\Delta S°$, and $\Delta G°$ for the process

$$Br_2(l) \longrightarrow Br_2(g)$$

$$\Delta H°_{vap} = (30.7 - 0.0)\text{kJ mol}^{-1}$$

$$= 30.7 \text{ kJ mol}^{-1}$$

$$\Delta S°_{vap} = (245.35 - 152.3)$$

$$= 93.05$$

$$\Delta G°_{vap} = \Delta H°_{vap} - T\Delta S°_{vap}$$

$$= (30{,}700) - (298)(93.05)$$

$$= 2971 \text{ J}$$

$$T_b = \frac{\Delta H°_{vap}}{\Delta S°_{vap}} = \frac{30{,}700}{93.05} = 329.93 \text{ K (or } 56.85°\text{C)}$$

The Handbook of Chemistry and Physics lists the boiling point of $Br_2$ as 58.78°C. The percent error is

$$\frac{58.78 - 56.85}{58.78} \times 100 = 3.3\%$$

2. We are asked to calculate $\Delta H°$, $\Delta S°$, and $\Delta G°$ for the process

$$CH_3CH_2OH(l) \longrightarrow CH_3CH_2OH(g)$$

$$\Delta H°_{vap} = (-235.4 + 277.63) \text{ kJ mol}^{-1}$$

$$= 42.23 \text{ kJ mol}^{-1}$$

$$\Delta S°_{vap} = (282 - 161) \text{ J/K mol}$$

$$= 121 \text{ J/K mol}$$

$$\Delta G°_{vap} = \Delta H°_{vap} - T\Delta S°_{vap}$$

$$= (42{,}230) - (298)(121)$$

The vapor pressure is calculated as follows:

$$\Delta G^\circ_{vap} = -RT \ln p_v$$

$$p_v = \exp \frac{\Delta G^\circ}{-RT}$$

$$= \exp \frac{6172}{-(8.314)(298)}$$

$$= 8.28 \times 10^{-2} \text{ atm}$$

Trouton's rule predicts that the entropy of vaporization will be approximately 90 J/K mol. Here, the calculated value of $\Delta S^\circ_{vap}$ is 121 J/K mol, which is significantly higher. It is likely that there is a great deal of hydrogen bonding in the liquid phase of ethanol. This would account for the higher value of $\Delta S^\circ_{vap}$.

3. The phase diagram will be similar to that for $CO_2$ in its general appearance. The positive slope of the solid-liquid equilibrium line indicates that $SiF_4$ will contract upon freezing, which is characteristic of most materials.

4. We are given the vapor pressures of water and ethanol at 25°C. We are asked to calculate the total vapor pressure and the mole fraction of ethanol above a solution that is 40% ethanol by weight. Using Raoult's law, we have:

$$P_{total} = P_A + P_B = X_A P^{\bullet}_A = X_B P^{\bullet}_B$$

$$= (0.21)(54.2) + (0.79)(23.6)$$

$$= 30.0 \text{ torr}$$

$$X_{\substack{\text{ethanol}\\ \text{in vapor}}} = \frac{P_{ethanol}}{P_{total}} = \frac{X_{ethanol} P^{\bullet}_{ethanol}}{P_{total}}$$

$$= \frac{(0.21)(54.2)}{30.0}$$

$$= 0.38$$

5. Freezing-point depression is a colligative property, which means it is dependent upon the number of particles present. In order of decreasing freezing point, we have: 0.1 m galactose, 0.1 m $Cr(NO_3)_3$ and 0.2 m $BaCl_2$. Because we are assuming complete dissociation of ionic compounds, $Cr(NO_3)_3$ has a lower freezing point than galactose because it dissociates into four particles.

6. We are given the mass of an unknown compound that is dissolved in 100.0 mL chloroform. We are also given the boiling point of the chloroform and unknown solution and the density of chloroform. We are asked to calculate the molecular weight of the unknown compound.

First, calculate $\Delta T$, the boiling-point elevation:

$$\Delta T_b = 62.5°C - 61.7°C = 0.80°C$$

Next, calculate the molality, $m$, of the solution.

$$m = \frac{\Delta T_b}{K_b} = \frac{0.80°C}{3.63 \text{ deg/mol} \cdot \text{kg}} = 0.22 \text{ m}$$

Calculate the number of kg of solvent.

$$100.0 \text{ ml chloroform} \times \frac{1 \text{ cm}^3}{1 \text{ mL}} \quad \frac{1.4832 \text{ g}}{\text{cm}^3} \times \frac{1 \text{ kg}}{1000 \text{ g}} = 0.148 \text{ kg}$$

Finally, calculate the molecular weight of the unknown.

$$\frac{0.22 \text{ mol}}{\text{kg}} \times 0.148 \text{ kg} = 0.0326 \text{ mol unknown}$$

$$\frac{12.884 \text{ g unknown}}{0.0326 \text{ mol unknown}} = 395 \text{ g mol}^{-1}$$

7. The osmotic pressure is calculated as follows:

Use the ratio of the densities of mercury and sap to calculate the height of 1 atm sap.

$$\frac{13.6 \text{ g/cm}^3}{1.00 \text{ g/cm}^3 \text{ sap}} \times 76.0 \text{ cm Hg} = 1033 \text{ cm sap/atm}$$

The height of the tree is:

$$30 \text{ ft} \times \frac{12 \text{ in}}{\text{ft}} \times \frac{2.54 \text{ cm}}{\text{in}} = 914 \text{ cm}$$

$$\text{osmotic pressure} = \frac{914 \text{ cm}}{1033 \text{ cm/atm}} = 0.885 \text{ atm}$$

$$\pi = CRT \qquad C = \frac{RT}{\pi} = \frac{(0.08206 \text{ L} \cdot \text{atm/mol} \cdot \text{K})(293 \text{ K})}{(0.885 \text{ atm})} = 27 \text{ M}$$

8. Use the Gibbs phase rule to predict the number of degrees of freedom.

$$f = 2 + c - p$$
$$= 2 + 1 - 1$$
$$= 2$$

There are two degrees of freedom.

9. We are asked to calculate the weight percent of ethylene glycol in an antifreeze solution whose freezing point is -10°F.

First, convert to degrees celsius.

$$°C = (F - 32)\ 5/9 = (-10 - 32)\ 5/9 = -23.3\ C°$$

Now, calculate the molality of ethylene glycol and the mass percent.

$$\frac{\Delta T_f}{-K_f} = m = \frac{(-23.3)}{-(1.86)} = 12.53 \text{ mol/kg}$$

$$12.53 \text{ mol } C_2H_6O_2 \times \frac{62.07 \text{ g}}{1 \text{ mol}} = 778 \text{ g}$$

$$\frac{778 \text{ g ethylene glycol}}{1000 \text{ g water}} = 77.8\%$$

10. We are given the vapor pressure of carbon tetrachloride at 23°C. We are asked to calculate the mass of iodine that must be dissolved in order to lower the $CCl_4$'s vapor pressure to 75.0 torr. The mole fraction of $CCl_4$ must be

$$P_{CCl_4} = P^{\bullet}_{CCl_4} X_{CCl_4}$$

$$X_{CCl_4} = \frac{75.0}{100.0} = 0.75$$

Therefore, the mole fraction of $I_2$ must be 0.25.

$$500 \text{ mL} \times \frac{1.5940 \text{ g } CCl_4}{\text{mL}} \times \frac{1 \text{ mol } CCl_4}{153.81 \text{ g}} = 5.81 \text{ mol } CCl_4$$

The number of moles of $I_2$ that must be present is $X$:

$$\frac{0.75}{5.81} = \frac{0.25}{X} \qquad X = 1.94 \text{ mol } I_2$$

The mass of $I_2$ that must be added is

$$1.94 \text{ mol } I_2 \times \frac{253.80 \text{ g}}{1 \text{ mol } I_2} = 492.4 \text{ g } I_2$$

11. Ethanol and water can be separated from mixtures of the two by fractional distillation, because the vapor is richer in ethanol than the solution.

## CHAPTER 18

1. Compare the $E°$ values to determine whether two substances will react together in a redox process.

   a. $F_2(g)$ and $Cl^-(aq)$ will react in a redox process.

   b. $Br_2(l)$ and $Cl^-(aq)$ will not react in a redox process.

   c. $Cl_2(g)$ and $I^-(aq)$ will react in a redox process.

   d. $I_2(s)$ and $Br^-(aq)$ will not react in a redox process.

   e. $I_2(s)$ and $F^-(aq)$ will not react in a redox process.

2. The anode reaction, oxidation, is the reverse of

$$Cu(s) \longrightarrow Cu^{2+}(aq) + 2\bar{e} \qquad E° = -0.34 \text{ V}$$

The cathode reaction, reduction, is

$$NO_3^- + 4H^+ + 3\bar{e} \longrightarrow NO + 2H_2O \qquad E° = 0.96\ V$$

The shorthand notation for the cell is

$$Cu \mid Cu^{2+}, NO_3^- \parallel H^+, NO_3^-, NO \mid Pt$$

The overall reaction is

$$3Cu(s) + 8HNO_3(aq) \longrightarrow 3Cu(NO_3)_2(aq) + 2NO(g) + 4H_2O(l)$$

$$E° = 0.96\ V - 0.34\ V = 0.62\ V$$

3. We are given two half-reactions. We are asked to calculate $E°$ for the cell. We are also asked to write the spontaneous cell reaction and to make a drawing of the cell.

$$MnO_2(s) + 4H^+(aq) + 2\bar{e} \longrightarrow Mn^{2+}(aq) + 2H_2O(l) \qquad E° = 1.21\ V$$

$$Cl_2(g) + 2\bar{e} \longrightarrow 2Cl^-(aq) \qquad E° = 1.36\ V$$

The spontaneous cell reaction is

$$Cl_2(g) + Mn^{2+}(aq) + 2H_2O(l) \longrightarrow 2Cl^-(aq) + MnO_2(s) + 4H^+(aq)$$

$$E° = 1.36\ V - 1.21\ V = 0.15\ V$$

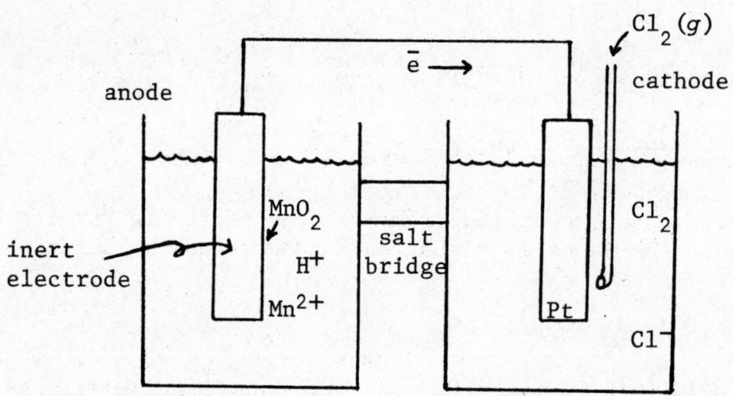


4. We are given the time and the current and asked to calculate the number of kg of $Br_2(l)$ that can be produced by the electrolysis of a NaBr solution. First, calculate the charge.

$$q = it = 5000\ A \times 8.0\ hours \times \frac{3600\ s}{hour} = 1.44 \times 10^8\ C$$

The half-reaction is $2Br^- \longrightarrow Br_2 + 2\bar{e}$. Use this reaction to calculate the mass of $Br_2(l)$ that forms.

$$1.44 \times 10^8\ C \times \frac{1F}{96485\ C} \times \frac{1\ mol\ Br_2}{2F} \times \frac{159.82\ g}{1\ mol\ Br_2} \times \frac{1\ kg}{1000\ g} = 119.3\ kg\ Br_2(l)$$

5. We are asked to calculate the time a solution of $Cr^{3+}(aq)$ must be electrolyzed to plate out 227 g of $Cr(s)$. The half-reaction for this process is $Cr^{3+}(aq)$ +

$3\bar{e} \longrightarrow Cr(s)$. First calculate $q$.

$$q = \frac{3F}{1 \text{ mol } Cr(s)} \times \frac{1 \text{ mol Cr}}{51.996 \text{ g}} \times 227 \text{ g } Cr(s) \times \frac{96{,}485 \text{ C}}{1F} = 1.26 \times 10^6 \text{ C}$$

$$t = \frac{q}{i} = \frac{1.26 \times 10^6 \text{ C}}{500 \text{ A}} = 2520 \text{ s} \times \frac{1 \text{ min}}{60 \text{ s}} = 42 \text{ minutes}$$

6. We are asked to design a cell to measure $K_{sp}$ for $Ag_2CrO_4(s)$. The cell reaction must be

$$Ag_2CrO_4(s) \rightleftharpoons 2Ag^+(aq) + CrO_4^{2-}(aq)$$

$$K_{sp} = [Ag^+]^2[CrO_4^{2-}]$$

The half-reactions are

$$Ag^+ + \bar{e} \longrightarrow Ag \qquad E° = 0.7996 \text{ V}$$

$$Ag_2CrO_4 + 2\bar{e} \longrightarrow 2Ag + CrO_4^{2-} \qquad E° = 0.4463 \text{ V}$$

$$E°_{cell} = (0.4463 - 0.7996)\text{V} = -0.3533 \text{ V}$$

To calculate $K_{sp}$, use the expression

$$\Delta G° = -RT \ln K_{sp} = -nFE°$$

$$\ln K_{sp} = \frac{-nFE°}{-RT} = \frac{-(2)(96{,}485)(-0.3533)}{-(8.314)(298)} = -27.517$$

$$K_{sp} = 1.12 \times 10^{-12}$$

7. We are asked to calculate the standard potential for the reaction between aluminum metal and water. The half-reactions are

$$2H_2O + 2\bar{e} \longrightarrow H_2 + 2OH^- \qquad E° = -0.8277 \text{ V}$$

$$Al^{3+} + 3\bar{e} \longrightarrow Al \qquad E° = -1.71 \text{ V}$$

The overall reaction is

$$2Al + 6H_2O \longrightarrow 2Al^{3+} + 3H_2 + 6OH^-$$

$$E° = -0.8277 \text{ V} + 1.71 \text{ V} = 0.88 \text{ V}$$

Unpainted aluminum canoes do not dissolve in lakes and rivers because a coating of $Al_2O_3(s)$ forms on the surface of the aluminum.

8. We are given a cell and asked to calculate $E$ at 25°. The two half-reactions are

$$Cd \longrightarrow Cd^{2+} + 2\bar{e} \qquad E° = 0.40 \text{ V}$$

$$Ni^{2+} + 2\bar{e} \longrightarrow Ni \qquad E° = -0.23 \text{ V}$$

The overall reaction is

$$Cd(s) + NiSO_4(aq) \longrightarrow CdSO_4(aq) + Ni(s)$$

$$E° = 0.40 - 0.23 = 0.17 \text{ V}$$

$$Q = \frac{[CdSO_4]}{[NiSO_4]} = \frac{(0.75 \text{ M})}{(1.5 \text{ M})} = 0.50$$

Using the Nernst equation, we have

$$E = E° - \frac{2.303 \, RT}{nF} \log Q$$

$$= 0.17 \text{ V} - \frac{(2.303)(8.314)(298)}{(2)(96485)} \log (0.50)$$

$$= 0.1789 \text{ V} = 0.18 \text{ V}$$

9. We are asked to calculate the electrode potential for the half-cell

$$Au \mid AuCl_4^-(0.10 \text{ M}),\ Cl^-(2 \text{ M})$$

The half-reaction for this process is

$$Au + 4Cl_4^- \longrightarrow AuCl_4^- + 3\bar{e} \qquad E° = -0.99 \text{ V}$$

$$Q = \frac{[AuCl_4]}{[Cl^-]^4} = \frac{(0.10 \text{ M})}{(2 \text{ M})^4} = 6.25 \times 10^{-3}$$

$$E = E° - \frac{2.303 \, RT}{nF} \log Q$$

$$= -0.99 - \frac{2.303(8.314)(298)}{3(96{,}485)} \log (6.25 \times 10^{-3})$$

$$= -0.947 \text{ V} = -0.95 \text{ V}$$

10. a. The half-reactions are

$$Cu \longrightarrow Cu^{2+} + 2\bar{e} \qquad E° = -0.34 \text{ V}$$

$$Ag^+ + \bar{e} \longrightarrow Ag \qquad E° = 0.80 \text{ V}$$

$$E°_{cell} = -0.34 \text{ V} + 0.80 \text{ V} = 0.46 \text{ V}$$

b. The potential could be increased above $E°$ by increasing the concentration of $AgNO_3$ or decreasing the concentration of $CuSO_4$. This would decrease the value of $Q$. Since the term in the Nernst equation that includes $Q$ is subtracted, the potential would be increased.

c. As the cell generates electricity, $E°$ decreases. The concentration of $Cu^{2+}$ increases, and the concentration of $Ag^+$ decreases. The mass of the Cu electrode decreases, and the mass of the Ag electrode increases.

d. When $E = 0$, the cell will be at equilibrium.

## CHAPTER 19

1. a. hexamminechromium(III) pentachlorocuprate(II)

   b. pentacarbonyliron(0)

   c. isothiocyanatopentaamminecobalt(III) chloride

   d. potassium tetranitroplatinate (IV)

   e. tris(ethylenediamine)nickel(II) nitrate

   f. fluoropentaaquochromium(III) sulfate

2. a. $[Cu(NH_3)_4]SO_4$

   b. $NaFeF_4$

   c. $[Pt(NH_3)_2ClBr]$

   d. $[Co(en)_3][Cr(CN)_6]$

   e. $K[Cr(ox)_2Cl_2]$

   f. $K_3[W(CN)_8]$

3. The complexes that have isomers are

   2(c)

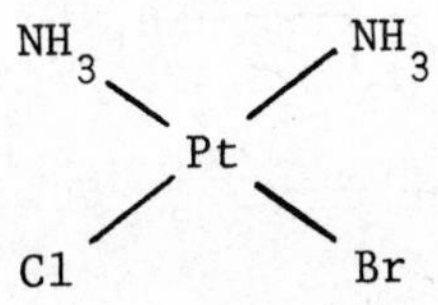

   NH3 NH3 Pt Cl Br — cis

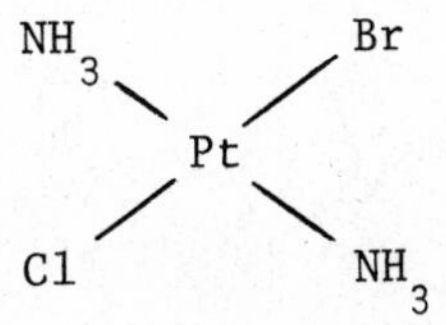

   NH3 Br Pt Cl NH3 — trans

   1(e) and 2(d)

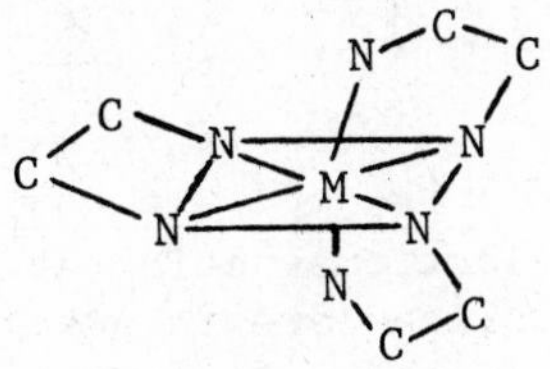

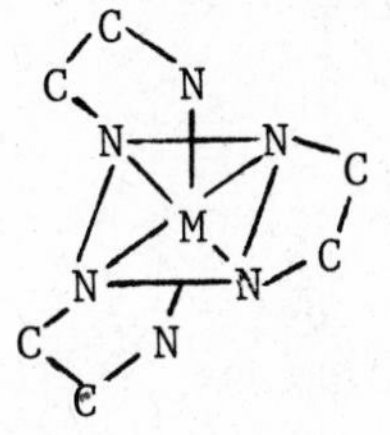

   2(e)

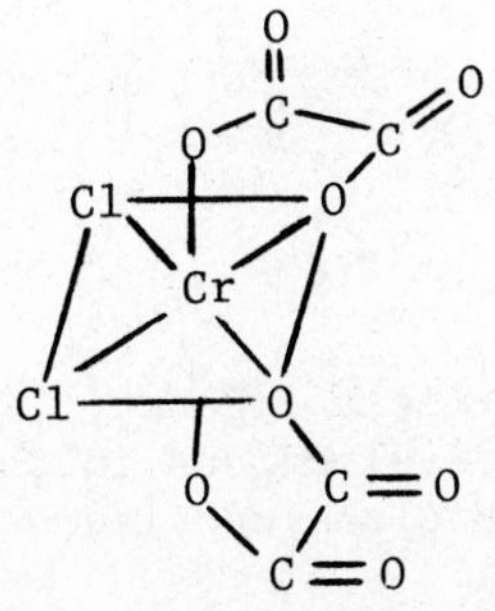

   cis

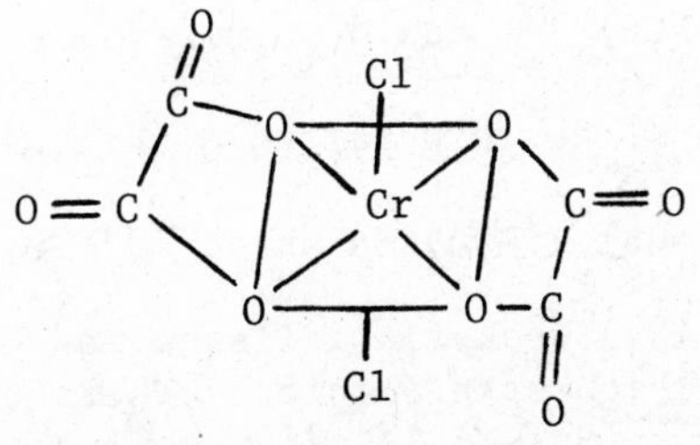

   trans

4. a. The valence configuration of $Cr^{3+}$ is $d^3$. There are three unpaired electrons.

   b. The valence configuration of $Ni^{2+}$ is $d^8$. There are two unpaired electrons.

   c. The valence configuration of $Pt^{+2}$ is $d^8$. The geometry is square planar. There are no unpaired electrons.

   d. The valence configuration of $Co^{3+}$ is $d^6$. There are no unpaired electrons because this octahedral complex is low-spin.

   e. The valence configuration of $Fe^{3+}$ is $d^5$. The geometry is tetrahedral. There are 5 unpaired electrons.

5. $[Co(NH_3)_5(NO_3)_2]SO_4$ dinitropentaamminecobalt(III) sulfate

   $[Co(en)_2(NO_2)_2]Cl$ dinitrobis(ethylenediamine)cobalt(III) chloride

6. In order of increasing crystal field energy ($\Delta_o$): $[CrCl_6]^{3-}$, $[CrF_6]^{3-}$, $[Cr(H_2O)_6]^{3+}$, $[Cr(NCS)_6]^{3-}$, $[Cr(NH_3)_6]^{3+}$, $[Cr(CN)_6]^{3-}$.

7. Yes, it is possible for diamagnetic Ni(II) complexes to exist. The geometry would be square planar. (See Figure 19-17 in the text.)

8.

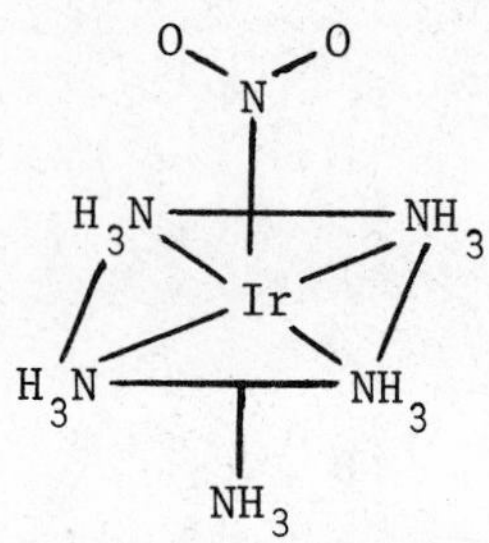


nitropentaammineiridium(III)

ONO
$H_3N$ $NH_3$
Ir
$H_3N$ $NH_3$
$NH_3$

nitritopentaammineiridium(III)

9. a. $\Delta_t$ $[Co(NCS)_4]^{2-}$ $\Delta_t$ $FeF_4^-$ $\Delta_o$ $e_g$ $t_{2g}$ $[Fe(NCS)_6]^{3-}$

   b. $FeF_4^-$ is colorless because it does not absorb electromagnetic radiation in the visible region. $[Fe(NCS)_x(H_2O)_{6-x}]^{3-x}$ complexes are intensely red because they absorb electromagnetic radiation in the visible region (∿ 500 nm) by a charge-transfer mechanism.

   c. $[Co(NCS)_4]^{2-}$ has 3 unpaired electrons.

   $[FeF_4]^-$ has 5 unpaired electrons.

   $[Fe(NCS)_6]^{3-}$ has 5 unpaired electrons.

10. a. $H_2O$ is a weak-field ligand and $CN^-$ is a strong-field ligand. $[Mn(H_2O)_6]^{2+}$ is a high-spin complex. There are five unpaired electrons in the *d* orbitals. $[Mn(CN)_6]^{4-}$ is a low-spin complex. It has one unpaired electron.

b. $[Mn(H_2O)_6]^{2+}$ outer orbital complex ($sp^3d^2$)

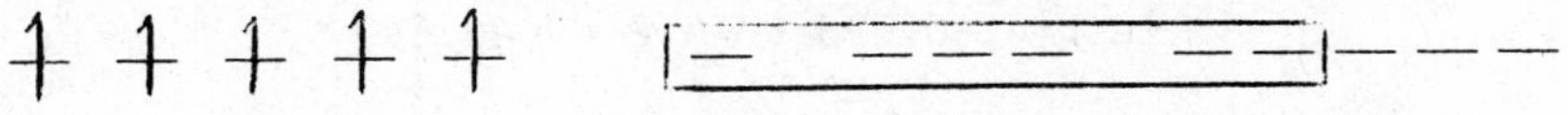

↑ ↑ ↑ ↑ ↑ [— — — — — —] — — —

3d 4s 4p 4d

$[Mn(CN)_6]^{4-}$ inner orbital complex ($d^2sp^3$)

⇅ ⇅ ↑ [— — — — — —]

3d 4s 4p

11. We are given the original concentration of $Pb^{2+}$ and asked to calculate the concentration of $Cl^-$ necessary to complex 99.9% of the $Pb^{2+}$ (0.10% remains uncomplexed).

$$Pb^{2+} + 4Cl^- \rightleftharpoons PbCl_4^{2-}$$

$$K_f = \frac{[PbCl_4^{2-}]}{[Pb^{2+}][Cl^-]^4} = 4 \times 10^2$$

$$[PbCl_4^{2-}] = (0.999)(0.010\ M) = 9.99 \times 10^{-3}\ M$$

$$[Pb^{2+}] = (0.0010(0.010\ M) = 1.0 \times 10^{-5}\ M$$

$$4 \times 10^2 = \frac{(9.99 \times 10^{-3})}{(1.0 \times 10^{-5})[Cl^-]^4}$$

$$[Cl^-]^4 = 2.498$$

$$[Cl^-] = 1.26\ M$$

## CHAPTER 20

1. a. Second order in NO

   b. First order in $H_2$

   c. Third order overall

2. a. First order in $H_2$, 3/2 order in $Br_2$, first order in HBr

   b. Increasing the concentration of HBr will decrease the rate of reaction.

3. a. Using the integrated rate law,

$$\ln \frac{c_0}{c} = kt,$$

we can substitute $p_0/p$ for $c_0/c$

$$\ln p_0 - \ln p = kt$$

$$\ln p = \ln p_0 - kt = \ln (0.500) - (9.2\ s^{-1})(5s)$$

$$\ln p = -0.693 - 46.0 = -46.693$$

$$p = 5.27 \times 10^{-21}\ \text{atm}$$

b. Percent decomposed $= \dfrac{c_0 - c}{c_0} = \dfrac{p_0 - p}{p_0} = \dfrac{0.500\ \text{atm} - 5.27 \times 10^{-21}\ \text{atm}}{0.500\ \text{atm}} \cong 100\%$

This reaction is extremely fast.

4. a. We are given the specific rate constant and asked to calculate the half-life of the process.

$$t_{1/2} = \frac{\ln 2}{k} = \frac{\ln 2}{2.2 \times 10^{-5}\ s^{-1}} = 3.15 \times 10^4\ \text{s or } 8.75\ \text{hr}$$

b. We are asked to calculate the time required for 90% of the $SO_2Cl_2$ to decompose.

$$\ln \frac{c_0}{c} = kt$$

$$\ln \frac{c_0}{0.1\ c_0} = 2.2 \times 10^{-5}\ s^{-1} t$$

$$1.05 \times 10^5\ \text{s} = t = 29.2\ \text{hr}$$

5. a. We are given the half-life of radium-223 and asked to calculate the rate constant for its decomposition.

$$t_{1/2} = \frac{\ln 2}{k}$$

$$k = \frac{\ln 2}{t_{1/2}} = \frac{\ln 2}{11.43\ \text{days} \times \frac{24\ \text{hr}}{\text{day}} \times \frac{3600\ \text{s}}{\text{hr}}} = 7.018 \times 10^{-7}\ s^{-1}$$

b. We are asked to calculate how many half-lives will pass before 99% of the sample has decomposed.

$$\ln \frac{c_0}{c} = kt$$

$$\ln \frac{c_0}{0.01\ c_0} = (7.018 \times 10^{-7}\ s^{-1})t$$

$$t = 6.56 \times 10^6\ \text{s}$$

$$t_{1/2} = 11.43\ \text{days} \times \frac{24\ \text{hr}}{\text{day}} \times \frac{3600\ \text{s}}{\text{hr}} = 9.87 \times 10^5\ \text{s}$$

$$6.56 \times 10^6\ \text{s} \times \frac{1\ \text{half-life}}{9.87 \times 10^5\ \text{s}} = 6.6 \cong 7\ \text{half-lives}$$

6. We are given the half-life of radium and the initial mass. We are asked to calculate the number of Ra atoms that are remaining.

$$1\ \text{g}\ RaCl_2 \times \frac{1\ \text{mol}\ RaCl_2}{296.9\ \text{g}} \times \frac{1\ \text{mol Ra atoms}}{1\ \text{mol}\ RaCl_2} \times \frac{6.02 \times 10^{2}\ \text{atoms}}{1\ \text{mol}}$$

$$= 2.03 \times 10^{21}\ \text{Ra atoms}$$

$$t = 1983 - 1921 = 62\ \text{years}$$

$$k = \frac{\ln 2}{t_{\frac{1}{2}}} \times \frac{\ln 2}{1600\ \text{yr}} = 4.33 \times 10^{-4}\ \text{yr}^{-1}$$

$$\ln \frac{c_0}{c} = kt$$

$$\ln c_0 - \ln c = kt$$

$$\ln c = -kt + \ln c_0$$

$$\ln c = -(4.33 \times 10^{-4}\ \text{yr}^{-1})(62\ \text{yr}) + \ln (2.03 \times 10^{21})$$

$$\ln c = 49.04$$

$$c = 1.98 \times 10^{21}\ \text{Ra atoms}$$

7.

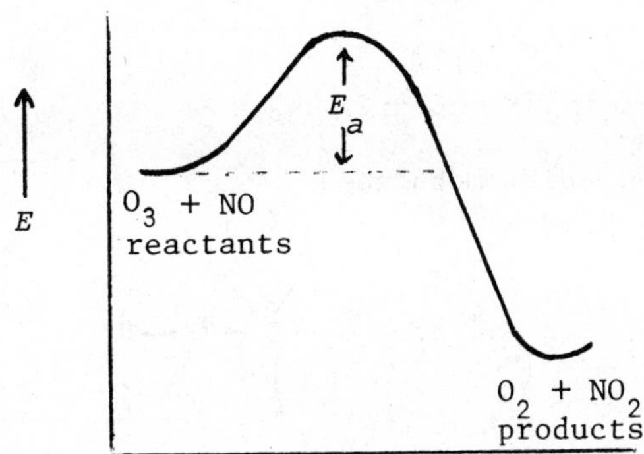


Rxn Coordinate

8. We are given the rate constant for the reaction in problem 7 at 25°C and asked to calculate the rate constant at 100°C.

$$\ln k_2 - \ln k_1 = -E_a/RT_2 + E_a/RT_1 = E_a/R(1/T_1 - 1/T_2)$$

$$\ln k_2 = \ln k_1 + E_a/R(1/T_1 - 1/T_2)$$

$$= \ln (2.2 \times 10^7) + \frac{10.29 \times 10^3}{8.314} \left(\frac{1}{298} - \frac{1}{373}\right)$$

$$\ln k_2 = 14.12$$

$$k_2 = 1.35 \times 10^6\ \text{L mol}^{-1}\text{s}^{-1}$$

9. a. $$\text{rate} = \frac{d[NO]}{dt} = \frac{2d[Cl_2]}{dt} = \frac{-[NOCl]}{dt}$$

b. $$\ln \frac{k_2}{k_1} = \frac{E_a}{R}\left(\frac{1}{T_1} - \frac{1}{T_2}\right)$$

$$\ln \frac{6.9 \times 10^{-4}}{9.3 \times 10^{-6}} = \frac{E_a}{8.314}\left(\frac{1}{350} - \frac{1}{400}\right)$$

$$4.31 = 4.3 \times 10^{-5}\ E_a$$

$$1.00 \times 10^5\ \text{J} = E_a$$

10. The decreased $E_a$ observed in acetone is due to the polarity of the solvent. Hexane is nonpolar and acetone is quite polar. The chemical species undergoing reaction are polar and the reaction is favored by a polar medium.

## CHAPTER 21

1. The carbon skeletons and locations of the bromine atoms are as follows:

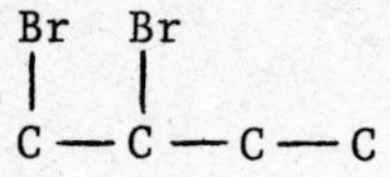

```
Br  Br                  Br       Br                 Br  Br
|   |                   |        |                  |   |
C — C — C — C           C — C — C — C          C — C — C — C
```

1,2-dibromobutane 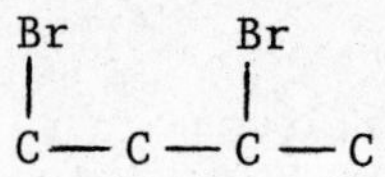    1,3-dibromobutane 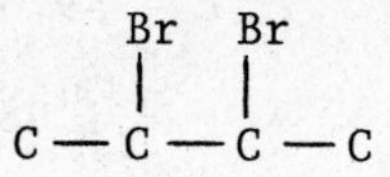    2,3-dibromobutane

$Br_2C$ — C — C — C

1,1-dibromobutane

C — $CBr_2$ — C — C

2,2-dibromobutane

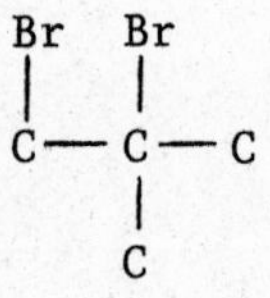

```
Br  Br
|   |
C — C — C
    |
    C
```

1,2-dibromo-2-methylpropane

```
Br — C — C — C — Br
         |
         C
```

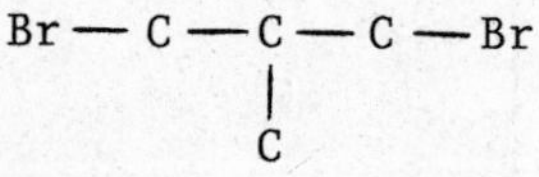

1,3-dibromo-2-methylpropane

```
C — C — CBr2
    |
    C
```

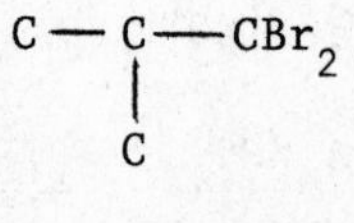

1,1-dibromo-2-methylpropane

2. a. $sp^3$

b. 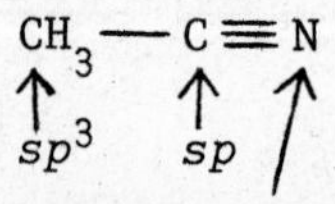 $CH_3$ — C≡N ($CH_3$: $sp^3$; C: $sp$; N: no hybrid orbitals needed)

c. 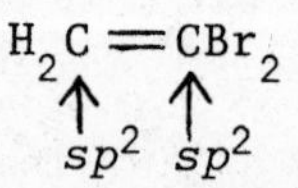 $H_2C$=$CBr_2$ (and isomers) ($H_2C$: $sp^2$; $CBr_2$: $sp^2$)

d. 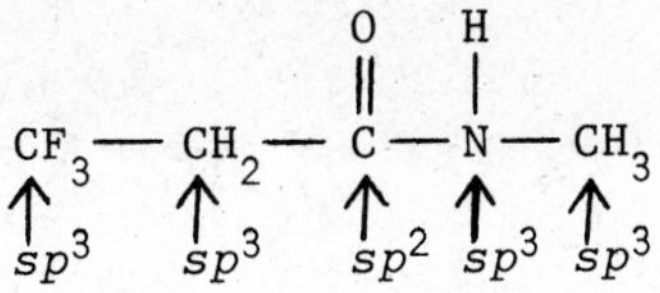 $CF_3-CH_2-C(=O)-N(H)-CH_3$

($CF_3$: $sp^3$; $CH_2$: $sp^3$; C: $sp^2$; N: $sp^3$; $CH_3$: $sp^3$)

e. 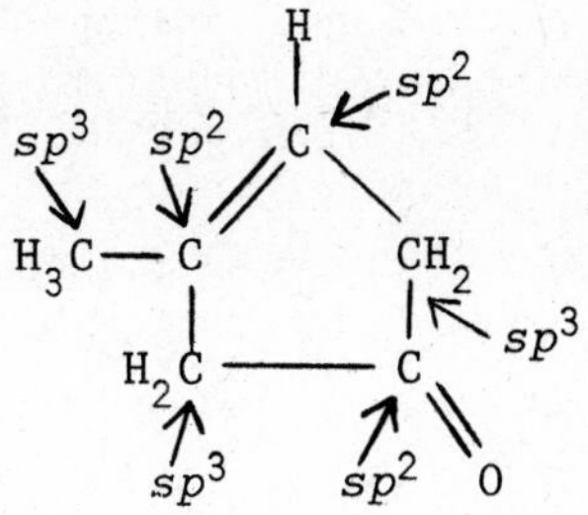 Five-membered ring: $H_3C-C$ (ring C, $sp^2$) $=$ C(H) ($sp^2$) $-CH_2$ ($sp^3$) $-C(=O)$ ($sp^2$) $-CH_2$ ($sp^3$) back to ring C; $H_3C$: $sp^3$

3. a. $BrCH_2-CH_2-C\equiv C-CH_2-CH_2-CH_3$

b. 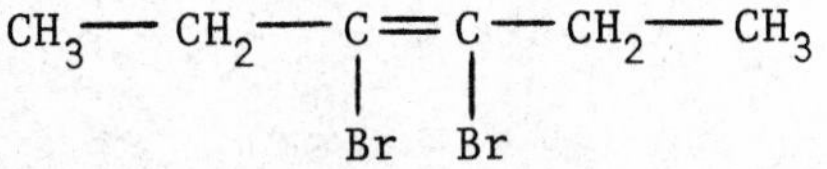 $CH_3-CH_2-C(Br)=C(Br)-CH_2-CH_3$

c. $CH_3-CH_2-CH_2-CH_2-CH_2-CH_2-C(=O)-O-CH_3$

d. 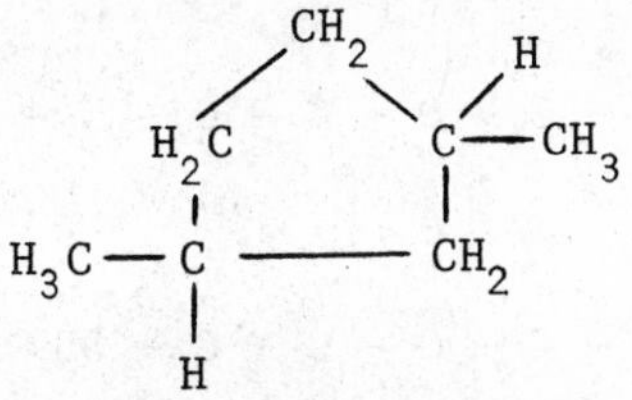 Five-membered ring: $H_2C-CH_2-C(H)(CH_3)-CH_2-C(H)(CH_3)$, ring closed back to $H_2C$ ($H_3C-C(H)$ ring carbon)

e. $CH_3-CH_2-CH_2-CH_2-CH_2-C(=O)OH$

f. 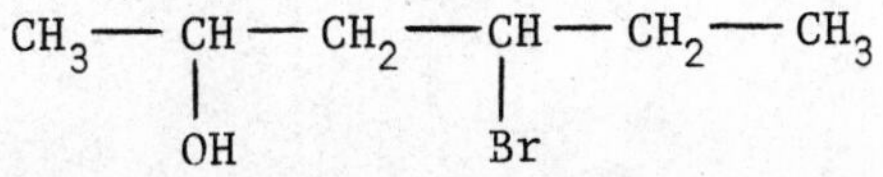 $CH_3-CH(OH)-CH_2-CH(Br)-CH_2-CH_3$

4. This compound contains one double bond or a ring. Carbon skeletons are as follows:

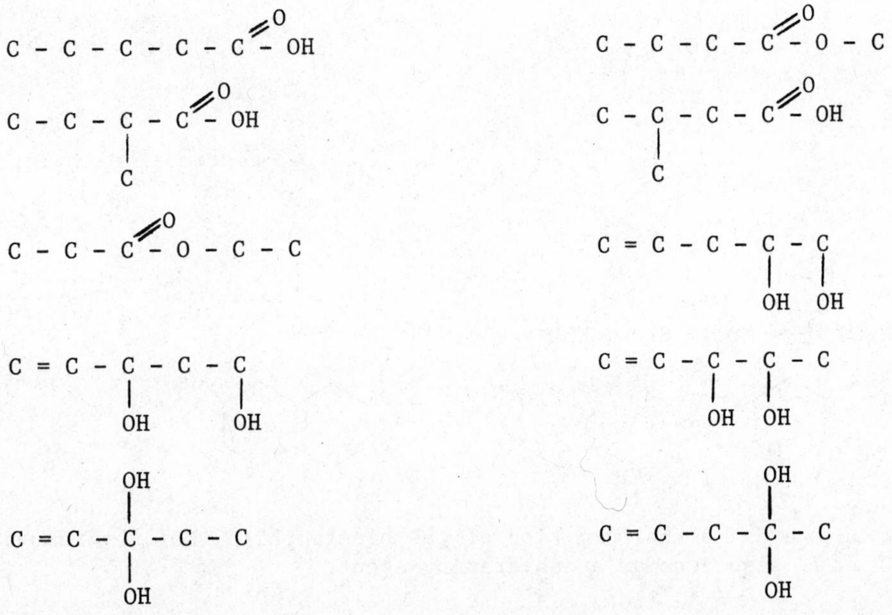

C - C - C - C - C(=O) - OH

C - C - C - C(=O) - O - C

C - C - C(C) - C(=O) - OH

C - C(C) - C - C(=O) - OH

C - C - C(=O) - O - C - C

C = C - C - C(OH) - C(OH)

C = C - C(OH) - C - C(OH)

C = C - C(OH) - C(OH) - C

C = C - C(OH)(OH) - C - C

C = C - C - C(OH)(OH) - C

```
C = C - C - C - C - OH
                |
                OH
```

```
HO - C - C = C - C - C
     |
     OH
```

```
C - C = C - C - C
|           |
OH          OH
```

```
HO - C - C = C - C - C - OH
```

```
C - C = C - C - C - OH
                |
                OH
```

```
          OH
          |
C - C = C - C - C
          |
          OH
```

```
                 //O
C - C - C - C - C - H
        |
        OH
```

```
                 //O
C - C - C - C - C - H
            |
            OH
```

```
                 //O
C - C - C - C - C - H
    |
    OH
```

```
                      //O
HO - C - C - C - C - C - H
```

```
                     //O
C - O - C - C - C - C - H
```

```
                     //O
C - C - O - C - C - C - H
```

```
            O
            ||
C - C - C - C - C - OH
```

```
        O
        ||
C - C - C - C - C - OH
```

```
            O
            ||
C - C - C - C - C
        |
        OH
```

```
        O
        ||
C - C - C - C - C
            |
            OH
```

```
            O
            ||
C - C - C - C - C
    |
    OH
```

```
                     O
                     ||
HO - C - C - C - C - C
```

```
     C
   /   \
  C     C — OH
  |     |
  C  —  C — OH
```

```
     C
   /   \   OH
  C     C /
  |     | \
  C  —  C   OH
```

```
          C
        /   \
       C     C — OH
       |     |
HO  —  C  —  C
```

5. $HNO_3 + H_2SO_4 \longrightarrow NO_2^+ + H_2O + HSO_4^-$

$NO_2^+$ + (naphthalene) $\longrightarrow$ (intermediate cation, + , H, $NO_2$) $\longrightarrow$ (2-nitronaphthalene, $NO_2$) + $H^+$

Sulfuric acid aids in the formation of the electrophile, $NO_2^+$, by removing $OH^-$ from $HNO_3$. It also acts as a dehydrating agent.

6. Compounds b and c have sufficiently large pi systems so that $\pi$ - $\pi^*$ transitions could occur in the visible region.

7. There are two possibilities:

(a)

(b)

8. Compound (a) contains an α-glycosidic link and can be digested by humans. Compound (b) is indigestible, however, because it contains a β-glycosidic link. To relate the structures of (a) and (b) to those of cellulose and starch in Figure 21-16 in the text, flip over the center β-glucose molecule in the cellulose chain.

9. Any of those having aliphatic or aromatic side groups are hydrophobic when incorporated into a protein.

10. Amino acids having hydrophobic side groups would be found in the interior of a globular protein.

11. Those having acidic or basic side groups would be the most strongly attracted to water. Amino acids containing polar uncharged groups would enhance the aqueous solubility of a protein to a lesser degree.

## CHAPTER 22

1. Since γ rays are electromagnetic radiation, $E = h\nu$.

$$\nu = \frac{E}{h} = \frac{(142.7 \times 10^3\ eV)(1.602 \times 10^{-19}\ J/eV)}{6.626 \times 10^{-34}\ J \cdot s} = 3.45 \times 10^{19}\ s^{-1}$$

$$\lambda = \frac{c}{\nu} = \frac{3.00 \times 10^8\ m/s}{3.45 \times 10^{19}\ s^{-1}} = 8.70 \times 10^{-12}\ m = 0.0870\ \mathring{A}$$

2. Nuclear radius is given by

$$r = 1.33 \times 10^{-13}\ A^{1/3}\ cm$$

For $^{99}Tc$, $r = 1.33 \times 10^{-13}(99)^{1/3}\ cm = (1.33 \times 10^{-13})(4.63)\ cm$

$$r = 6.15 \times 10^{-13}\ cm$$

For $^{12}C$, $r = 1.33 \times 10^{-13}(12)^{1/3}\ cm = (1.33 \times 10^{-13})(2.29)\ cm$

$$r = 3.04 \times 10^{-13}\ cm$$

While $^{99}Tc$ is 8.25 times as heavy as $^{12}C$, its radius is only twice as large.

3\. a. $^{191}_{78}Pt \xrightarrow{EC} {}^{191}_{77}Ir$ Electron capture decreases the number of protons by one.

b. Radioisotopes decay with first-order kinetics.

$$\ln \frac{n_0}{n} = kt$$

$$k = \frac{\ln 2}{t_{1/2}} = \frac{0.693}{3.0\ d} = 0.231\ d^{-1}$$

The initial mass of $^{191}Pt$ can be converted to atoms before the rate law is applied. Alternately, the rate law can be applied first, followed by conversion of the mass of $^{191}Pt$ remaining to atoms.

The second method allows you to work with smaller numbers.

$$\ln = \frac{25\ \text{mg}}{X\ \text{mg}} = (0.231\ \text{d}^{-1})(2\ \text{wk})(7\ \text{d/wk})$$

$$\ln 25 - \ln X = 3.234$$

$$\ln X = 3.219 - 3.234 = -0.025$$

$$X = 0.975\ \text{mg}\ {}^{191}\text{Pt remaining}$$

$$\text{atoms}\ {}^{191}\text{Pt} = (6.022 \times 10^{23}\ \text{atoms/mol})(0.975 \times 10^{-3}\ \text{g})/(191\ \text{g/mol})$$

$$\text{atoms}\ {}^{191}\text{Pt} = 3.1 \times 10^{18}\ \text{atoms}$$

(Note: This is an approximate number because the atomic weight of $^{191}Pt$ was estimated as 191.)

4\. Positron emission and electron capture both decrease the number of protons by one.

$$^{207}_{84}Po \longrightarrow \beta^+ + {}^{207}_{83}Bi \xrightarrow{EC} {}^{207}_{82}Pb$$

5\. Alpha emission decreases *A* by four and *Z* by two. Beta decay increases *Z* by one.

$$^{215}_{84}Po \longrightarrow \alpha + {}^{211}_{82}Pb \longrightarrow \beta^- + {}^{211}_{83}Bi$$

$$^{211}_{83}Bi \nearrow \alpha + {}^{207}_{81}Tl \longrightarrow \beta^- + {}^{207}_{82}Pb$$

$$^{211}_{83}Bi \searrow \beta^- + {}^{211}_{84}Po \longrightarrow \alpha + {}^{207}_{82}Pb$$

6\. a. $^{123}_{52}Te \xrightarrow{EC} {}^{123}_{51}Sb$

b. In this process, $^{123}Te$ and 52 electrons is converted to $^{123}Sb$ and 51 electrons. Only energy is emitted. The mass loss is just the difference between the masses of the isotopes.

$$\Delta m = (122.9042 - 122.9041)\ \text{amu} = 0.0001\ \text{amu}$$

$$E = mc^2 = (1 \times 10^{-4}\ \text{amu})(931.5\ MeV/\text{amu})$$

$E = 0.093\ MeV = 93\ keV$

7. The ratio of $n$ to $p$ in $^{115}In$ is 66/49 = 1.3. $^{124}In$ and $^{121}In$ contain too many neutrons. Thus one would expect these isotopes to decay by $\beta^-$ emission, which increases protons and decreases neutrons. On the other hand, the $n$ to $p$ ratio for $^{109}In$ is only 60/49 = 1.2. This isotope has too few neutrons, and should decay by electron capture or positron emission, both of which decrease protons and increase neutrons.

8. $^{45}Sc$ contains 21 protons and 24 neutrons. $^{40}Sc$ and $^{41}Sc$ contain too few neutrons, and thus should decay by EC or $\beta^+$ emission. $^{50}Sc$, however, is neutron-rich, and thus is expected to emit $\beta^-$.

9. The specific activity of $^{14}C$ in living organisms is 15.3 c/m•g. The ratio of disintegration rates is used in the first-order rate law.

$$t = \frac{1}{k} \ln \frac{d_0}{d} = \frac{t_{\frac{1}{2}}}{0.693} \ln \frac{d_0}{d}$$

$$t = (5570\ \text{yr}/0.693)(\ln 15.3 - \ln 8.6)$$

$$t = (8037.5)(2.73 - 2.15) = (8037.5)(0.58)$$

$$t = 4660\ \text{yr}$$

10. Substitute $^{18}O$ for the oxygen in ethanol. If the $^{18}O$ is present in the product, then the O-H bond in ethanol is broken. If $^{18}O$ does not show up in the ester, the O-C bond is broken. Substitution of $^{18}O$ in acetic acid is not a good idea, because acetate ion is present in equilibrium with the acid. Recall that oxygen atoms in a carboxylate group are equivalent.

$CH_3C(=O)O^- \longleftrightarrow CH_3C(O^-)=O$

Substitution of $^{18}O$ at either oxygen position in acetic acid would guarantee that some $^{18}O$ appear in the ester, since the oxygen atoms in acetate ion get scrambled. Thus at least one of them is retained in the ester.

11. The ratio of activities equals the ratio of millimoles of $^{35}S$.

$$\frac{5.64 \times 10^9\ \text{counts/min}}{3.29 \times 10^{15}\text{counts/min}} = \frac{x\ \text{mmol}}{1\ \text{mmol}}$$

$$x\ \text{mmol} = \text{mmol}\ Hg^{2+} = 1.71 \times 10^{-6}\ \text{mmol}$$

$$[Hg^{2+}] = 1.71 \times 10^{-6}\ \text{mmol}/2.00\ \text{mL} = 8.55 \times 10^{-7}\ M$$

12. $^{224}_{86}Rn \longrightarrow \beta^- + {}^{224}_{87}Fr \longrightarrow \beta^- + {}^{224}_{88}Ra \longrightarrow \alpha + {}^{220}_{86}Rn \longrightarrow \alpha + {}^{216}_{84}Po$

$^{216}_{84}Po \longrightarrow {}^{212}_{82}Pb + \alpha$

$^{212}_{82}Pb \longrightarrow {}^{212}_{83}Bi + \beta^-$

$^{212}_{83}Bi \longrightarrow {}^{208}_{81}Tl + \alpha \longrightarrow {}^{208}_{82}Pb + \beta^-$

$^{212}_{83}Bi \longrightarrow {}^{212}_{84}Po + \beta^- \longrightarrow {}^{208}_{82}Pb + \alpha$

13. a. $^{40}_{19}K \xrightarrow{EC} {}^{40}_{18}Ar$ or $^{40}_{19}K \longrightarrow {}^{40}_{19}Ar + \beta^{+}$

b. If there is 2.5 times as much $^{40}Ar$ as $^{40}K$ in the sample, then

$$\frac{K_{remaining}}{K_{original}} = \frac{1}{3.5}$$

Use the first-order rate law to find the age:

$$\ln \frac{n_0}{n} = kt$$

$$\ln (3.5/1) = (0.693/1.28 \times 10^9 \text{ yr})\ t$$

$$t = \frac{(\ln 3.5)(1.28 \times 10^9 \text{ yr})}{0.693} = 2.3 \times 10^9 \text{ yr}$$

c. In using this technique, you assume that argon is trapped in the sample. Since argon is a gas at room temperature, this assumption may not be valid for all materials.